d 15 r

HUMAN BIOLOGY AND HYGIENE
BIOLOGY BOOK II

SECONDARY SCIENCE SERIES

The books in this series adopt the latest approach to science teaching for secondary schools and the new middle schools. The students are encouraged to discover as much as possible for themselves rather than simply to verify what they are told to be true. Scientific knowledge is acquired through a largely experimental approach, related always to everyday life and experience.

Most of the experiments are simple and require the minimum of equipment. To help readers who do not have access to full laboratory facilities, the conclusions to be drawn from investigations are incorporated later in the text. At the end of most chapters there is a *Test Your Understanding* section to reinforce knowledge and understanding of important points. SI units have been used throughout the series.

These volumes, **General Plant and Animal Biology,** Biology Book I, and **Human Biology and Hygiene,** Biology Book II, are designed to follow on from the first volume, **Foundation Science,** which provides a two-year course in basic science. They are intended to take pupils up to the standard required by the CSE Biology Examination. The majority of topics required by the various GCE Boards, particularly with regard to the newer syllabuses, have also been covered.

The parallel volumes are **Chemistry**;
General Science Book I: **Matter and Energy**;
General Science Book II: **Man and His Environment**;
Physics Book I: **Force and Energy**
Physics Book II: **Atoms and Waves**

SECONDARY SCIENCE SERIES

HUMAN BIOLOGY AND HYGIENE

Biology Book II

E. J. Ewington and D. F. Moore

Illustrated by David and Maureen Embry

Routledge & Kegan Paul
London, Boston and Henley

First published in 1971
by Routledge & Kegan Paul Ltd
39 Store Street, London WC1E 7DD,
Broadway House, Newtown Road,
Henley-on-Thames, Oxon RG9 1EN and
9 Park Street, Boston, Mass. 02108, USA

Printed in Great Britain by
Redwood Burn Ltd
Trowbridge, Wiltshire

Reprinted 1972, 1973, 1974, 1977
Reprinted with corrections, 1980
Reprinted 1982

ISBN 0 7100 7079 9

SECONDARY SCIENCE SERIES

N. E. Savage

Senior Physics Master, Technical High School for Girls, Canterbury.
Formerly member of Science Panel and Physics and Integrated Science
sub-Panels, South East Regional Examinations Board for the CSE.

Contents

TOPIC C: HEALTH AND HYGIENE

Introduction

This volume, *Human Biology and Hygiene*, Biology Book II, together with its companion volume, *General Plant and Animal Biology*, Biology Book I, presents a course of biology suitable for pupils in the age range 13–16. Those who have worked through the introductory book in the series, *Foundation Science*, will find these volumes a natural extension of that work.

The authors have, throughout, kept in mind the requirements of the various Examining Boards, particularly those of the Certificate of Secondary Education. Together, the two volumes provide adequate preparation for CSE papers in biology and for the General Certificate of Education biology papers at Ordinary level. Moreover, this second volume, *Human Biology and Hygiene*, provides a full treatment of those aspects of human anatomy, physiology and hygiene required by candidates presenting Human Biology at the CSE or GCE at Ordinary level.

Whilst some topics are necessarily dealt with in a descriptive manner, the general approach is experimental. The investigations are an integral part of the text and, through them, the students are led to discover the facts for themselves rather than to verify what they have been told. The apparatus used is of the simple, unsophisticated type which is likely to be available in schools in quantities which make group and individual practical work possible. However, schools that are unable to carry out the investigations, or do not wish to, will find that the conclusions to be drawn from them are incorporated later in the text. Where an investigation involves any element of danger, hazard warning symbols appear in the margin.

Much biological knowledge can be taught through accurate line drawings and, for this reason, the text is very fully illustrated. In many cases the drawings are sufficiently simple for pupils to copy, if required.

As in the other books in this series, SI units have been used throughout.

The vocabulary has been kept as simple as possible, commensurate with accuracy of description. Where technical terms are desirable, their first mention has been printed in bold type for easy back reference.

At the end of each chapter a 'Test your understanding' section provides a simple yet searching inquiry into the knowledge gained by the pupil. Completion of these tests will also provide a useful summary of the important factual content.

Whilst this volume approaches biology mainly from the human standpoint, in places the authors have felt the need to widen the pupil's scope. Particularly is this so in the chapter on reproduction, where it is felt that a full understanding of the process in humans can best be gained from a general study of animal reproduction. Again, man's place in evolution is brought into perspective through a general consideration of the origin and evolution of animals and plants.

E. J. E.
D. F. M.

TOPIC A: HOW THE BODY WORKS

Chapter 1

Food and Digestion

1.1. Why food is necessary

All living things must obtain a constant supply of food in order to provide:

a. substances rich in **energy**, to act as 'fuel' for the body;

b. materials for the **growth** of new tissues and for repair or replacement of damaged parts;

c. substances essential for **health**, to protect the body against disease.

Each day we must take into our bodies food of the correct type and in the correct quantity, to satisfy these three requirements. Before we can examine the problem in a little more detail, it is necessary for us to consider something of the chemistry of foods.

1.2. Types of foodstuff

The number of different foods is, of course, very large. Some are natural foods, such as vegetables, meat and honey. Others are manufactured, as in the case of biscuits. cornflakes and hamburgers. Although there are so many different foods, we can divide them into six basic groups. These are carbohydrates, proteins, fats, mineral salts, water and vitamins.

a. Carbohydrates

Carbohydrates are chemicals containing the elements carbon, hydrogen and oxygen. The hydrogen and oxygen are present in the same proportion as they are in water (that is, two hydrogen atoms to each oxygen atom). An example of a simple carbohydrate is the sugar **glucose**, which has the chemical formula $C_6H_{12}O_6$. This type of sugar occurs naturally in grapes. The substance we call 'sugar' in the kitchen is really **sucrose**, or cane-sugar. Here the molecule is slightly more complex, for it comprises a molecule of glucose linked to a molecule of fructose, by the removal of the elements of water.

2

Fructose is a simple sugar having the same formula as glucose, but with a slightly different arrangement within the molecule. Thus:

$$GLUCOSE + FRUCTOSE \longrightarrow SUCROSE + WATER$$

Starch is another carbohydrate. A molecule of starch is very large, for it comprises many glucose molecules linked together to form a 'long-chain' compound. Compounds formed in this way, by the joining together of smaller molecules, are called **polymers**. The common plastic, polythene, is a man-made polymer.

Whilst sugars dissolve readily in water, starches do not. Starches are important storage substances in plants.

b. Proteins

In addition to the three elements that are present in carbohydrates, proteins contain nitrogen, and often sulphur and phosphorus. Like starches, proteins are polymers. The units which are linked together to form the giant protein molecules are members of a group of substances called **amino acids**. Proteins are the most important chemicals in living matter (protoplasm). They also form the main ingredients of such materials as wool, fur, leather, horn and silk. Like starches, most proteins are insoluble in water.

c. Fats

Like carbohydrates, fats contain the elements carbon, hydrogen and oxygen. They are compounds of propane – 1, 2, 3 – triol (glycerol) and fatty acids. The resultant molecules are insoluble in water, but dissolve in such solvents as ethoxyethane (ether), ethanol and benzene. At room temperature, fats may be solids, as in the case of meat fat, butter and margarine, or they may be oils, as in cod-liver oil, olive oil and linseed oil. Fats may be stored by plants, especially in fruits and seeds (for example, coconut oil, palm oil and peanut oil). Animals also store fats under the skin and around the body organs. The camel's hump is full of fat, and not of water as is generally supposed. Fats help some animals to conserve heat, as in the case of the blubber fat of whales.

d. Mineral salts, water and vitamins

See Sections 1.7 and 1.9.

1.3. Testing foods for their chemical content

It is possible, using fairly simple tests, to find out which of the basic foodstuffs are present in a particular food.

Investigation 1a. Testing food for the presence of a reducing sugar, for example glucose

Method 1. Benedict's test

Harmful

Into a test-tube place 2 cm³ of the blue liquid called Benedict's solution. Add as much glucose as you are able to pick up on a spatula tip. Shake, so as to mix the contents of the tube. Now heat the tube gently in a bunsen flame. What happens to the blue colour of the solution? Does this change happen if Benedict's solution is heated alone, or for a short time with starch?

Method 2. Fehling's test

Corrosive

The test is carried out as above, but Fehling's solution is used instead of Benedict's solution. This is a mixture of equal volumes of Fehling's A and Fehling's B. (*Note*. The mixture should be prepared freshly before the test.) How does the blue colour of Fehling's solution change when boiled with a reducing sugar?

Investigation 1b. Testing for the presence of starch

Harmful

Place a little starch in a test-tube or watchglass. Add a few drops of 'iodine solution' (iodine dissolved in potassium iodide solution). How does the colour of the starch change? Does glucose change in this way if 'iodine solution' is added?

Investigation 1c. Testing for the presence of protein

Method 1. Millon's test

Toxic

Corrosive

Into a test-tube place 2 cm³ of the clear fluid called Millon's reagent. With a spatula add a little flour, shake, and heat the tube gently in a bunsen flame. What colour change occurs? Repeat the test, using glucose and starch instead of flour.

Method 2. Biuret test

Harmful

Place a little flour in a test-tube and add 1 cm³ of 5% sodium hydroxide solution followed by a drop of 1% copper (ii) sulphate (vi) solution. Do not heat. Notice any colour change in the reagents. Repeat the test, using glucose and starch instead of flour. (*Note*. The final colour depends on the concentration of protein in the food under test.)

Investigation 1d. Testing for the presence of fat

Method 1. Grease-spot test

Flammable

Place a little margarine or lard in a watchglass. Add a few drops of ethoxyethane (ether) and mix with a spatula. Pour the resulting

4

liquid on to the centre of a clean filter paper and allow it to dry in the air. Hold the dry filter paper to the light and compare it with an unused piece. How has the fat affected the paper?

Method 2. Emulsion test

Using a spatula, place a little fat in the bottom of a test-tube. Add 2 cm³ of ethanol. Shake well, and then pour the resultant liquid into a clean tube. To this ethanol–fat solution add 2 cm³ of cold water. How do you describe the appearance of the final liquid?

Flammable

Summary of tests

TABLE 1.1. TABLE OF FOOD TESTS

Test for	Reagent	Change if Substance Present
Reducing sugar	Benedict's solution	Colour change: blue to green/red
Reducing sugar	Fehling's solution	Colour change: blue to brick red
Starch	Iodine solution	Colour change: orange to blue-black
Protein	Millon's reagent	Colour change: colourless to deep red
Protein	Sodium hydroxide and copper (ii) sulphate (vi)	Colour change: blue to pink/violet
Fat	Ethoxyethane (ether)	Translucent grease ring on paper
Fat	Ethanol and water	Cloudy emulsion produced

Investigation 1e. Testing a variety of foods for their chemical content

Select a variety of common foods, such as potatoes, meat, milk, egg yolk, egg white, bread, oatmeal, honey, etc. Test each food for the presence of (a) a reducing sugar, (b) starch, (c) protein and (d) fat, using the methods chosen from those given in Table 1.1. Record your results in the form of Table 1.2, as shown.

★ WARNING. *Note the hazards associated with each test as in Investigations 1b, 1c, 1d.*

TABLE 1.2. TESTING FOOD

Food	Test for			
	Reducing Sugar	Starch	Protein	Fat
Flour Potato Meat	Absent	Present	Present	Absent

In Investigation 1e you may have chosen cane-sugar (sucrose) as one of the foods to test. If so, you will no doubt have been surprised to discover that the Benedict's or Fehling's test was negative. This showed the absence of a reducing sugar in sucrose, which is, in fact, a more complex sugar of the type known as a **disaccharide** (*di*, two; *saccharum*, sugar). As explained in Section 1.2, sucrose comprises a molecule of glucose linked to a molecule of fructose, by the removal of the elements of water.

The test for sucrose is, therefore, first to split, or **hydrolyse**, the molecule by warming with dilute acid, and then to test for the reducing sugars which will form the products. Proceed as follows:

Corrosive

Place a little cane-sugar in a test-tube and add 2 cm³ of dilute hydrochloric acid. Boil very gently for two minutes, taking care to point the tube away from the face. Now cool the tube in a stream of tap water. Add solid sodium hydrogen carbonate until no more fizzing occurs. The solution is now neutral. Apply Benedict's or Fehling's test to this solution.

Repeat the test, using some of the foods tested in Investigation 1e.

1.4. What should we eat?

We are fortunate that in this country the number of different foods that we are able to buy is very large. We have seen that each of these foods will contain one or more of the basic foodstuffs, carbohydrates, proteins, fats, mineral salts, vitamins and water. The question arises, therefore, as to which foods it is best to eat, and in what quantity.

In Section 1.1 it was stated that the body needs food for energy, growth and good health. Foods differ in their value to the body, so, for instance, one food may be a good fuel but a poor supplier of growth materials, whilst another food may be the reverse. It is necessary, therefore, that we should eat a range of foods, in order to satisfy all of the body's requirements. Meals that do this are said to constitute a **balanced diet**. One of the world's outstanding problems is that more than half of its people fail to receive a balanced diet and are, therefore, undernourished.

1.5. The energy requirement: carbohydrates and fats

In many ways the body is like a machine and, like any other machine, will not function unless it receives a supply of fuel, from which it can release energy. We measure energy in joules (before metrication, the unit used was the food calorie), and the amount of energy present in a food may be measured by means of a **calorimeter** (see Figure 1.1).

The food is ignited in a stream of oxygen so that the energy is released as heat (and light). This heat is passed to water, the rise in temperature of which is an indication of the amount of heat released. Whilst this apparatus does not give an accurate indication of the energy content of a food, it does show which foods are good energy suppliers and which are poor suppliers. The energy content of some common foods is given in Table 1.3.

TABLE 1.3. ENERGY CONTENT OF SOME COMMON FOODS

1 gram portion of	Kilo-joules	1 gram portion of	Kilo-joules	1 gram portion of	Kilo-joules
Bread	10·2	Milk	2·8	Runner beans	0·6
Rice	15·1	Cheese	17·7	Cabbage	1·0
Cornflakes	15·3	Sardine	12·5	Lettuce	0·5
Butter	33·4	Beef	9·2	Apple	1·9
Margarine	33·4	Pork	17·6	Chocolate	22·9

(*Note:* 1 food calorie = 4·184 kilojoules)

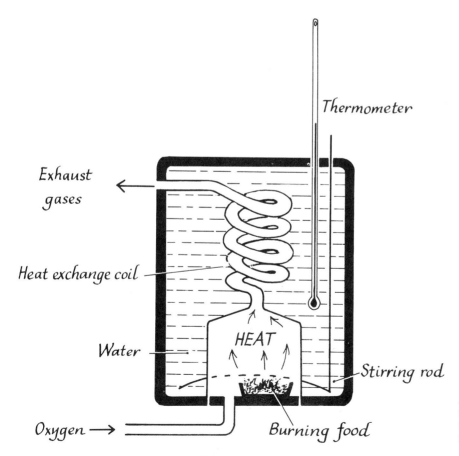

Figure 1.1 Simple calorimeter for measuring the energy content of a food

7

From the table of energy values you will see that the foods which are rich sources of energy are those containing either carbohydrates (starches and sugars) or fats. Although carbohydrates contain less energy per gram-portion than fats, they are eaten in much larger quantities. Fats are ideal substances for storage, for a small quantity of fat stores considerable energy. Where do we store fat in our bodies? Can you think of any fats or oils that are extracted from plants? From which parts of the plant are they extracted?

The next question that we must consider is the daily requirement of energy. This will not be the same for everyone, for some of us work harder, physically, than others. Thus a miner who hews coal all day will obviously require more energy-giving food each day than, say, an office worker. Other factors affecting our energy requirement are our sex, size and age. Again, we shall require more energy-giving food in winter than in summer. Why should this be so? Table 1.4 gives the daily energy requirement for various persons.

TABLE 1.4. DAILY REQUIREMENTS OF ENERGY

Person	Daily Requirement (kilojoules)
Child, aged 3 years	5 000
Boy, aged 10 years	10 500
Girl, aged 10 years	9 000
Boy, aged 15 years	16 000
Girl, aged 15 years	13 500
Man, in bed all day	7 000
Office worker (male)	12 500
Office worker (female)	10 500
Carpenter	14 500
Woodcutter	21 000 or more
Old-age pensioner	9 000

What can you conclude, from the table, about the relationship between energy requirement and age? It follows that the more energetic we are, the more carbohydrates and fats we shall need to eat. During the last war, heavy manual workers, such as miners, were given extra rations of fats to supplement their carbohydrate diet, and so provide them with the energy they needed. Remember that being a schoolboy or schoolgirl is also a very energy-demanding occupation.

1.6. The growth requirement: proteins

Our bodies are built largely from proteins which, you will remember, are complex substances comprising long chains of amino acids. Some of these amino acids are made by the body, but others have to be obtained by the breakdown of the proteins in our food. It is generally considered that each day we require one gram of protein food for each kilogram of our body weight. For an average man, this means some seventy grams of protein per day. The protein requirement for various persons is given in Figure 1.2.

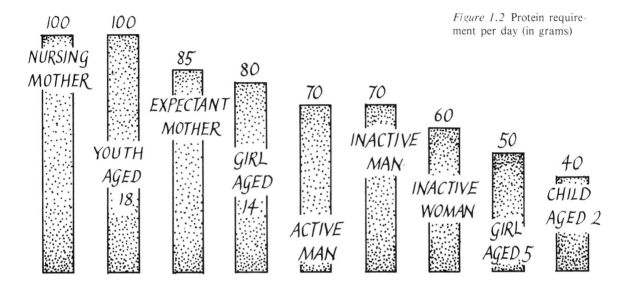

Figure 1.2 Protein requirement per day (in grams)

The main sources of protein are meat and fish, but it is also obtained from such foods as milk, cheese, egg, potato, flour, peas and beans. Some plant proteins do not contain all the amino acids that we require, so at least half of our daily protein intake should be of animal origin. Moreover, vegetable proteins are not digested as readily as those from animals.

1.7. The health requirement: vitamins and minerals

Whilst a diet comprising pure starches, sugars, proteins and fats might satisfy our energy and growth requirements, it would certainly not lead to good health. This is because the body requires small amounts of other substances, which are present in natural foods. Without a daily intake of these substances the body develops **deficiency diseases**. The first group of these substances that we will consider is called the **vitamins**. Let us take an example of one of these.

The disease called **scurvy** has serious effects, for the sufferer becomes very weak, blood vessels burst beneath the skin, the gums develop ulcers and teeth may fall out. Those most likely to develop scurvy are sailors, soldiers, members of expeditions, and people such as Laplanders who live in very cold places. In 1601, Sir James Lancaster introduced the provision of fruit juice on board ships after it was realized that this prevented the sailors from developing scurvy. We now know that as little as half an orange per day will suffice to hold the disease at bay. The substance present in fruit juice which has such powerful effects is known as **vitamin C** (now known to be ascorbic acid). Apart from citrus fruits, which are the richest source, the vitamin occurs in green vegetables, such as cabbages and Brussels sprouts. The vitamin is destroyed by prolonged boiling and by keeping food hot for some time before serving.

At one time, only four vitamins were known to be essential for man's health; these are known as vitamins A, B, C and D. We now know that there are many such substances. Thus vitamin B is actually a group of vitamins (the vitamin B complex). Further information about vitamins will be found in Table 1.5.

TABLE 1.5. SOME ESSENTIAL VITAMINS

	Vitamin	Use in Body	Good Sources
Fat-soluble vitamins	A	Essential for health of certain glands (for example, tear glands), normal night vision, normal growth of cells and prevention of skin infections. Deficiency causes night-blindness and skin infections.	Cod-liver oil, sardines, halibut oil, milk, butter, eggs, carrots, green vegetables, tomatoes.
	D	Essential for healthy growth of bones and teeth. Deficiency in young children leads to rickets Cod (soft, deformed bones).	Formed in skin if exposed to sun's rays (or sun lamp). Cod and halibut oils, eggs, butter.
	E	Necessary for normal reproduction. In rats, deficiency causes sterility.	Green vegetables, cereals, wheat germ.
Water-soluble vitamins	B_1	Essential for healthy nerves. Deficiency leads to nervous disorders such as beri-beri (paralysis of limbs).	Wholemeal bread, wheat and rice germ, yeast, Marmite, liver, peas, beans, egg yolk.
	B_2 complex	Essential for healthy nerves and skin. Deficiency may cause pellagra (dry skin, nervous and digestive trouble).	Liver, kidney, eggs, milk, cheese, yeast, green vegetables, wholemeal bread.
	C	Essential for healthy skin, to maintain the linings of blood vessels and to increase resistance to infection. Deficiency causes scurvy (common in sailors and explorers of earlier times).	Citrus fruits (lemons, limes, oranges, grapefruit). Also other fruits, for example, tomatoes, blackcurrants, pineapples and green vegetables.

Other substances that are essential for our normal health are **minerals.** Important minerals which are used in the body are **calcium,**

iodine and **iron**. Table 1.6 summarizes their uses and indicates foods which are good sources.

TABLE 1.6. THREE ESSENTIAL MINERALS

Mineral	Use in Body	Daily Requirement	Good Sources
Calcium	Necessary for the proper hardening of teeth and bones and to assist in blood clottings.	800 mg (adult). 1 300 mg (child).	Milk (1 750 mg per litre), cheese, green vegetables.
Iron	Necessary for the production of haemoglobin, the red pigment in blood. Deficiency leads to anaemia.	15–20 mg.	Meat (especially liver), eggs, spinach, peas, beans, wheat, oatmeal, potatoes.
Iodine	Necessary for the production of thyroxin, the hormone of the thyroid gland in the neck. Deficiency leads to goitre (swollen neck).	0·1 mg.	Sea-foods, for example whelks and winkles, some natural drinking waters, iodized table salt.

It will be noticed that the amounts of vitamins and mineral salts that are required each day are very small indeed. Compared with the others, calcium is needed in large quantities, but even here one gramme per day will suffice. This can be obtained by drinking half a litre (roughly one pint) of milk. The amount of iodine required each day is minute (0·1 mg). We see, therefore, that vitamins and mineral salts have been well named 'tremendous trifles'.

1.8. The value of milk

During the early part of its life the young mammal relies on its mother's milk for its entire nourishment. It follows that milk must contain the essential requirements for healthy growth. Apart from water, the main constituents are as follows:

Proteins: caseinogen
lactalbumin
lactoglobulin
Sugar: lactose
Fat: milk fat
Minerals: calcium salts
potassium salts
iron salts
Vitamins: mainly A and B_2

To 'drink a pint of milk a day' is obviously sound advice.

11

1.9. Water

Around 75% of our body mass is water. This water occurs both within the cells and around them. The watery fluid which bathes the cells is called **lymph** (see Section 3.8). Water is essential for the chemical processes of the body, and it is vital that any loss should be made good. A 'balance sheet' showing the water gained and lost by an average man in one day is given in Table 1.7.

TABLE 1.7. DAILY BALANCE SHEET FOR WATER

Intake	cm^3	Output	cm^3
Food	1 000	Sweat	350
Drinks	1 200	Evaporation from lungs	500
From respiration	300	Urine	1 500
		Faeces	150
	2 500		2 500

Most foods contain a good proportion of water, especially fruit and vegetables. Even dry foods yield water when the products of their digestion are respired (see Chapter 2). This water is known as the **water of respiration**. Certain insects and other animals that live in very dry conditions rely on this water of respiration for their survival.

HOW THE BODY DEALS WITH FOOD

1.10. The purpose of digestion

Examine Figure 1.3, which shows the organs concerned with nutrition in the earthworm. Notice that the organs form a tube extending through the body, this tube being known as the **alimentary canal**, or **gut**. Food enters this canal through the **mouth** and waste matter leaves it through the **anus**. Notice, also, that although the alimentary canal of the earthworm is almost a straight tube it has various parts. These serve various functions in dealing with food. The alimentary canal of man is shown in Figure 1.9. Again, it is a tube which extends from mouth to anus, and is composed of various parts. How does it differ from the simple canal of the earthworm?

Further examination of Figure 1.3 will show that the cavity, or **lumen**, of the canal is in direct connection with the surroundings of the animal, and any food within the canal is not really within the tissues of the body, any more than it would be if it were placed on the outside skin. Thus food in the alimentary canal is separated from body tissues by the wall of the gut.

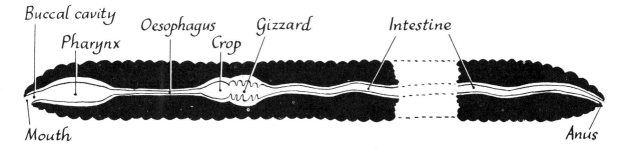

Buccal cavity Oesophagus Gizzard Intestine
Pharynx Crop

Mouth Anus

In Figure 1.4 you will see that the wall of the earthworm's intestine is well supplied with blood vessels, and this is true, also, of the intestines of higher animals. For food materials to be delivered to the tissues of the body, it is necessary for them to first pass into the blood stream. They can only do this by passing through the lining of the intestine itself, or, as we say, they must be **absorbed** into the blood.

In the following investigations we will represent the lining of the gut by a length of cellulose tubing.

Figure 1.3 Diagram to show the alimentary canal of the earthworm

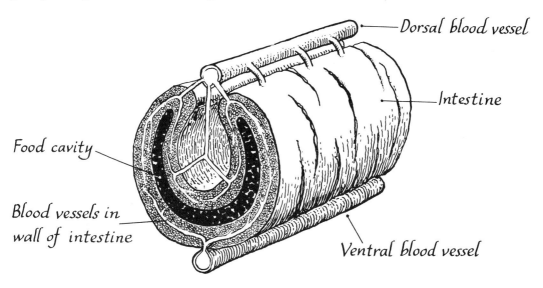

Dorsal blood vessel

Intestine

Food cavity

Blood vessels in wall of intestine

Ventral blood vessel

Investigation 1g. To compare the ability of glucose and starch to pass through a membrane

Figure 1.4 Part of the intestine of the earthworm

Begin by adding a mixture of glucose and starch to some water. Cut off a 300 mm length of cellulose (Visking) tubing, wet one end and tie a knot in it. Using a syringe, run some of the starch–glucose 'solution' into the tubing and then knot the open end. Rinse the outside of the tubing to remove any of the solution that has run down the side. Now set up the tubing as shown in Figure 1.5. Leave the apparatus for a few minutes and then, using a clean syringe, remove some of the water surrounding the Visking tubing. Test this water

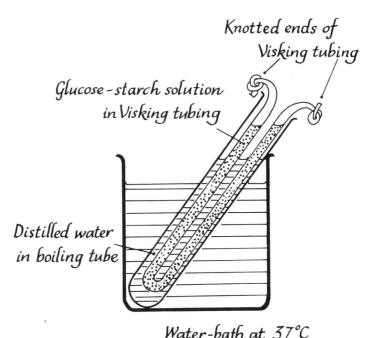

Knotted ends of
Visking tubing

Glucose-starch solution
in Visking tubing

Distilled water
in boiling tube

Water-bath at 37°C

Figure 1.5 Investigating which substances are digested

Harmful

Corrosive

with (a) 'iodine solution' for the presence of starch (see Investigation 1b) and (b) Benedict's or Fehling's solution for the presence of a reducing sugar (see Investigation 1a). Repeat these tests with samples taken from the boiling tube at intervals of several minutes.

Which of the following statements summarizes the results of your investigation?

1. Neither starch nor glucose can pass through the tubing.
2. Both starch and glucose can pass through the tubing.
3. Starch, but not glucose, can pass through the tubing.
4. Glucose, but not starch, can pass through the tubing.

The lining of the alimentary canal acts very much like the tubing in your investigation, for it permits the passage of some substances but not others. This raises the question as to what decides whether a particular substance is absorbed or not. We may get an insight into the answer to this question if we remind ourselves of the difference between the molecules of glucose and starch (see Section 1.2). Glucose, you remember, is a relatively simple molecule naving the formula $C_6H_{12}O_6$. Starch, on the other hand, is a 'long-chain' molecule, or polymer, formed by the linkage of many molecules of glucose, accompanied by the removal of water.

$$\begin{array}{ccc} n \text{ molecules of} & \text{one molecule} & n \text{ molecules} \\ \text{glucose} & \text{of starch} & + & \text{of water} \end{array}$$

We can represent this process with 'poppit' beads (see Figure 1.6). Each bead represents a glucose unit, whilst the whole necklace repre-

14

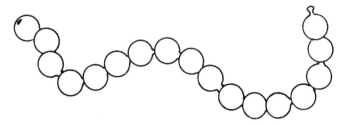

BEADS REPRESENT GLUCOSE MOLECULES

NECKLACE REPRESENTS STARCH MOLECULE

Figure 1.6 Comparing glucose and starch

sents the starch molecule. This is an over-simplification, for we know that the starch molecule is branched.

We are now in a position to understand why glucose can pass through the lining of the gut, but the starch cannot. It is as if the lining was porous and the pores allow the passage of the small glucose molecules but hold back the larger starch molecules. We can imitate this in the following investigation.

Investigation 1h. Imitating absorption

Divide some 'poppit' beads into two groups. Leave the beads in one group unconnected, but join the others up to form a necklace. Now place all of the beads on a coarse sieve, the meshes of which are a little larger than the bead. Shake the sieve and observe how it separates the individual beads from the necklace. Think of the sieve as the lining of the gut, the beads as the glucose molecules and the necklace as the starch molecule.

Our work has shown us that only small molecules are able to be absorbed by the gut. You will remember, however, that most of our food comprises substances with large molecules, like those of starch. It follows, therefore, that before absorption can occur, these large molecules must be broken down to smaller ones. This process, whereby complex, insoluble substances, such as starch, are broken down to simple, soluble substances, such as glucose, is called **digestion** (see Figure 1.7).

In the case of starch digestion, the process will be the reversal of the equation given earlier in this section. The large starch molecule will be split, accompanied by the taking up of water. This process is referred to as **hydrolysis**.

1.11. The agents of digestion: enzymes

The hydrolysis of starch can be brought about in a test-tube, as shown in the following investigation.

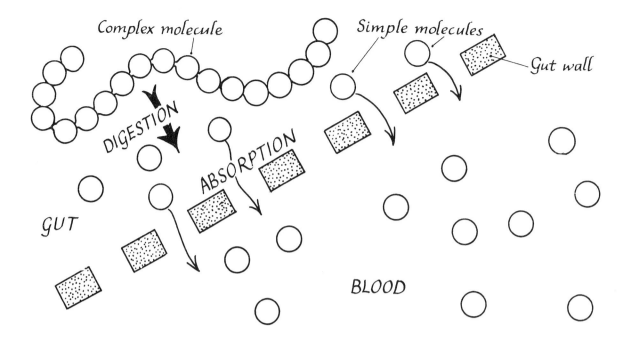

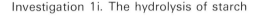

Figure 1.7 Diagram to illustrate the purpose of digestion

Harmful   Corrosive

Harmful

Investigation 1i. The hydrolysis of starch

Into each of two test-tubes place 2 cm^3 of 0·5% starch solution. Put one tube aside as a control. To the starch solution in the other tube add 1 cm^3 of dilute hydrochloric acid and boil gently for ten to fifteen minutes. Cool, and add solid sodium hydrogen carbonate until no more fizzing occurs. The solution is now neutral. Test both the boiled and the control tube for the presence of starch (see Investigation 1b) and a reducing sugar (see Investigation 1a). Does your investigation indicate that any hydrolysis has occurred?

It is obvious that the body cannot bring about the breakdown of complex molecules in this way. The next investigation will show just how easily it can accomplish the hydrolysis.

Investigation 1j. The action of saliva and diastase on starch

Using a wax pencil, mark out a white tile as shown in Figure 1.8b. Also mark three boiling tubes as follows: C (for control), D (for diastase) and S (for saliva). Into each tube place 10 cm^3 of 0·5% starch solution. Add nothing further to the control tube. To tube D add 10 cm^3 of 2·5% diastase solution. To tube S add saliva from your mouth (as much as you can). Place all three tubes in a water-bath (see Figure 1.8a), which is maintained approximately at body temperature (37 °C). Using glass rods, place a drop of solution from each tube on the white tile, in squares C1, D1 and S1 respectively. To each add one drop of 'iodine solution' from a dropping bottle.

16

Compare the colour and grain size of the precipitate in each square. Repeat the tests at one-minute intervals. using a new line of squares for each set of tests.

In which tubes has the starch been hydrolysed? What brings this about most rapidly? What result would you expect if, at the end of these tests, you were to test each tube for the presence of a reducing sugar? Perform such tests and see if your deductions are correct.

We see, therefore, that the breakdown of starch can be brought about (without the need for boiling) by diastase. a substance extracted from barley seeds. Moreover, saliva must contain a substance similar to diastase as it also breaks down starch. Such substances, which cause difficult chemical changes to occur so readily, are called **enzymes**. The diastase-like enzyme in saliva is called **ptyalin** (pronounced *tie-ah-lin*). As food passes down the alimentary canal, digestive juices, of which saliva is an example, are added to it. These juices contain many different enzymes which help to bring about digestion of the various sorts of food.

The name enzyme is derived from two words, *en* (in) and *zymos*

Figure 1.8 Action of saliva and diastase on starch

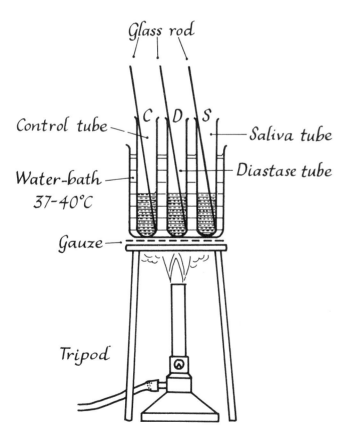

TEST	C	D	S
1			
2			
3			
4			
5			
6			
7			
8			

LAYOUT OF WHITE TILE

A   B

17

(yeast), reminding us of Louis Pasteur's early work on these sub-stances, when he was investigating the fermentation of sugar by yeast.

It should be realized that in their action enzymes closely resemble the substances known to chemists as catalysts. Indeed, enzymes are often referred to as **biological catalysts**. Enzymes do not function only in digestion, but are widespread in plants and animals, playing a vital part in many of their chemical processes.

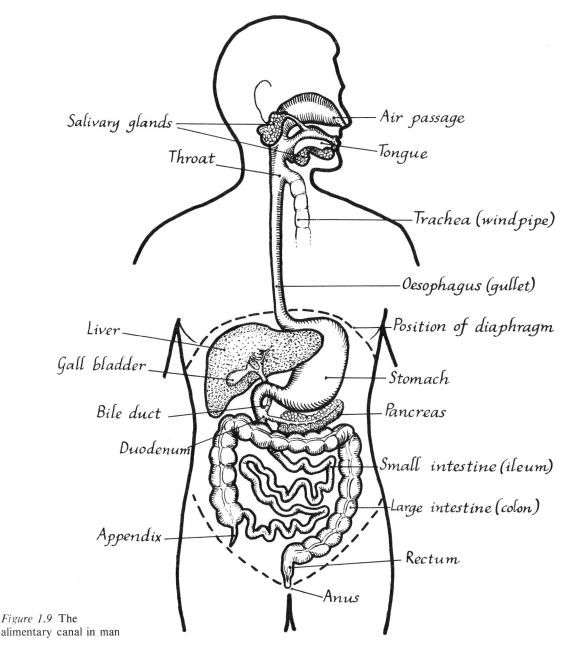

Figure 1.9 The alimentary canal in man

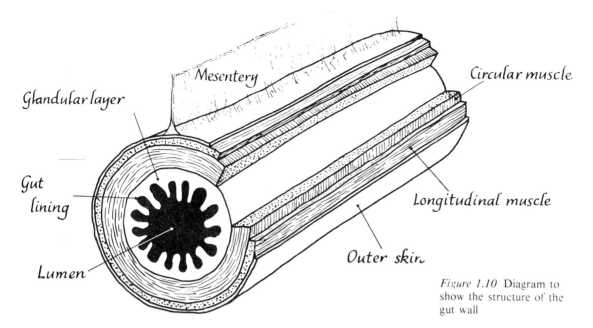

Glandular layer

Mesentery

Circular muscle

Gut lining

Longitudinal muscle

Lumen

Outer skin

Figure 1.10 Diagram to show the structure of the gut wall

1.12. How food is moved through the alimentary canal

We have seen that the alimentary canal is a tube extending from mouth to anus. Food in the mouth is swallowed and is then moved through the alimentary canal by the action of the muscles in the wall of the gut. Figure 1.10 shows the structure of this wall. Notice the thick layer of circular muscle fibres. Contraction of these fibres causes the gut to become drawn in, or constricted, just as a purse string draws in the neck of a purse. Contraction of the longitudinal muscles returns the gut to its former shape.

When there is no food in the gut these muscles are relaxed. Food causes the tube to become swollen, or distended, and this stimulates the circular muscles in this region to contract. The food is squeezed and is forced to an adjacent part of the tube, where the muscles are relaxed. Distension will now occur in this region and the contraction of the muscles will move the food on again. This process whereby food is moved along the gut is called **peristalsis** (see Figure 1.11).

Investigation 1k. To imitate peristalsis

Obtain a piece of bunsen tubing (the length is not important). Into one end force a marble, ball-bearing or orange pip, which is large enough to cause the tube to bulge. With your fingers, pinch the tubing behind the object and progressively move it along. When you have reached the halfway point, flood the tubing with soapy water and see if this makes any difference to the rate of progress of the object as you force it along the second half of the tubing. Can the

19

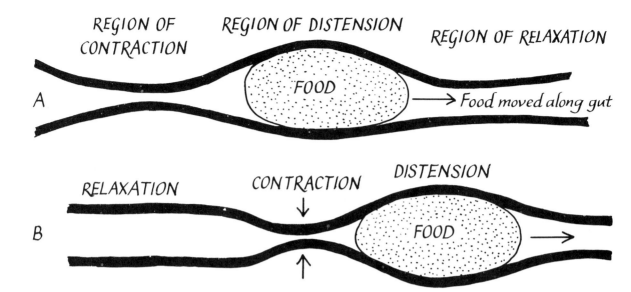

REGION OF CONTRACTION   REGION OF DISTENSION   REGION OF RELAXATION

A   FOOD   → Food moved along gut

RELAXATION   CONTRACTION   DISTENSION

B   ↓   FOOD   →   ↑

Figure 1.11 Diagram to illustrate peristalsis

process be reversed? Can you think what lubricates the alimentary canal? When is peristalsis reversed?

1.13. Digestion in the mouth

In the mouth food is chewed, or **masticated**, by the action of the jaws and teeth, and is mixed with **saliva**. Mastication renders the food small enough to be swallowed and allows saliva to mix thoroughly with it. Saliva is produced by three pairs of salivary glands, whose ducts carry the saliva to the buccal cavity. The secretion of saliva is reflexly controlled (see Chapter 7), so that even before food is eaten our mouth 'waters'.

The most important constituents of saliva are ptyalin and mucin. Ptyalin is a starch-splitting enzyme, which accelerates the breakdown of cooked starch to maltose (malt sugar). This action was demonstrated in Investigation 1j. Ptyalin is unable to act on uncooked starch because such starch is encased in starch grains, the walls of which contain cellulose (the material which also forms the cell walls of plants). Ptyalin cannot act on cellulose and is, therefore, unable to reach the starch within. **Mucin** is a lubricative substance, which helps to make swallowing easier.

1.14. Swallowing

The first stage of swallowing is voluntary; that is, it is under the control of the will. The ball of chewed food is projected to the back of the throat by the tongue. The second stage is involuntary, as the muscles of the pharynx take over the action. The larynx (Adam's apple) is raised so that the opening of the trachea (windpipe) is

20

brought under the flap of tissue called the epiglottis (see Figure 1.12).
The ball of food must pass into the oesophagus (gullet), because the
entrance to the trachea is closed. The raising of the larynx prevents
food 'going down the wrong way'. Once in the oesophagus, food is
conveyed by peristalsis to the stomach.

1.15. Digestion in the stomach

The stomach is a pouch with a thick, muscular wall. The muscles
produce a churning action, causing food to be mixed thoroughly with
gastric juice, secreted by glands in the stomach lining. We will now
consider the main constituents of gastric juice and their action on
food.

a. **Pepsin** is an enzyme which acts on proteins, breaking the long-
chain molecules into shorter lengths (polypeptides).

b. **Hydrochloric acid** is secreted by special cells in the stomach
lining. This acid is needed for pepsin. Pepsin is an unusual enzyme,
for it requires fairly strong acid conditions for its action.

c. **Mucin**, in addition to its lubricative action, may serve to protect the delicate stomach lining from the damaging effects of the
acidic gastric juice.

d. **Rennin** is an enzyme which acts on the soluble protein (caseinogen) of milk, a protein which cannot be acted on by pepsin. Rennin
renders this protein partly insoluble, forming curds which separate
from the soluble fraction, or whey. The curds are then acted on by
the pepsin. Extracts containing rennin, called 'rennet', are used in the
making of junket and in the manufacture of some types of cheese.
In the process of digestion, rennin is of most importance in the young
mammal, when the diet is entirely milky.

Figure 1.12 The action of
swallowing

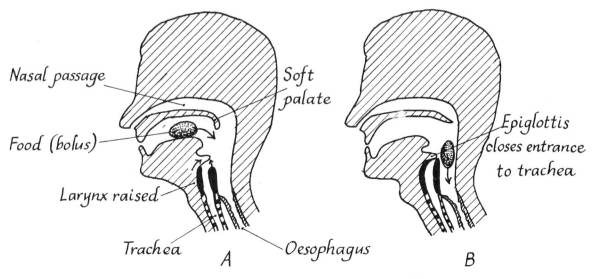

Food remains in the stomach until the churning action and the gastric juice have rendered the food down to a porridge-like consistency (now called chyme). Thus the harder the food is to liquefy, the longer it will remain in the stomach. Meat is retained longer than carbohydrates, whilst fats are retained longest of all. Hence the saying that a very greasy meal lies 'heavy on the stomach' has truth in it. An ordinary mixed meal is through the stomach in about three hours.

1.16. Digestion in the small intestine

The exit from the stomach is controlled by a muscular ring called the **pyloric sphincter**. This opens at intervals, allowing the contracting stomach to force food into the small intestine. The term 'small' refers only to diameter, for this part of the alimentary canal is very long, being some six to seven metres in man. The first part of the small intestine is called the **duodenum**, and this houses the **pancreas** in its loop. The pancreas is a thin sheet of glandular tissue which secretes **pancreatic juice**. This passes down a duct which is joined by the bile duct from the liver. It should be realized that the pancreas is also an important endocrine organ, for it secretes the hormone insulin (see Chapter 8). Bile juice has little digestive function, though it does assist in the breakdown of fats to small droplets (emulsification).

Pancreatic juice, on the other hand, is a vital digestive juice, for it contains three important enzymes:

a. **Trypsin** is a powerful, protein-splitting enzyme which only becomes active when combined with enterokinase, a substance secreted by the intestinal wall. Trypsin converts the proteins in meat, fish, eggs, etc., into simpler, soluble polypeptides.

b. **Amylase** is an enzyme having the same effect on starches as the ptyalin in saliva; it converts them to maltose.

c. **Lipase** is an enzyme which converts fats to propane – 1, 2, 3, – triol (glycerol) and fatty acids.

The wall of the small intestine also contains glands which secrete a digestive juice (**intestinal juice** or succus entericus). The enzymes in this juice complete the digestion of food. They are as follows:

a. **Peptidase** (erepsin) converts polypeptides to amino acids.

b. **Sucrase** converts sucrose (cane-sugar) to glucose and fructose.

c. **Maltase** converts maltose to glucose.

d. **Lactase** converts lactose (milk-sugar) to glucose and galactose.

e. **Lipase** converts fats to glycerol and fatty acids.

1.17. Absorption of the digestive products

The surface area of the inner lining of the small intestine is greatly increased by means of folds bearing tiny projections called **villi** which extend like the hairs on a carpet (see Figure 1.13). These projections cover the whole lining. There are over five million of them, which are constantly lengthening, shortening and swaying as they come into contact with digested food. Within the villus are blood and lymph vessels, into which the products of digestion are absorbed.

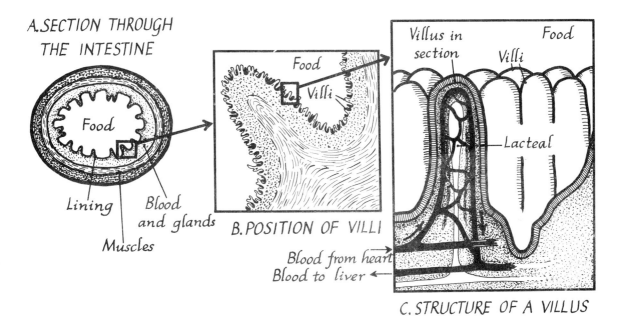

A. SECTION THROUGH THE INTESTINE

B. POSITION OF VILLI

C. STRUCTURE OF A VILLUS

Figure 1.13 Structure of the small intestine

Simple sugars (glucose, fructose and galactose) from carbohydrate digestion and amino acids from protein digestion pass into the blood stream and are carried to the **liver**. This vital organ controls the food content of the blood, storing surplus sugar as **glycogen**, and breaking down unwanted amino acids. Blood leaving the liver has a constant composition.

The products of fat digestion pass into the lacteals and are carried into the **lymphatic system**. Eventually, they reach the general circulation via a duct which joins the vena cava at the base of the neck. Fats which are not used immediately are stored under the skin or around vital organs such as the heart and kidneys.

1.18. Fate of the undigested matter

The food that we eat contains some substances, such as cellulose, that we are unable to digest. These substances, together with large quantities of water, pass into the **large intestine** or **colon**, which is wider in diameter but less than a quarter of the length of the small intestine. Some four-fifths of the water content is absorbed into the blood, leaving a semi-solid waste. Glands in the wall of the colon add much mucin to this waste, to lubricate its passage through the

23

bowel (the descending part of the colon). The bowel depends for its action on the presence of solid matter, or **roughage**. This distends the wall and promotes peristalsis (see Section 1.12). Failure of peristalsis is called constipation, and leads to the accumulation of waste matter in the bowel. Apart from the discomfort caused, constipation is not conducive to good health, and may lead to poor complexion, etc. A regular routine of bowel evacuation, together with a diet containing ample cellulose roughage, will prevent constipation. Frequent use of purgatives, such as castor oil, senna, Epsom salts, etc., is to be avoided.

Test your understanding

Copy and complete the following paragraphs:

Food provides a source of . . . .[1] as well as materials for the . . . .[2] of the body. Starches and . . . .[3] are both carbohydrates and are rich in energy. Proteins are body-building substances and are composed of units called . . . .[4] Proteins and starches are similar, chemically, in that they are both . . . .[5] or long-chain compounds. The type of food having the highest energy content is . . . .[6], and is commonly stored by plants in their . . . .[7]

Food comprises substances many of which are not . . . .[8] in water and cannot be . . . .[9] through the wall of the gut. The process whereby these substances are rendered simple and soluble is called . . . .[10] Digestive juices contain substances called . . . .[11] which accelerate the breakdown process.

1. Give three examples of each of the following: foods containing sugar; foods containing starch; foods containing protein; foods containing fat.
2. Explain why a girl of fourteen years needs more protein in her diet than a blacksmith.
3. Why do some people take halibut oil capsules regularly?
4. Name three foods which have vitamins added by the manufacturer. In each case state which vitamins are added.
5. Why are citrus fruits of special importance in our diet?
6. Why is it necessary to add iodine to table salt?
7. In what sense is milk the ideal food? Has it any deficiencies?
8. What do we mean by a balanced diet?
9. Mention three important ways in which the alimentary canal of man differs from that of the earthworm.
10. What is peristalsis and how is it brought about?
11. What are the functions of saliva?
12. Why is rennin of less importance in an adult than in a baby?
13. List four substances which are the end-products of the digestive process. Which of these substances can be stored in the liver and in what form?
14. How is it that the internal surface of the small intestine is so large?
15. What is roughage, and why is it an important constituent of our diet?

Chapter 2

The Release of Energy: Respiration

2.1. The meaning and purpose of respiration

Respiration is frequently confused with the process of breathing. Respiration is in fact concerned with the liberation of energy which is so vital to the body, whilst breathing is the process of filling and emptying the lungs to bring air into contact with the blood. Energy is obtained from food which contains complex chemicals such as glucose. The glucose molecule contains atoms of carbon, hydrogen and oxygen held together by chemical bonds. Energy is required for the formation of these chemical bonds, and when they are broken this energy is released. Respiration is an **oxidation** process which occurs in a living cell. Oxygen is usually necessary for this process.

2.2. Combustion of glucose

It has been stated that the basis of respiration is the oxidation or burning of glucose in oxygen. Let us try to investigate this and the nature of the by-products.

Investigation 2a. To see what is produced when glucose is burnt in oxygen

Take a clean gas jar filled with dry oxygen. Place a small piece of solid glucose in a deflagrating spoon and set fire to it by holding it for a moment or two in a bunsen flame. When it is burning with a pale blue flame, plunge it into the gas jar of dry oxygen. Watch carefully and record what happens (see Figure 2.1). (*Try to prevent molten glucose from spilling over the gas jar as it is difficult to clean off and may even crack the jar.*)

Feel the side of the gas jar. Is it warm? Have any drops of a colourless liquid condensed on the side of the gas jar? What liquid do you think it is? Test for water by allowing a drop of the liquid to fall on white anhydrous copper (ii), sulphate (vi), or blue cobalt (ii) chloride paper. Only remove the top of the gas jar for a moment. Have any gases been produced in the gas jar? If so, what sort of gases? Carefully lower a drop of limewater suspended on a glass rod into the

Harmful

25

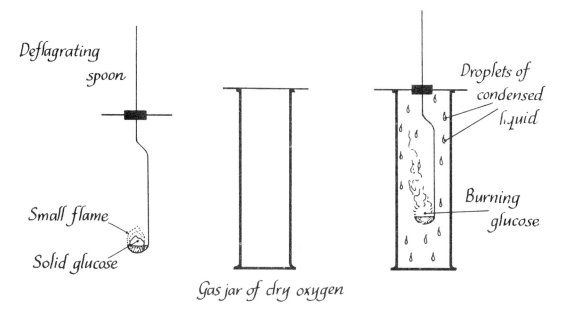

Deflagrating spoon

Small flame

Solid glucose

Droplets of condensed liquid

Burning glucose

Gas jar of dry oxygen

Figure 2.1 Combustion of glucose

gas jar for about half a minute and then examine it carefully. Has anything happened? If so, what does it indicate? Alternatively, add a few drops of methyl red indicator to the gas jar. Does the colour change? What does this indicate? Complete this equation:

$$\text{GLUCOSE} + \text{OXYGEN} \longrightarrow \dots + \dots + \dots$$

We know that air is necessary for burning and it has been suggested that respiration is a burning process.

Investigation 2b. To compare the capacities of atmospheric and exhaled air to support combustion

Take two similar gas jars, A and B. Invert gas jar A over a trough of water, as shown in Figure 2.2. Insert a piece of rubber tubing into the gas jar, put the other end in your mouth and breathe in all the air (not the water!). Now breathe out, filling the gas jar with your exhaled air. Repeat this process about six times before placing the top on the gas jar.

Place a lighted candle in both gas jar A and gas jar B (see Figure 2.3). Record how long each candle burns. Try to draw some conclusion from your results.

2.3. Respiration and combustion

Respiration can be compared with a familiar physical process, the action of the internal combustion engine of a motorcycle. A motorcycle will not run without petrol. The motorcycle engine also needs air which is mixed with petrol vapour in the carburettor. In the

26

cylinder the spark plug ignites the mixture, which burns as the oxygen oxidizes the petrol to water vapour, carbon dioxide and carbon monoxide. Useful energy is released in the form of the motion of the motorcycle, and useless energy in the form of heat and noise. The waste products are the water vapour, carbon dioxide and carbon monoxide gas forced from the exhaust.

In man, this process of energy release, called respiration, takes place in all the living cells of the body. Let us consider a muscle fibre. The fuel or respiratory substrate is glucose, which is obtained from the food as a result of digestion. The oxygen enters the blood stream in the lungs. The blood carries both the glucose and the oxygen to the muscle where the glucose is oxidized and converted to water vapour and carbon dioxide. The energy released brings about the contraction of the muscle fibre and the waste carbon dioxide and water are carried by the blood to the lungs for excretion.

GLUCOSE + OXYGEN $\longrightarrow$ ENERGY + CARBON DIOXIDE + WATER

2.4. Detecting respiration

Investigation 2c. To discover the effect of carbon dioxide gas on a clear solution of limewater

Harmful

Take two small test-tubes and prepare a cork and delivery tube to fit into one of them. Place a marble chip (calcium carbonate) in one tube and a few cubic centimetres of limewater (calcium hydroxide) in the other. Add a few cubic centimetres of dilute hydrochloric acid to the marble chip. The fizzing shows that carbon dioxide gas is being produced. Connect the test-tubes by means of the delivery tube,

Figure 2.2 (left) Obtaining re-breathed air

Figure 2.3 (below, A and B) Comparing the capacities of atmospheric and exhaled air to support combustion

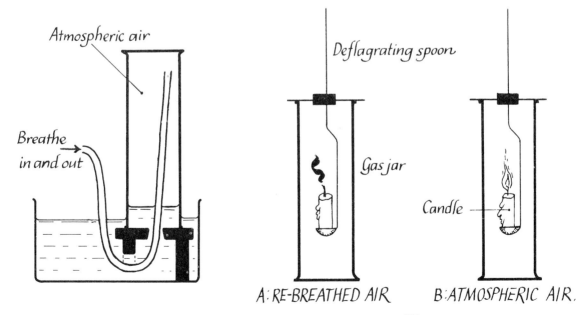

so that the carbon dioxide bubbles through the limewater (see figure 2.4).

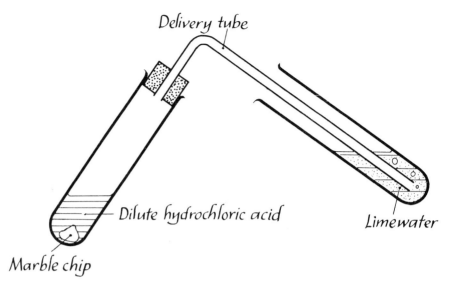

Delivery tube

Dilute hydrochloric acid

Limewater

Marble chip

Figure 2.4 A test for carbon dioxide

Record what happens to the limewater. Does the same thing occur in the test-tubes of the other members of your class? If so, this can be used as a test to indicate the presence of carbon dioxide gas.

The milkiness produced in this test is an insoluble precipitate of calcium carbonate (chalk, a different type of calcium carbonate from marble).

Investigation 2d. Does exhaled air contain carbon dioxide?

Blow air through a straw into limewater (see Figure 2.5). What happens? Does this show that you are producing carbon dioxide and therefore respiring?

Toxic

Flammable

A rather more delicate test for the presence of carbon dioxide is the use of hydrogen carbonate/indicator solution. When carbon dioxide gas passes through water, it combines with it to form a very weak acid (carbonic acid). The hydrogen carbonate/indicator solution contains two very sensitive indicators, cresol red and thymol blue, which change from orange to yellow in the presence of weak carbonic acid.

Investigation 2e. To compare the carbon dioxide content of inhaled air with that of exhaled air

Toxic

Flammable

Connect two wash bottles by means of a T-piece, as in Figure 2.6, noting carefully the arrangement of the tubes. Place limewater or hydrogen carbonate/indicator solution in the two flasks. Place the T-piece in the mouth and steadily breathe in and out (not too hard or the

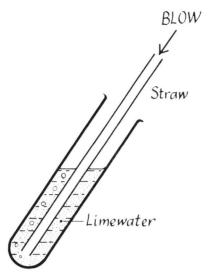

BLOW

Straw

Limewater

Figure 2.5 Blowing into limewater

solution may enter your mouth). Note that inhaled atmospheric air is drawn through the indicator in the left-hand flask and exhaled air is blown through the indicator in the right-hand flask. After a few minutes, compare the contents of the two flasks and draw your conclusions.

Investigation 2f. To find out whether other living organisms produce carbon dioxide

Place a few cubic centimetres of hydrogen carbonate/indicator into two boiling tubes, marked A and B. Place a platform of perforated zinc

Toxic

Flammable

Figure 2.6 The 'Huff and Puff' apparatus

BREATHE IN AND OUT

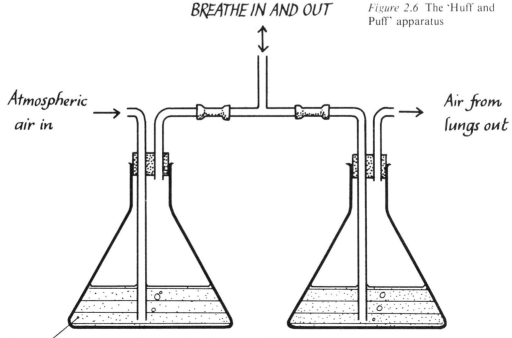

Atmospheric air in

Air from lungs out

Limewater or hydrogencarbonate/indicator solution   29

or a loose plug of steel wool inside tube A, and place several wood-lice on it (see Figure 2.7). Cork both boiling tubes. Observe the tubes after about ninety minutes. Has there been any change? If so, what? Why is tube B necessary? Repeat the investigation using other small invertebrates, such as gentles, mealworms, etc. Do you obtain similar results? What does this show?

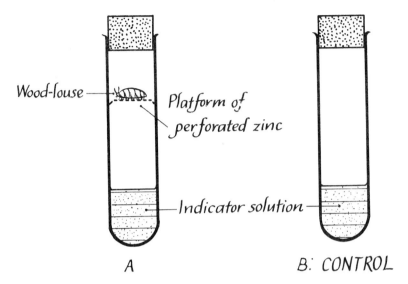

Figure 2.7 Apparatus used to discover if small creatures produce carbon dioxide

2.5. Internal and external respiration

Our discussion so far has dealt with the chemical process of energy release which is vital to every living cell. The capacity of a cell or an organism to store, liberate and utilize energy is, perhaps, the primary indication of life. This process is variously called cellular, tissue or internal respiration. External respiration, on the other hand, is concerned with supplying all living cells of the body with the raw materials needed for the process, and with removing all the waste products.

Man's main problem is the oxygen supply. We learnt in the previous chapter how food was digested and distributed to the cells of the body which needed it. At sea-level 21% of the atmospheric air is oxygen, so there is plenty available. But how is it to get to the cells if man is covered by an impervious, protective skin? It must enter the blood stream by diffusion, and for this to happen an enormous area of blood must be exposed to a similarly large surface area of air. Man, in common with the other terrestrial vertebrates, has lungs to enable this to happen.

Investigation 2g. To examine the structure and contents of the thorax

Examine the chest region of a skinned rabbit. Can you see the outlines of the ribs within the muscle? Can you see the position of the sternum or breast-bone? Notice the **intercostal** muscles between the ribs. The intercostal muscles are arranged in two sets, the internal intercostal muscles which are inserted on the inner side of the chest wall and the outer intercostal muscles which are inserted on the outer side of the chest wall. These are very important for breathing. With the tip of a pair of large scissors, pierce the intercostal muscle between the lower two ribs. Cut through this muscle on each side and sever the sternum. Now cut through the ribs along each side of the animal so that the ventral surface of the thorax can be raised to display the contents of the thorax.

Biological

The pinkish, spongy organs occupying much of the space are the lungs. Why are they this colour? The dark red organ more or less in the centre is the heart. Can you see the large blood vessels connecting the heart to the lungs? Note the sheet of muscle separating the thorax from the abdomen; this is the **diaphragm.** It is very important in breathing.

Investigation 2h. To examine the lungs and heart of a large mammal

Obtain a 'pluck', the contents of the thorax of a sheep or a pig. The heart is easily identified. Try to discover the large pulmonary arteries and the pulmonary veins. Notice how the windpipe or **trachea** divides into two bronchi, one **bronchus** passing into the right lung and the other into the left lung. At the top of the trachea is the voice box, or **larynx.** What is the function of the rings of cartilage around the trachea? Are these rings complete?

Biological

To see how elastic the lungs are, insert a glass tube or pump connector into the trachea. Seal it to prevent leakage of air by tying a piece of string or wire around it, and then blow up the lungs.

2.6. External respiration

External respiration can be considered in three stages:
a. Ventilation of the lungs, or breathing.
b. Gaseous exchange in the lungs and in the body tissues.
c. The transport of oxygen and carbon dioxide by the blood. See Section 3.2a.

2.7. Ventilation of the lungs, or breathing

Inhalation

The lungs are enclosed inside the air-tight rib cage (see Figure 2.8). To breathe in, the dome-shaped diaphragm contracts and is pulled down and flattened. At the same time, the external intercostal muscles contract, pulling the ribs and sternum upwards and outwards (see

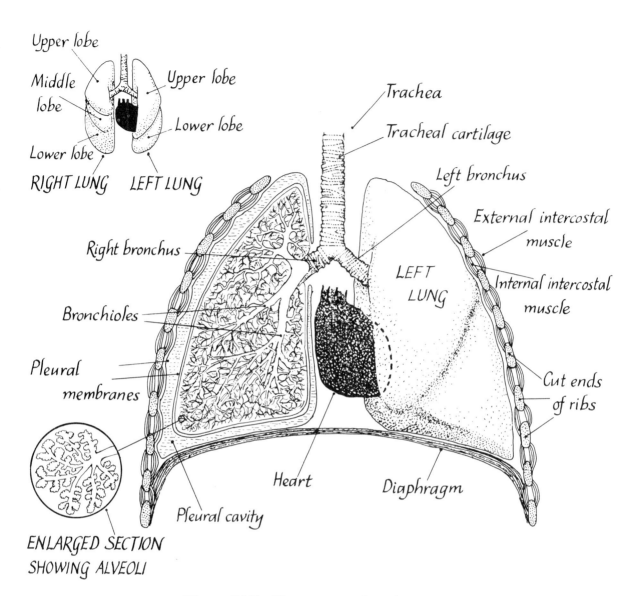

Upper lobe

Middle lobe

Lower lobe

RIGHT LUNG

Upper lobe

Lower lobe

LEFT LUNG

Right bronchus

Bronchioles

Pleural membranes

Trachea

Tracheal cartilage

Left bronchus

External intercostal muscle

Internal intercostal muscle

LEFT LUNG

Cut ends of ribs

Heart

Pleural cavity

Diaphragm

ENLARGED SECTION SHOWING ALVEOLI

Figure 2.8 The contents of the thorax of man

Figure 2.11). These two actions increase the volume inside the thorax, thereby reducing the internal pressure relative to the external pressure. This difference in pressure causes air to rush in through the nose or the mouth and down the air passages to the lungs (see Figure 2.9). Air passing through the nose is treated before it reaches the lungs: it is warmed as it passes over the scroll-like bones in the nose, it is filtered as it passes over cells with hair-like projections, and it is moistened by mucus secreted by some of the cells of the nose. Air breathed through the mouth misses this treatment and could increase the likelihood of infection in the throat and lungs.

The air then passes over the vocal cords, in the larynx, into the trachea. The trachea splits into the right and left bronchi. The bronchi split into **bronchioles** which become finer and finer, ending

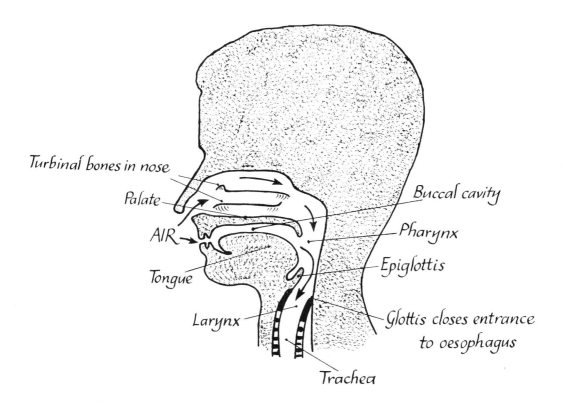

Turbinal bones in nose

Palate

AIR

Tongue

Larynx

Buccal cavity

Pharynx

Epiglottis

Glottis closes entrance
to oesophagus

Trachea

eventually in tiny air sacs called **alveoli** (see Figure 2.10). The walls of the alveoli are so thin that the air is in close proximity to the blood.

Figure 2.9 The respiratory passages

Exhalation

This is the reverse of inhalation. The external intercostal muscles relax and the internal intercostal muscles contract allowing the ribs

Figure 2.10 A terminal cluster of alveoli

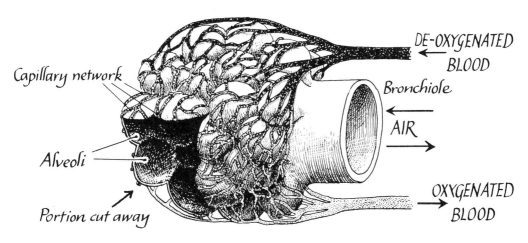

Capillary network

Alveoli

Portion cut away

DE-OXYGENATED
BLOOD

Bronchiole

AIR

OXYGENATED
BLOOD

and sternum to return to their former position. The diaphragm relaxes and is pushed by the abdominal organs back to its dome shape (see Figure 2.11). This increases the internal pressure relative to the external pressure and air is forced out of the lungs.

The normal respiratory rate of an adult, at rest, is about eighteen breaths per minute.

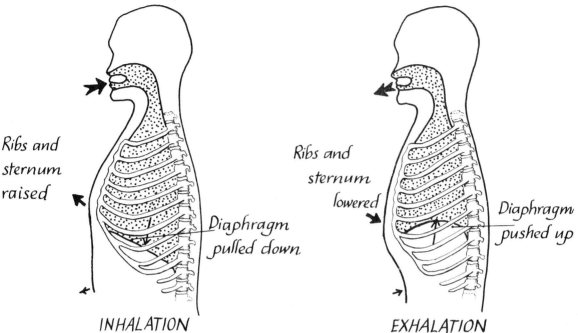

Figure 2.11 The action of breathing

Investigation 2i. To examine the action of the intercostal muscles

Use meccano or wooden spatulas to construct the model shown in Figure 2.12. Fix an elastic band between A and B. What happens? (This is how the fibres of the external intercostal muscles are arranged.). Now fix the elastic between points C and D. What happens? (This is how the fibres of the internal intercostal muscles are arranged.)

Investigation 2j. To determine the effect of exercise on the respiratory rate

Sit quietly in a chair and get a friend to count the number of breaths you take per minute. Then do some vigorous exercise, such as stepping up on to a chair and down again about a dozen times or running twice round the playground, and then get your friend to measure your respiratory rate again. Compare the two results. Are your classmates' results similar? How do you account for your results?

An investigation to determine the effect of exercise on carbon dioxide production can be incorporated with this investigation.

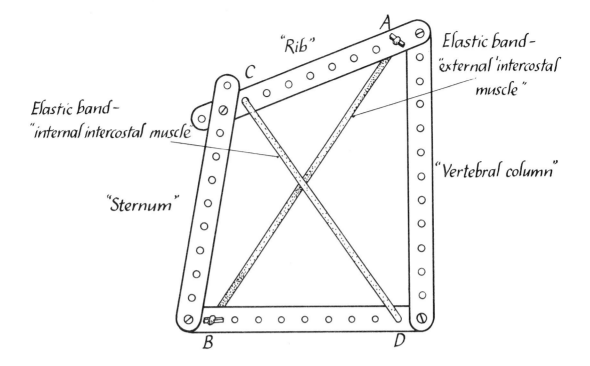

Investigation 2k. To determine the effect of exercise on the rate of carbon dioxide production

Figure 2.12 Model to show rib action

Into two wash bottles (see Figure 2.13) place equal volumes of hydrogen carbonate/indicator. Before taking the exercise suggested in Investigation 2j, and while sitting quietly, blow into the first wash bottle. With a stop-watch, or a wrist-watch with a 'sweep' second hand, record the time for the indicator to change colour from red to yellow. After exercise, repeat this procedure with the second wash bottle, and compare and explain the results.

Toxic

Flammable

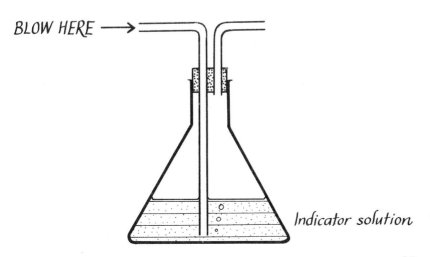

Figure 2.13 A wash bottle as used in Investigation 2k

If hydrogen carbonate/indicator is not available, limewater can be used. Place equal volumes of limewater into each wash bottle. Before taking exercise breathe into the first wash bottle and record the time taken for it to become a definite milky colour. Keep this first flask carefully on one side as your standard. After exercise, repeat the process with the second flask, carefully timing the period necessary for the limewater in the second flask to reach the same degree of milkiness as the standard in the first flask. Compare and explain your results.

2.8. Lung capacity

The average person's lungs hold about $5\,500$ cm^3 of air, but this is not changed at every breath. In a normal breath, about 500 cm^3 of air passes in and out of the lungs. This is known as **tidal air**. In an extra deep breath, a further $3\,000$ cm^3 may pass in and out of the lungs. This is known as **complemental air**. If a person breathes out vigorously he can expel another $1\,000$ cm^3, called **supplemental air**. The total amount of air that can be expelled from the lungs by forced expiration after a deep breath is known as a person's **vital capacity**. Even after this there is about $1\,000$ cm^3 of **residual air** which cannot be expelled.

TABLE 2.1. THE CAPACITY OF THE LUNGS

TOTAL CAPACITY 5 500 cm³			VITAL CAPACITY 4 500 cm³
	TIDAL AIR 500 cm³	Changed at every breath.	
	COMPLEMENTAL AIR 3 000 cm³	Changed by a deep breath.	
	SUPPLEMENTAL AIR 1 000 cm³	By forced expiration.	
	RESIDUAL AIR 1 000 cm³	Never expelled.	

Investigation 21. To measure the vital capacity

Set up the apparatus as shown in Figure 2.14. Close tap A, open tap B and turn the sink tap on. If all the joints are air-tight, water will be drawn up into the bell jar. When it reaches level 0, close tap B and turn the sink tap off. Take a very deep breath, hold your nose and place the rubber tube between your lips. Open tap A, and immediately blow all the air you possibly can from your lungs. When you can blow no more, immediately close tap A. Read off the volume of air exhaled, in cubic centimetres. This is your vital capacity.

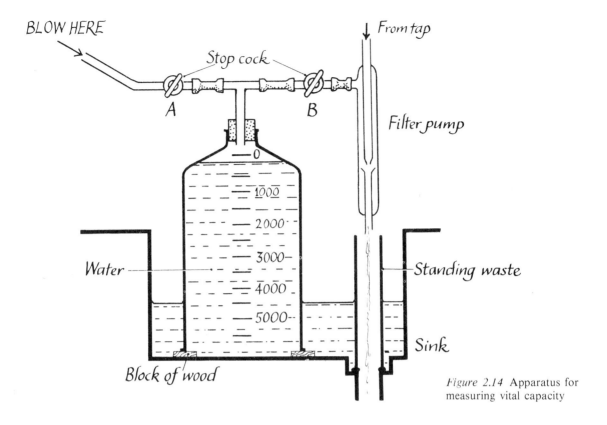

Figure 2.14 Apparatus for measuring vital capacity

Although the investigation is simpler and quicker with the apparatus used in Figure 2.14, it can also be carried out with a bell jar, a sink and a piece of rubber tubing. Invert the bell jar, fill it with water and cover the bottom with a piece of glass. Carefully turn it the correct way up and place the open end below the water-level in the sink (see Figure 2.15). Remove the sheet of glass, insert the rubber tube under the edge of the bell jar and blow. Be sure that there is enough room in the sink to take the water that you expel from the bell jar.

2.9. Failure of breathing

The contraction and relaxation of the chest muscles which bring about the breathing movements are stimulated by electrical impulses carried by the nerves. If the nerves are damaged by an accident or by a disease, such as poliomyelitis, the patient cannot breathe and would soon die if it were not for a mechanical device which breathes for him. The patient is placed in an air-tight chamber, called an iron lung, in which the air pressure is rhythmically increased and decreased. Lowering the pressure around the chest enables atmospheric air to pass into the lungs in the usual way.

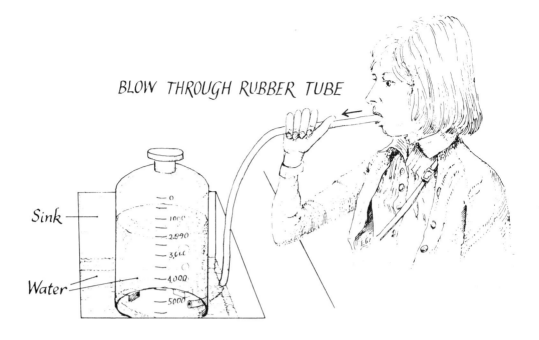

BLOW THROUGH RUBBER TUBE

Sink

Water

— 0
— 1000
— 2.090
— 3,000
— 4,000
— 5000

Figure 2.15 Alternative apparatus for measuring vital capacity

Investigation 2m. To construct a model of an iron lung

Construct the model as shown in Figure 2.16, and attach it by rubber tubing to a filter pump. Moisten a finger and periodically place it over the end of tube A. Carefully watch what happens.

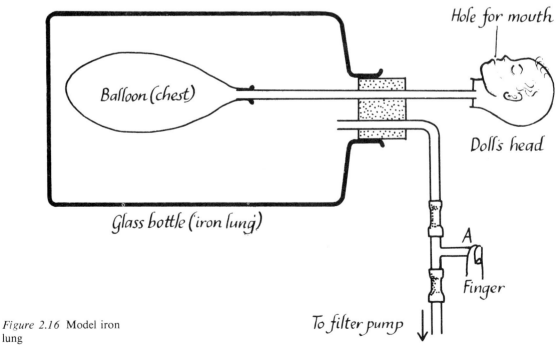

Balloon (chest)

Glass bottle (iron lung)

Hole for mouth

Doll's head

A

Finger

To filter pump

Figure 2.16 Model iron lung

2.10. Artificial respiration

A person who has been removed from the water, or who is suffering from severe gas poisoning or electric shock, or who has an obstruction in the throat, may stop breathing. The patient will be very pale and have a weak pulse. In this state, the brain is being deprived of oxygen. If nervous tissue is deprived of oxygen for more than four minutes, the damage may be irreparable, so speed is vital—literally, 'seconds count'. Mouth to mouth resuscitation, sometimes called the 'kiss of life', is probably the most effective method of artificial respiration, except for the direct use of oxygen apparatus. If you are able to carry out this method, you may save a life.

Figure 2.17 Support the patient's shoulders with a cushion so that the head falls back

Lay the patient on his back and place a folded jacket or cushion under the shoulders, thus allowing the head to drop back so that the tongue is not obstructing the air passage (see Figure 2.17). Remove any obstruction, such as false teeth, from the mouth. Pinch the patient's nostrils with the thumb and forefinger of the left hand so that no air can escape, and blow air directly into the patient's mouth. Watch for the chest to rise (see Figure 2.18).

★ WARNING. *You must never practise this technique on other people. It can be dangerous. Always use a training model.*

Figure 2.18 Blowing air into the patient's lungs

Then take your mouth away and release your fingers from the nostrils to allow the air to escape and the chest to lower (see Figure 2.19). Repeat at about four-second intervals until the patient starts to breathe on his own. Then wrap the patient in warm blankets and turn him on his side until a doctor arrives. The patient should, however, not be allowed to become overheated.

Figure 2.19 Allowing the air to escape

If your school has a training model, you will be taught this method of resuscitation. If this equipment is not available, it can be borrowed from the local branch of the Schools' Swimming Association, who will probably also be able to provide an instructor. The Ambulance Service will also be delighted to send an instructor with a model to your school to teach you this technique. There is a good film on the subject entitled *That They Might Live*, which can be obtained on loan from the Headquarters of the St John Ambulance Brigade.

2.11. Gaseous exchange in the lungs and in the tissues

Study the figures in Table 2.2 carefully and then answer these questions. Where does oxygen enter the blood stream? Where does it leave the blood stream again? Does gaseous exchange of nitrogen occur? Where does carbon dioxide enter the blood stream and where does it leave again? Is there any change in water vapour concentration? How do you account for this?

Gaseous exchange is illustrated in Figure 2.20.

Figure 2.20 Gaseous exchange

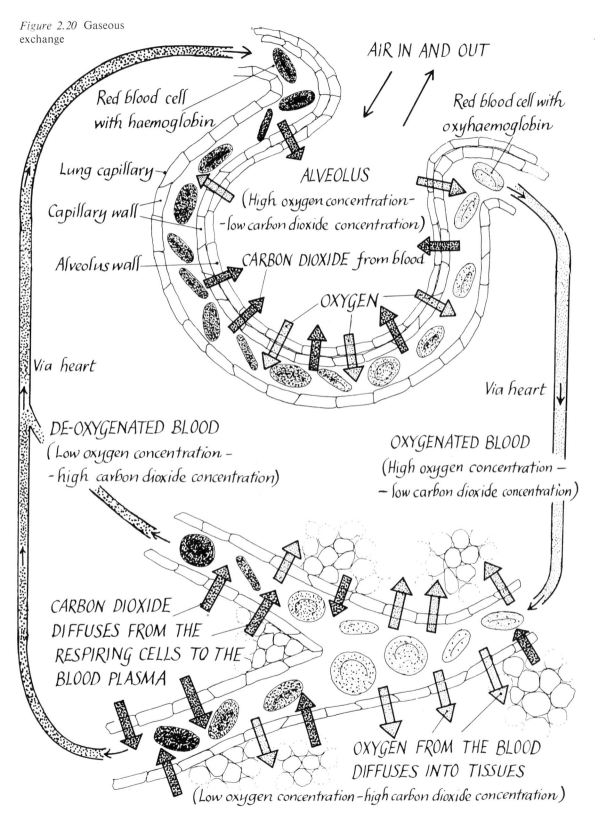

Red blood cell with haemoglobin

Lung capillary

Capillary wall

Alveolus wall

Via heart

AIR IN AND OUT

Red blood cell with oxyhaemoglobin

ALVEOLUS
(High oxygen concentration–
–low carbon dioxide concentration)

CARBON DIOXIDE from blood

OXYGEN

Via heart

DE-OXYGENATED BLOOD
(Low oxygen concentration –
–high carbon dioxide concentration)

OXYGENATED BLOOD
(High oxygen concentration –
– low carbon dioxide concentration)

CARBON DIOXIDE DIFFUSES FROM THE RESPIRING CELLS TO THE BLOOD PLASMA

OXYGEN FROM THE BLOOD DIFFUSES INTO TISSUES
(Low oxygen concentration – high carbon dioxide concentration)

TABLE 2.2. CHANGES IN THE COMPOSITION AND VOLUMES
OF RESPIRATORY GASES

	Approximate Composition of Air	
Gas	Inhaled	Exhaled
Nitrogen	79%	79%
Oxygen	21%	17%
Carbon dioxide	A trace	4%
Water vapour	Variable—less than saturation	Saturated

	Volume of Gas Carried by 100 cm³ of Blood	
Gas	Entering Lungs	Leaving Lungs
Nitrogen	0·9 cm³	0·9 cm³
Oxygen	10·6 cm³	19·0 cm³
Carbon dioxide	58·0 cm³	50·0 cm³

2.12. Internal or tissue respiration

At the beginning of this chapter, we established the following overall equation for respiration.

$$GLUCOSE + OXYGEN \longrightarrow ENERGY + CARBON\ DIOXIDE + WATER$$

This process takes place in all living cells and, even within the cell, there are special organelles called **mitochondria** concerned with the process. Tissues which need lots of energy, such as muscle cells or liver cells, have many mitochondria.

The energy produced may be converted into different forms of energy. If it is needed for storage, it will be converted to chemical energy. Excess energy may be liberated as heat energy. Some animals, such as members of the plankton (the drifting aquatic creatures) and the glow-worm, convert the energy into light energy. In the nervous system, some of the energy may be converted to electrical energy. Perhaps the most obvious use is its conversion into mechanical energy for walking or running. This energy is used for muscle contraction.

How is the energy harnessed and stored for these activities? A special chemical compound called **ATP** (short for **adenosine triphosphate**) has the phosphate part of the molecule attached by special energy bonds. When one of the phosphates is removed, energy is released and **adenosine diphosphate (ADP)** is formed. Energy is required to rebuild ATP from ADP and phosphate. ATP is thus present in cells for instant energy supply, and, like a battery, is 'recharged' for further use, the recharging process using up energy (see Figure 2.21).

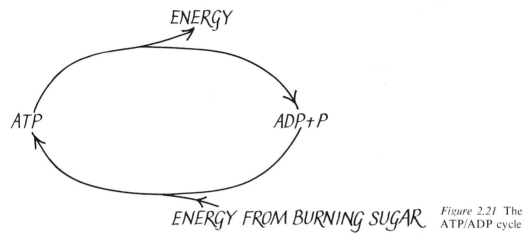

ENERGY

ATP

ADP+P

ENERGY FROM BURNING SUGAR

Figure 2.21 The ATP/ADP cycle

Investigation 2n. To investigate the effect of ATP on muscle fibre

Place a strand of muscle on a glass microscope slide which is lying on graph paper. The muscle may be taken direct from very fresh, lean meat or may be meat stored in 50% propane – 1, 2, 3 – triol (glycerol). Measure the length of the strand with the aid of the graph paper and record it. Using a syringe, add a few drops of ATP solution to the muscle. After about a minute, measure the strand of muscle again. To a second strand of muscle add a few drops of distilled water. Comment on any differences in reaction.

2.13. Energy release without oxygen

In a hundred-metre race, completed in perhaps ten seconds, a runner takes in very little oxygen—certainly not enough to liberate the energy required. Is this energy obtained from ATP? Unfortunately, ATP could supply only enough energy for about one second of such exertion, not ten. The body must therefore obtain energy on some sort of 'credit plan'. If blood is examined after severe exertion, it is found to contain more than its normal quantity of 2-hydroxy-propanoic (lactic) acid. When there is a heavy demand for energy during such exertion, glycogen in the muscles is converted to 2-hydroxypropanoic (lactic) acid; this releases energy without the use of oxygen. The accumulation of 2-hydroxypropanoic (lactic) acid is called 'oxygen debt', and its presence in the muscles gives a feeling of tiredness. After the race the runner pants, taking in oxygen in huge gulps. The 2-hydroxypropanoic (lactic) acid is then converted by the oxygen into carbon dioxide, water and energy, the latter being used to re-build ATP.

2.14. Control of respiration

The respiratory rate varies with age—from forty breaths per minute at birth, twenty-four at the age of one and about eighteen in an adult. The rate is controlled by the respiratory centre in the hind brain, or **medulla oblongata**. This respiratory centre monitors the amount of carbon dioxide in the blood flowing to the brain. If the carbon dioxide content of the blood is above normal, the respiratory rate increases. If carbon dioxide is removed from the lungs by forced breathing, then the breathing rate slows down until the carbon dioxide content of the blood returns to normal.

2.15. The lungs and health

The lining of the lungs is in constant contact with the atmosphere and is, therefore, very easily damaged. It is only recently that health authorities have realized that certain jobs are particularly hazardous to the health of the lungs. Coal miners are prone to the disease **pneumoconiosis**, which is caused by the frequent entry of coal dust into the lungs. Workers in any dusty atmosphere are liable to **silicosis**, while constant breathing of asbestos dust may lead to the very dangerous disease **asbestiosis**.

The fumes from a motorcar exhaust can present a hazard as they contain the poisonous gas carbon monoxide, which, if inhaled, drastically reduces the oxygen-carrying capacity of the blood and leads to suffocation.

The incidence of **tuberculosis**, a bacterial disease of the lungs, is rapidly falling with the stricter supervision of milk supplies and the introduction of mass X-ray for earlier detection.

However, the incidence of chronic **bronchitis** and lung **cancer** has risen in the last fifty years. Cigarette smoking has also risen over the same period. Is there any correlation between the two? Is the increase in cigarette smoking related to the increase in lung cancer? American scientists examined the records of people who had died from lung cancer. They found that there was a higher proportion of heavy smokers than the proportion of light or non-smokers! They also investigated the smoking habits of doctors and servicemen, and then recorded the numbers that died from lung cancer. It was found that those smoking twenty cigarettes per day are twenty times more likely to die of lung cancer than a non-smoker. A thirty-a-day man was thirty times more likely to die than a non-smoker. Perhaps you can draw your own conclusions.

Test your understanding

Copy and complete the following paragraphs:

Respiration is the liberation of . . . .[1] from . . . .[2] Oxygen is necessary to . . . .[3] or burn the food which is usually . . . .[4] The waste gases produced are . . . .[5] and water vapour.

The breathing movements of the chest are performed by the . . . .[6] muscles and the diaphragm. Air enters the lungs through the . . . .[7] or windpipe, which divides into two . . . .[8], one supplying each lung. The tiny branches are known as . . . .[9], and end in . . . .[10] or air sacs.

Carbon dioxide enters and . . . .[11] leaves the air sac by the process of . . . .[12] Respiration occurs in the part of the cell called the . . . .[13] Energy can be stored in the cell by the chemical called . . . .[14] . . . .[15] is a lung disease no longer common, but . . . .[16] is increasing and is probably caused by . . . .[17]

1. Distinguish between breathing and respiration.
2. Describe an investigation to establish the equation for respiration.
3. Compare respiration within a muscle cell with combustion in a motor-cycle engine.
4. Describe how you would show that both humans and woodlice breathe out carbon dioxide.
5. Explain the difference between internal respiration and external respiration.
6. Describe how you would find the average lung capacity of the children in your class.
7. Describe when and how you would administer oral resuscitation.
8. How is the rate of respiration controlled?
9. Write a short essay on the lungs and health.

Chapter 3

The Transport System: Blood

It is common knowledge that blood is a vital part of the body and that any loss of blood causes concern, demanding immediate attention. What is blood and why is it so vital to life? In the last chapter, we learnt that blood is required to transport respiratory gases. In this chapter, we shall learn that blood transports many other substances in our bodies.

3.1. The nature of blood

Let us begin our study of blood by trying to find out something about its nature. At first sight, it appears simply to be a red fluid. One of the problems in studying this red fluid is that as soon as it is released from the body it clots, or sets to a jelly. This takes only a matter of minutes. If we are to study the structure of blood, clotting must be prevented. Fortunately there are several substances which, when mixed with fresh blood, prevent clotting. Examples are sodium oxalate and magnesium sulphate.

Investigation 3a. Separating the components of blood

In this investigation a centrifuge is used. This machine enables a tube of fluid to be whirled at speed round a central pivot. This enables us to separate substances having different densities, the denser substance being thrown to the bottom of the tube leaving the less dense substance at the top.

In a centrifuge, place a tube of fresh blood to which a substance has been added to prevent clotting. Spin the tube for several minutes at as high a speed as possible. Examine the contents and compare with an untreated tube. What does this investigation tell us about whole blood? Compare your final tube with Figure 3.1.

Our investigation has shown us that blood cannot be as simple as it appears. Firstly, it must contain some 'mechanism' which brings about clotting, a mechanism which is stopped by certain chemicals. Secondly, blood is divisible into two fractions. One is a pale, straw-coloured fluid (called **plasma**) which occupies just over half the

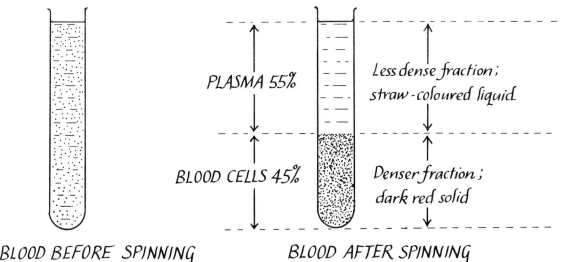

PLASMA 55%

Less dense fraction;
straw-coloured liquid

BLOOD CELLS 45%

Denser fraction;
dark red solid

BLOOD BEFORE SPINNING
IN CENTRIFUGE

BLOOD AFTER SPINNING
IN CENTRIFUGE

volume of blood. The other fraction is red and more dense, occupying just under half by volume. In the next investigation, we will discover the nature of the denser fraction.

Figure 3.1 Effect of spinning blood in a centrifuge

Investigation 3b. Making a blood smear

For this investigation you will need a microscope, two clean glass slides, a cover-slip, some 0·9% saline (solution of common salt), some ethanol, a bunsen or spirit burner, a sharp needle and a short length of string.

Make sure that the glassware is perfectly clean and ready to hand. Sterilize the needle by first dipping the end in ethanol and then heating it in a flame. Bind the string very tightly round the index finger, just below the nail. Tightness is absolutely essential; the tip of the finger should be felt to be under great pressure, due to blood being forced into it. With the needle, jab the skin just below the white 'half-moon' of the nail. A drop of blood should be exuded. Without delay, release the string and place this drop of blood on one end of one of the glass slides. Hold this slide still with one hand and, with the other hand, bring the second slide to the first at an angle of about 45°. Use this second slide to draw the blood along the first slide, making a smear. It is best to allow the blood to run sideways to the corners of the second slide, before moving lengthwise. The blood may be pushed in front of the moving slide, but better results may be obtained by drawing the blood along after it. Some practice is required to achieve an even smear (see Figure 3.2). It is important not to waste any time in smearing the drop after its release from the body. Why?

Once the smear has been made, allow it to dry in the air. Finally, add a drop or two of saline, which has a similar concentration to

Biological   **Flammable**

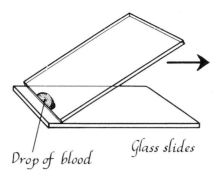

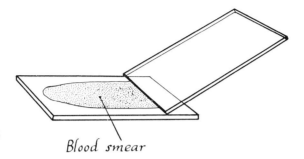

Drop of blood   Glass slides

Figure 3.2 Making a blood smear

Blood smear

blood plasma and prevents the contents of the blood from undergoing unwanted changes. Cover with a cover-slip and examine first under the low power and then under the high power of the microscope. Are you able to see disc-shaped structures? Are there many of these? What colour are they? Why is this surprising? What is their exact shape? Compare what you see with Figure 3.3. Red blood cells appear red when light reflects from them, but greenish when light passes through them.

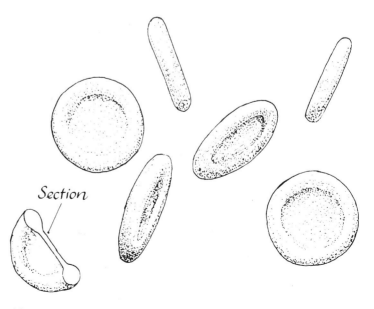

Section

Figure 3.3 Red blood cells ($\times 3\,000$)

48

These bi-concave discs which are so numerous in blood are living cells, called **red blood cells** (**erythrocytes**: *erythro*, red). In what important respect do these cells differ from cells that you have studied before?

Investigation 3c. Looking for white cells

Repeat the process of making a blood smear, outlined in Investigation 3b. After drying the smear in the air, pipette on a few drops of Leishman's stain (methylene blue and eosin in methanol). Rock the slide to distribute the stain over the whole smear. Leave for about twenty seconds and then add an equal quantity of distilled water. Rock again, and leave for ten minutes. Finally, rinse with distilled water and cover with a cover-slip. Examine under the low and high powers of the microscope. Among the red cells, are you able to see any of the structures shown in Figure 3.4?

 Flammable

 Harmful

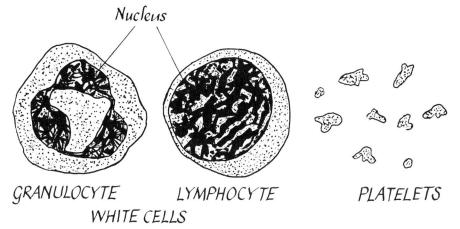

Nucleus

GRANULOCYTE   LYMPHOCYTE   PLATELETS
    WHITE CELLS

Figure 3.4 White blood cells and platelets

Unlike the red cells, the so-called **white cells**, or **leucocytes** (*leukos* means white, but actually they are colourless), have a nucleus. In some white cells the nucleus is divided into lobes, joined by fine connections; such cells are called **granulocytes**. In other white cells, the nucleus is not lobed and nearly fills the cell; these cells are called **lymphocytes**.

Return to your slide and see if you are able to see any granulocytes and lymphocytes. What effect has Leishman's stain on white cells?

In addition to the red and white cells, you should be able to see smaller, irregular structures known as **platelets** if you look carefully. These have no nucleus and appear to be fragments of cells. We will return to these when we consider the mechanism of clotting.

The structure of whole blood is summarized in Table 3.1 and the parts are shown in Figure 3.5.

TABLE 3.1. COMPONENTS OF BLOOD

WHOLE BLOOD

PLASMA
(straw-coloured, liquid
part of blood)

BLOOD CELLS
(solid part of blood)

RED CELLS
(bi-concave, red
discs, without nuclei)

WHITE CELLS
(colourless
cells, with
nuclei)

PLATELETS
(colourless
fragments)

GRANULOCYTES
(lobed nucleus)

LYMPHOCYTES
(non-lobed nucleus)

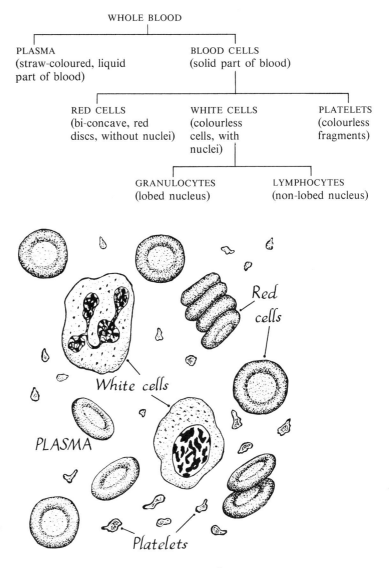

Figure 3.5 Components of
blood

3.2. The functions of the blood system

In all animals it is necessary for certain substances such as the
digestive products and respiratory gases to be transported from one
part of the body to another. Simple animals, such as the amoeba,
hydra and planarians (see Book I, Chapter 4), rely on diffusion for
the movement of such substances. Diffusion results from the fact
that the molecules and ions of dissolved substances are in constant
motion. This causes them to jostle about and to bombard each other,
resulting in a spread of molecules and ions. For any particular molecule or ion, the spread will be from a region of high concentration to
a region of low concentration. Diffusion is a very slow process and

50

can only be relied upon by animals having a small body volume relative to the area of their surface.

Even in the earthworm diffusion is not sufficient for the transportation of substances, and a simple blood system is present (see Book I, Chapter 5). All of the more complex invertebrate animals, and all of the vertebrates, have well-developed blood systems. The exact function of the blood system in the human body will now be considered.

a. Transport of respiratory gases

Oxygen. We have learnt in Chapter 2 that a supply of oxygen is essential for the life of every living cell, as it is there that internal respiration and the release of energy occur. Oxygen is taken into the body through the respiratory surface, which, in the human body, is the inner surface of the lungs. It is one of the functions of the blood to transport oxygen from the lungs to the other living cells of the body (generally referred to as the 'tissues'). The oxygen-carrying capacity of the blood is increased enormously by the presence of a pigment called **haemoglobin** in the red cells. Because of this substance, our blood can carry about fifty times the amount of oxygen that it could without it.

In the lungs, where oxygen is abundant, the haemoglobin combines with oxygen to form a compound known as **oxyhaemoglobin**. Whilst ordinary (or reduced) haemoglobin is bluish-red in colour, oxyhaemoglobin is bright scarlet. It follows, therefore, that the blood leaving the lungs will be a brighter red than that arriving.

In the tissues, oxygen is in low concentration, for it is constantly being consumed in cellular respiration. Here the oxyhaemoglobin breaks down, releasing oxygen for the use of the cell and returning to reduced haemoglobin. The latter will pick up more oxygen when the red cell, which carried it, arrives again in the lungs. We may summarize this process thus:

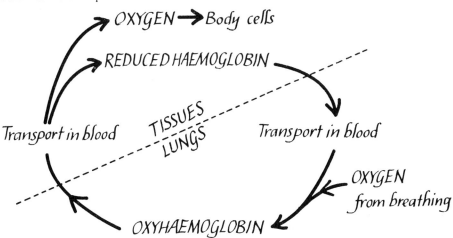

The body's demand for oxygen is high. In order to meet this demand, the number of red cells is very large, and one cubic millimetre of blood (about the size of a pinhead) contains about five million red cells. Since an average person has some five million cubic millimetres of blood, you can see that the total number of red cells is very large indeed.

Red cells have an average life of 120 days, and about one million old cells are disposed of every second, mainly by the spleen. New cells are formed in the red bone marrow, from cells which initially possess a nucleus and have no haemoglobin. During their development into red cells, they produce haemoglobin, and eject the nucleus. The spleen acts as a store for red cells, as well as disposing of them. During prolonged exercise, such as a long run, the spleen contracts and discharges red cells into the blood stream, increasing the total blood volume by as much as 25%. Why do you think it does this?

Carbon dioxide. In Chapter 2 we learnt that the release of energy from glucose results in the production of carbon dioxide as a waste product. This gas is harmful, for in solution it produces acidity:

$$\text{carbon dioxide} + \text{water} \longrightarrow \text{carbonic acid}$$
$$CO_2 \qquad + H_2O \longrightarrow H_2CO_3$$

It is vital, therefore, that the carbon dioxide should be excreted from the body; this occurs through the lungs when we breathe out. The blood must transport the carbon dioxide from the tissues where it is produced to the lungs where it is excreted. To avoid acidity, the carbon dioxide is carried in combination with other substances. About two-thirds is carried in the plasma as sodium hydrogen carbonate, and the remainder in the red cells in combination with the haemoglobin.

The transport of respiratory gases was illustrated in Figure 2.20.

b. Transport of digestive products

In Chapter 1 we learnt that digestion of food results in the production of simple, soluble substances, such as glucose and amino acids. In the intestine, these pass through the walls of the villi and enter the blood capillaries. These connect with the heptic portal vein, which conveys the digestive products to the liver. This vital organ serves to regulate the food content of the blood, so that the body cells are constantly supplied with blood containing, for example, the correct amount of glucose.

c. Transport of excretory products

Carbon dioxide is not the only waste product that has to be

excreted. The breakdown of proteins yields the poisonous substance ammonia. In the liver, this is converted into **urea**, a less harmful substance. The blood then transports urea to the kidneys, which remove it from the body. In the kidneys excess water is also removed from the blood. The liquid which leaves the body as urine contains dissolved urea and water (see Chapter 4).

d. Transport of hormones

Hormones are chemical 'messengers', produced in certain glands called endocrine organs. The chemicals are distributed by the blood stream to all parts of the body and have far-reaching effects on body metabolism. We shall learn more about these important substances in Chapter 8.

e. Transport of heat

Heat is generated in our bodies in the process of cellular respiration, for a large proportion of the energy converted by this process is released as heat. The most active cells from this point of view are, of course, those in the muscles, especially during exercise. The blood system serves to distribute this heat to all parts of the body, so helping to maintain a constant body temperature (see Chapter 5).

f. Transport of cells which combat disease

We have seen that in addition to the red cells the blood contains another type of cell called white cells. There is only one white cell to about 600 red, but, nevertheless, one cubic millimetre of blood contains about 8 000 white cells. The granulocytes are the most abundant of the white cells. They resemble the amoeba in their ability to extend pseudopodia and engulf other organisms. In our bodies, these cells ingest harmful bacteria and other germs, so helping to prevent disease (see Figure 3.6). Like red cells, granulocytes are produced in the red bone marrow.

Lymphocytes are another type of white cell. They cannot ingest germs, but are able to release substances, called **antibodies** or antitoxins, which neutralize bacterial poisons (toxins). Lymphocytes are produced in the lymph nodes (see Section 3.8).

g. Transport of clotting factors

The mechanism of clotting is complex and will be considered briefly in Section 3.9. In this mechanism the platelets, together with certain substances dissolved in the plasma, play an important part.

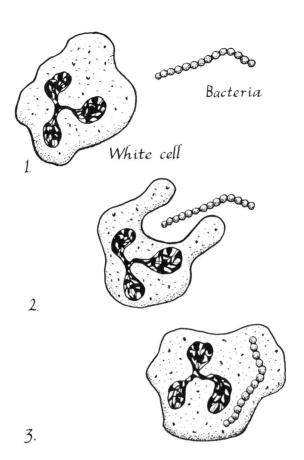

Bacteria

White cell

1.

2.

Figure 3.6 A white cell ingesting a chain of bacteria

3.

The functions of the blood are summarized in Table 3.2.

3.3. How blood is circulated

Blood travels round the body in tubes called **vessels.** It is caused to move along these vessels by the pumping action of the **heart,** a muscular organ in the chest cavity. Vessels carrying blood away from the heart are called **arteries,** whilst those returning blood to the heart are called **veins.** In order to reach every cell of the body, the blood is carried down finer and finer arteries (called **arterioles**) until the tubes become so fine that their walls are one cell thick (see Figure 3.7). These microscopic vessels exist in almost every tissue of the body, and are called **capillaries.** Only a few tissues, such as the lens and cornea of the eye, have no capillaries in them. From the capillaries, some of the plasma seeps out and bathes the surrounding cells as **lymph.** Lymph is returned to the general flow of blood by special **lymphatic vessels.** The rest of the blood passes through small veins, or **venules,** to the large veins, which return it to the heart.

54

TABLE 3.2. SOME IMPORTANT FUNCTIONS OF THE BLOOD

Transport of	From	To	How Carried	Purpose
Oxygen	Lungs	Tissues	As oxyhaemoglobin in red cells	Cellular respiration
Carbon dioxide	Tissues	Lungs	As hydrogen carbonate in plasma, also in haemoglobin in red cells	Excretion
Glucose	Intestine	Liver and rest of body	Dissolved in the plasma	Cellular respiration
Amino acids	Intestine	Liver and rest of body	Dissolved in the plasma	Growth
Urea	Liver	Kidneys	Dissolved in the plasma	Excretion
Hormones	Endocrine organs	All parts of body	Dissolved in the plasma	Regulation of metabolism
Heat	Muscles	All parts of body	By whole blood	Regulation of body temperature
White cells	General circulation	Site of infection	In plasma	Prevention of disease
Clotting factors	General circulation	Wound	In plasma	Prevention of blood loss

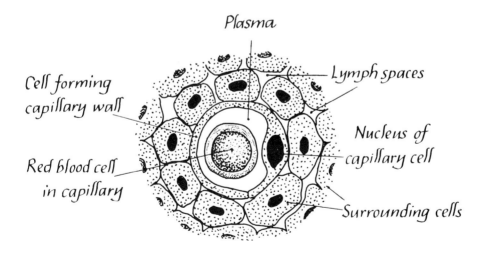

Figure 3.7 A capillary in cross section, with surrounding cells

This flow of blood, from the heart to the capillaries and back again to the heart, is called the **blood circulation**. **Valves** are required in certain parts of the system, to keep the blood flowing in one direction only (see Figure 3.8).

55

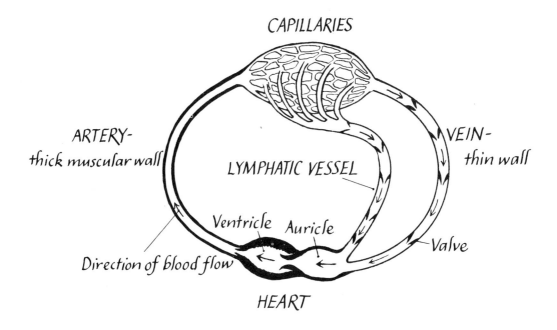

CAPILLARIES

ARTERY-
thick muscular wall

VEIN-
thin wall

LYMPHATIC VESSEL

Ventricle   Auricle

Direction of blood flow

Valve

HEART

Figure 3.8 Diagram to show the relationship between the various parts of the circulatory system

3.4. Blood vessels

Investigation 3d. Comparing arteries and veins

With the low power of the microscope, examine a prepared slide of a transverse section of an artery and of a vein. Compare the specimens with Figure 3.9 and identify the layers forming the walls of the vessels. Which type of vessel has the thickest wall? Why do you think that this is so? Which vessel has the largest lumen (cavity)? Can you explain this?

Investigation 3e. Vein valves in the arm

Roll up your sleeve and tie a handkerchief fairly tightly just above the elbow. Open and close the hand a few times and notice the

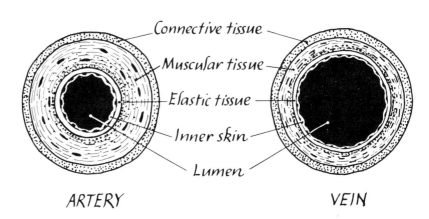

Connective tissue
Muscular tissue
Elastic tissue
Inner skin
Lumen

ARTERY   VEIN

Figure 3.9 Blood vessels in transverse section

56

bumps which appear on the inside of the lower arm (see Figure 3.10). These mark the position of valves in the veins lying near the surface of the arm. Why do you think that this method makes the valves show up? *Do not leave the arm tied for more than a minute or so.*

If a vein is blocked just above a valve by pressing it, and the vein is then flattened towards the heart, the vein remains flat until the original pressure is released. This demonstrates the direction of blood flow.

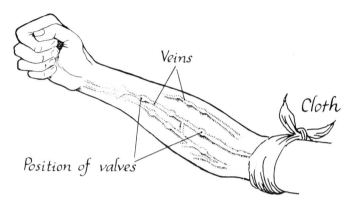

Figure 3.10 Demonstrating vein valves

The demonstration of vein valves was first performed by the English physician **William Harvey** (1578–1657). Although it may seem unbelievable, until Harvey's work in 1628 doctors did not know that blood circulated in the body. The Greek philosopher **Aristotle** (384–322 B.C.) believed that blood ebbed and flowed in the veins, whilst the arteries contained air (hence *arteria*, a Greek word meaning 'windpipe'). Later, the Greek physician **Galen** (A.D. 130–200) showed that arteries contained blood, but he still held the belief that blood passed to an organ in a vessel and returned in the same vessel. Moreover, this belief continued to be held for the next 1 400 years, until Harvey established that the heart pumped blood to the organs through arteries, whilst veins returned the blood to the heart. Since the microscope had yet to be invented, Harvey could not see how blood passed from arteries to veins, but he reasoned that there must be a connection. The Italian biologist **Marcello Malpighi** (1628–94) first used a microscope to show capillaries, thus completing Harvey's work.

Investigation 3f. Examination of capillaries in the tail of a tadpole

Place a tadpole in a watchglass with a little water. Add a drop or two of trichloromethane, thus rendering the tadpole inactive. Alternatively, a 0·1% solution of MS 222 (freshly made) may be used. Focus the low power of the microscope on the thin skin of the tail fin. Notice the blood flowing in the capillaries. The large, spider-like cells are pigment cells (see Figure 3.11).

Harmful

Flammable

★ *Replace the stopper of the trichloromethane bottle immediately after use. Do not breathe the vapour or allow near a naked flame.*

57

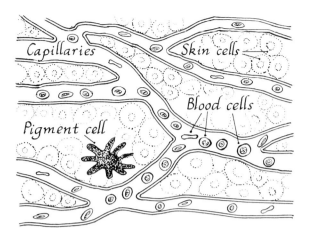

Figure 3.11 Capillaries in the tail of a tadpole

3.5. Types of blood circulation

Examine Figure 3.12. Notice that in the fish blood passes through the heart only once during a complete circulation of the body. This is known as a **single circulation**. The two-chambered heart contains de-oxygenated blood, which it pumps to the gills. Only the gills, therefore, receive blood under high pressure.

In the mammal, on the other hand, blood passes through the heart twice during a complete circulation of the body; in other words, there is a **double circulation**. The heart has four chambers and, whilst the two chambers on the left side contain oxygenated blood, those on the right contain de-oxygenated blood. Most organs receive

Figure 3.12 Comparison between the circulatory patterns of a fish (a single circulation) and a mammal (a double circulation)

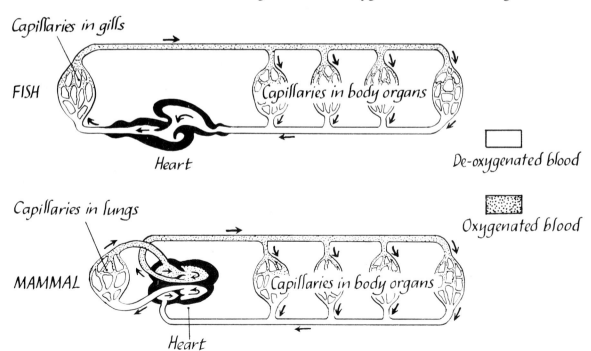

58

blood under high pressure from the heart. This type of circulation is a considerable improvement on that of the fish.

If you examine a chart showing the distribution of the main blood vessels of man, you will find the pattern rather complicated. The artery carrying blood to any particular organ often runs alongside the vein carrying blood away from it. Blood vessels cross each other, and the organs are close together. The pattern is simpler to understand if the vessels and organs are represented as in Figure 3.13, but

Figure 3.13 Diagram of the circulatory system of man

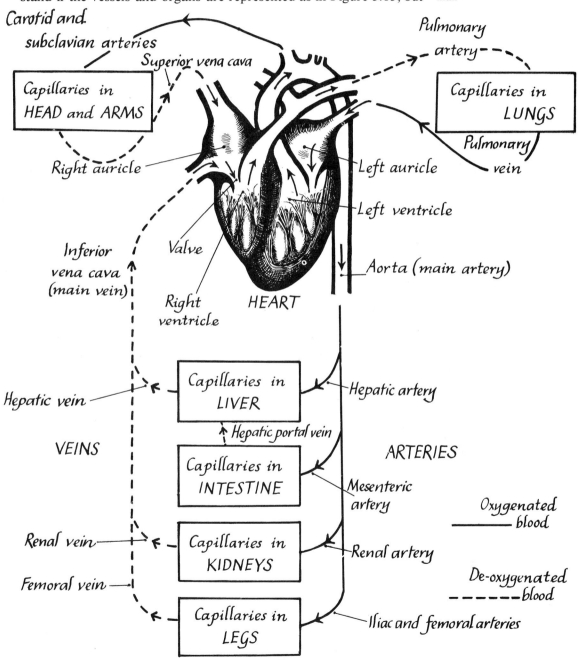

Carotid and subclavian arteries

Superior vena cava

Pulmonary artery

Capillaries in HEAD and ARMS

Capillaries in LUNGS

Pulmonary vein

Right auricle

Left auricle

Left ventricle

Inferior vena cava (main vein)

Valve

Aorta (main artery)

Right ventricle

HEART

Hepatic vein

Capillaries in LIVER

Hepatic artery

Hepatic portal vein

VEINS

Capillaries in INTESTINE

ARTERIES

Mesenteric artery

Oxygenated blood ——

Renal vein

Capillaries in KIDNEYS

Renal artery

Femoral vein

De-oxygenated blood - - - - - -

Capillaries in LEGS

Iliac and femoral arteries

you should realize that this does not show the true position of the vessels and organs.

3.6. The heart

The heart is a cone-shaped structure lying in the chest cavity between the lungs, with the point of the cone directed towards the left side. In the adult human, it is about the size of a fist, and weighs from 280 to 340 g (9–11 oz). Surrounding the heart is a delicate membrane, the **pericardium**, which contains a clear fluid.

The heart is divided into left and right sides by a central partition, and each side has an upper and lower chamber. The two upper chambers are called **auricles**, (atria), and these serve to receive blood from the veins. The two lower chambers are called **ventricles**. These pump the blood received from the auricles into the arteries. Guarding the entrance from the left auricle to the left ventricle is the **bicuspid valve**, which has two parts or cusps. The valve in the similar position on the right side has three cusps (the **tricuspid valve**). The openings that these valves guard would be wide enough to allow two or three fingers to be inserted. The entrances to the main arteries are also guarded by valves, which are pocket-like, **semi-lunar valves**.

Biological

Figure 3.14 External views of the mammalian heart: (a) dorsal view and (b) ventral view

Investigation 3g. Heart structure

Examine the heart of a sheep, pig or other mammal, and identify the external structures shown in Figure 3.14. Then examine a dissected heart (see the diagram in Figure 3.15), in which part of the walls of the chambers has been removed. With a blunt, curved, mounted needle ('seeker'), explore the various connections between the chambers and the main vessels. Compare the thickness of the walls of the auricles and ventricles. Which type of chamber has the

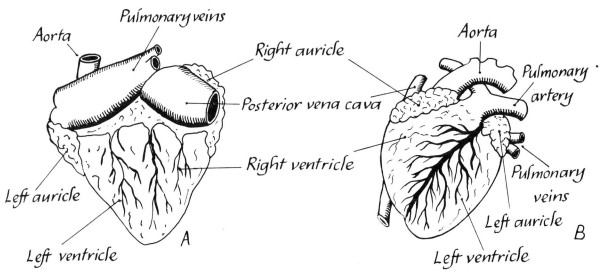

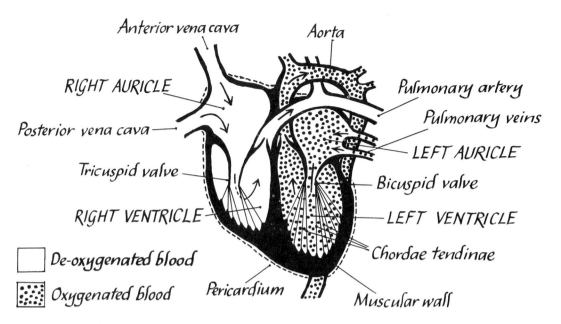

Anterior vena cava

Aorta

RIGHT AURICLE

Pulmonary artery

Pulmonary veins

Posterior vena cava

LEFT AURICLE

Tricuspid valve

Bicuspid valve

RIGHT VENTRICLE

LEFT VENTRICLE

De-oxygenated blood

Chordae tendinae

Oxygenated blood

Pericardium

Muscular wall

thickest wall? Why should this be so? Is there any difference between the thickness of the wall of the left and right ventricle? Can you explain this? Notice the tough cords attached to the bicuspid and tricuspid valves. What purpose do you think they serve? Why do you think that there are such prominent vessels extending over the surface of the heart?

Figure 3.15 The heart of a mammal in longitudinal section, showing adjoining arteries and veins (diagrammatic)

The working of the heart

To follow the working of the heart, it is best to refer to Figure 3.16. The heart is a pump which undergoes a series of events which repeat themselves about seventy times a minute. This series of events is called the **heart cycle**. The stages of this cycle are as follows:

1. Filling of auricles

The whole heart is relaxed. De-oxygenated blood enters the right auricle from the venae cavae, whilst oxygenated blood enters the left auricle from the pulmonary veins. The valves between the auricles and ventricles are closed. The semi-lunar valves are also closed, preventing arterial blood from entering the heart.

2. Opening of valves

The bicuspid and tricuspid valves open, and some of the blood pours through into the ventricles, which are still relaxed. At this stage, both auricles and ventricles contain blood.

3. Contraction of auricles

The auricles contract and force the remainder of their blood into the ventricles, which become stretched.

61

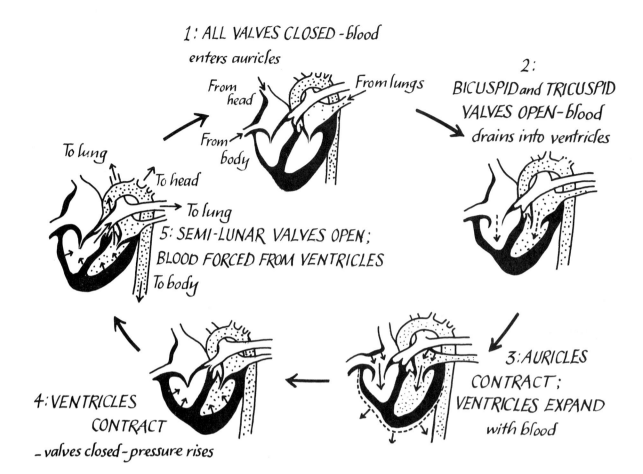

1: ALL VALVES CLOSED - blood enters auricles

From head
From lungs
From body

To lung
To head
To lung

5: SEMI-LUNAR VALVES OPEN; BLOOD FORCED FROM VENTRICLES
To body

2: BICUSPID and TRICUSPID VALVES OPEN - blood drains into ventricles

4: VENTRICLES CONTRACT
_ valves closed - pressure rises

3: AURICLES CONTRACT; VENTRICLES EXPAND with blood

Figure 3.16 Diagrams to illustrate the heart cycle

4. Contraction of ventricles

The ventricles contract, closing the bicuspid and tricuspid valves. Pressure rises in the ventricles, but blood has no way out as yet.

5. Discharge of blood into arteries

Suddenly, the semi-lunar valves open, and the pressure of the ventricles forces blood into the arteries. De-oxygenated blood from the right ventricle passes into the pulmonary arteries, which carry it to the lungs. Oxygenated blood from the left ventricle passes into the main aorta and is distributed to the rest of the body.

The whole series of events takes less than one second, and is repeated immediately. What we call 'heartbeat' is, in fact, two beats, the auricular contraction and the ventricular contraction. Which do you think is the more powerful beat? If you have an amplifier and microphone available, try holding your breath and listening to your heartbeat.

Experiments have shown that heartbeat continues even if all of the nerves to the heart have been cut, though the heart does not continue to beat at the correct rate. The nervous impulses which cause the heart cycle to occur originate in a centre in the right auricle. However, the rate of heartbeat varies according to the body's requirements, and is under the control of the autonomic nervous system (see Chapter 7).

3.7. Blood pressure

We have seen that the heart pumps blood into the arteries in a series of spurts. When you performed Investigation 3f, did you find that the blood spurted along capillaries or was the flow continuous? When the heart contracts and forces blood into the arteries, the elastic walls of these vessels allow them to be stretched. In the interval between heartbeats, the arterial walls recoil, so forcing blood along further. Thus the spurting flow in the arteries becomes a continuous flow in the capillaries.

The force with which blood is pushed along is called **blood pressure**. Whilst this pressure normally varies with exercise, emotional stress, etc., a permanent high or low pressure may be a sign of disease. In consequence, measurement of blood pressure is a test normally performed by a doctor when examining a patient. The instrument used is a **sphygmomanometer** (see Figure 3.17).

Figure 3.17 A sphygmomanometer: an instrument used to measure blood pressure

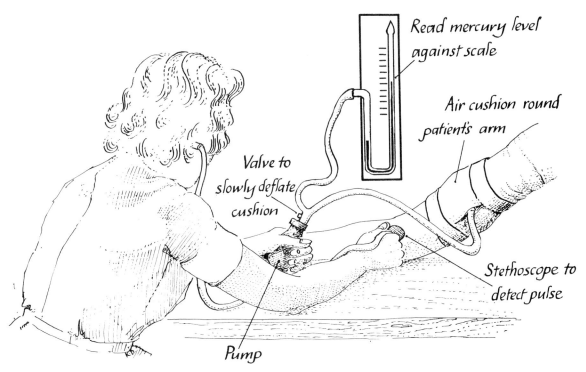

Read mercury level against scale

Air cushion round patient's arm

Valve to slowly deflate cushion

Stethoscope to detect pulse

Pump

63

The instrument consists of a flat rubber bag, enclosed in cloth to prevent stretching. A tube connects the bag to a manometer (a U-tube containing mercury) and another tube connects it to a small hand-pump. When the latter is operated, air is forced into the rubber bag, and the manometer registers the air pressure within it. The doctor wraps the rubber bag fairly tightly round the patient's upper arm, securing it in place with its attached straps. The bag is then inflated until the pulse at the wrist can no longer be felt. This means that the air pressure in the bag is holding back the blood supply in the main brachial artery of the arm. The doctor then places the end of his stethoscope over this artery between the elbow and the rubber armlet. There comes a point, as he gradually lets air out of the bag, when he hears the pulsation of the artery as blood seeps through to it. The reading on the manometer is now taken, and indicates the patient's blood pressure. Normal blood pressure for an adult is about 16 kilonewtons per square metre (120 millimetres of mercury), but in cases of chronic disease it may reach 40 kN m^{-2} (300 mm Hg).

Pressure points and the pulse

At certain points in the body, such as the wrist and temple, an artery lies over a bone and close to the surface of the skin. Here we can feel the contraction and expansion of the artery, in time with the heartbeat. This is called the **pulse**, and the place where it is felt is called a **pressure point**. The rate of the pulse, and its force and regularity, are all checked by the doctor when he examines a patient.

Investigation 3h. The effect of exercise on the pulse

Ask your partner to measure your pulse rate. To do this, the number of beats at the wrist are counted over two periods of one minute, and the results are then averaged. Now perform some vigorous exercise for about half a minute, such as stepping on and off a chair or running up and down stairs. Then get your partner to re-measure your pulse rate over two separate minutes, again averaging the result. What has been the effect of exercise on heartbeat? If you wish, you can continue the measurement, and find out how long it takes for the heartbeat to return to normal. Is the time the same for all members of the class?

3.8. Lymph and the lymphatic system

In Section 3.3 we learnt that, as blood circulates through capillaries, some of its liquid seeps out and bathes the surrounding cells. This escaping fluid is called lymph. It is similar to plasma, but contains less protein, for the walls of the capillaries hold back some of the larger protein molecules. Lymph carries substances such as oxygen and glucose to the cells, and picks up waste products from them. Minute lymph capillaries carry the lymph into lymphatic vessels which return it to the main veins just before they enter the heart (see Figure 3.18).

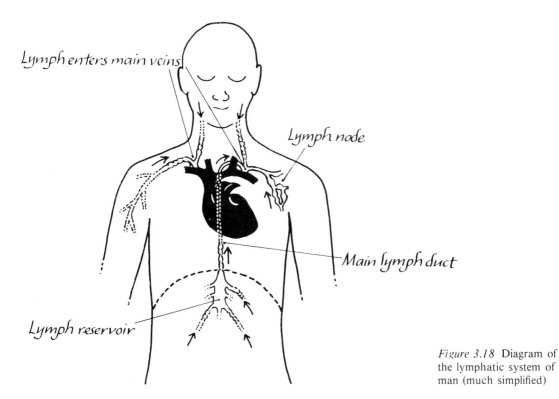

Figure 3.18 Diagram of the lymphatic system of man (much simplified)

In certain parts of the body, such as in the neck, groin and under the armpits, the lymphatic vessels bear swellings called **lymph nodes**. Tonsils and adenoids are lymph nodes, and are not 'glands', as sometimes stated. The lymph nodes act as filters, removing harmful bacteria and other germs from the lymph. Many white cells (lymphocytes) are formed in the nodes, and infection may cause the nodes to swell near the region of infection. This is the reason why tonsils swell during a throat infection or the armpit swells when a finger becomes septic. The swelling results from the 'battle' which rages in the lymph node between the germs and the defending lymphocytes. The structure of a lymph node is shown in Figure 3.19.

3.9. Blood clotting

Once released from the body, blood clots to a jelly within six minutes. The clot is due to the formation in the plasma of a fibrous protein called **fibrin**. Threads of fibrin radiate from the platelets, and

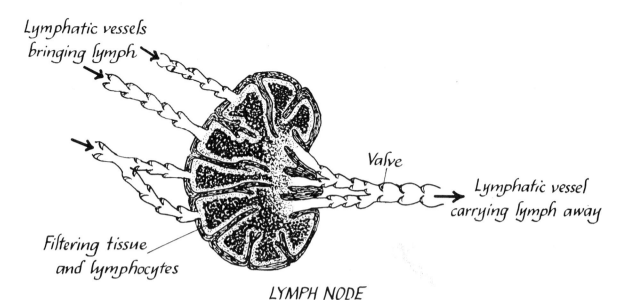

Lymphatic vessels bringing lymph

Valve

Lymphatic vessel carrying lymph away

Filtering tissue and lymphocytes

LYMPH NODE

Figure 3.19 Structure of a lymph node

form a network in which the blood cells become entangled (see Figure 3.20).

Fibrin is present in normal blood in a soluble form. At a wound, soluble fibrin is converted into insoluble threads by a special clotting enzyme, released by damaged cells and by platelets. Clotting is important, for it controls the loss of blood from a wound and also prevents the entry of germs.

3.10. Blood groups and transfusion

If the blood of two different animals, such as a monkey and a rabbit, is mixed, clumping results, for the red cells become massed and fused together. In 1900 it was discovered that a similar clumping

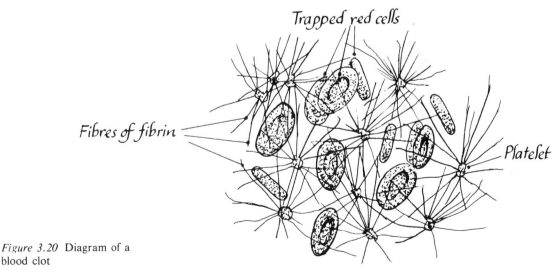

Trapped red cells

Fibres of fibrin

Platelet

Figure 3.20 Diagram of a blood clot

66

sometimes results when the blood of two different human beings is mixed, for example, in a blood transfusion. This can be very dangerous, for the red cells of the person giving the blood (the donor) form clumps which block the blood vessels of the person receiving the blood (the recipient). This can cause death.

The entire human population can be divided into four groups according to the reaction of the blood when mixed. These blood groups are known as group A, group B, group AB and group O. Of every hundred persons, on average, forty will be group A, eleven group B, four group AB and forty-five group O.

The red cells of a person in group A contain a substance which we may call 'substance A'. If these cells are given to a person whose own cells do not contain this substance (for example, a person in group O) clumping results, for the recipient's plasma produces an antibody ('anti-A') which destroys the 'foreign' red cells. Similarly, a person in group B has 'substance B' in the red cells which evokes 'anti-B' in blood which does not contain this substance. Group AB has both substance A and substance B, whilst group O has neither. The following table shows the results of mixing blood of different groups.

TABLE 3.3. THE EFFECT OF MIXING BLOOD OF DIFFERENT GROUPS

		Donor's Red Cells			
		GROUP A	GROUP B	GROUP AB	GROUP O
		Substance A	Substance B	Substances A and B	—
Recipient's Plasma	GROUP A Anti-B	Mix	Clump	Clump	Mix
	GROUP B Anti-A	Clump	Mix	Clump	Mix
	GROUP AB —	Mix	Mix	Mix	Mix
	GROUP O Anti-A and anti-B	Clump	Clump	Clump	Mix

Every year, many thousands of people donate some of their blood to the Blood Transfusion Service, to help to save lives. Which group do you think is most valued at the blood 'bank'? Why is this so? If you were unfortunate enough to need a blood transfusion, which group would it be best to be? We have no choice, of course, for it has been shown that the group we belong to is decided by our inheritance.

Persons in group O are called **universal donors**, while those in group AB are called **universal recipients**.

In order to find out to which blood group a particular sample belongs, it is necessary to obtain some serum from blood groups A and B. Serum is blood plasma without its clotting factor (fibrin). Large hospitals and pathology laboratories keep stocks of these sera, and will probably give a small quantity of each type for the school's use.

Prepare a clean microscope slide and set up a microscope on low power. Using the technique described in Investigation 3b, obtain two drops of blood from the finger and place them on the slide, sufficiently apart to prevent mixing. Quickly add a drop of test serum A to one drop of blood, and a drop of test serum B to the other. Examine under the microscope and observe whether any clumping of blood cells has occurred. The blood group is determined as follows:

TABLE 3.4

Result of Test	Blood Group
No clumping	Group O
Both drops clump	Group AB
Clumping only with serum A	Group B
Clumping only with serum B	Group A

3.11. The Rhesus factor

Until 1940 only the ABO series of blood groups was understood, and doctors were puzzled that even when these groups were checked deaths from transfusions sometimes occurred. Such deaths were found to have occurred either in persons receiving a blood transfusion for the second time, or in pregnant women, or in women who had just given birth. It was found that 85% of the human population has a substance in the blood called the Rhesus substance (after work done on the Rhesus monkey), whilst the other 15% do not. If blood containing the Rhesus substance (called Rh positive blood) is injected into a person lacking the substance (Rh negative), nothing serious happens immediately, but an antibody is produced in the recipient's blood ('anti-Rh'). Any second transfusion of Rh positive blood causes immediate clumping, and possibly death. A Rh negative mother may carry a Rh positive baby. Should any of the baby's blood enter the mother's circulation, the mother reacts by producing the antibody, anti-Rh. This can, in turn, have a destructive effect on the baby's blood. A massive transfusion of Rh negative blood may be needed to save the baby's life. If the Rh negative mother has a second Rh positive baby, the danger is increased, since the mother's blood will most probably have produced anti-Rh through the mixing of her blood and that of the previous baby at the time of its birth. However, provided that the facts are known, and the proper precautions taken, the baby will not suffer.

Test your understanding

Copy and complete the following paragraphs:

Blood is carried in tubes called blood . . . .[1] Those that carry blood . . . .[2] the heart are called . . . .[3], whilst those that carry blood . . . .[4] the heart are called veins. Veins have . . . .[5] walls because they do not have to withstand the . . . .[6] of the . . . .[7] Veins have . . . .[8] along their length, to prevent the blood from flowing . . . .[9] All tissues are permeated by very fine blood . . . .[10] Here, some of the liquid part of the blood seeps out, this escaped fluid being called . . . .[11] Special . . . .[12] vessels are required to return this fluid to the general circulation.

The heart is the organ which . . . .[13] the blood round the body. The . . . [14] are the main . . . .[15] chambers, whilst the . . . .[16] are the main receiving chambers. De-oxygenated blood from the body enters the . . . .[17] at the same time as oxygenated blood from the . . . .[18] enters the . . . [19] At this stage the . . . .[20] and . . . .[21] valves are closed. When they open, blood pours into the . . . .[22] Pressure is built up by the . . . .[23] of the ventricle walls. When the . . . .[24] valves open, blood is discharged from the ventricles. De-oxygenated blood from the . . . .[25] passes into the . . . .[26] and is carried to the . . . .[27] Oxygenated blood from the . . . .[28] passes into the . . . .[29] and is carried all over the body. The sequence of actions performed by the heart is called the heart . . . .[30]

1. Write down five important facts about red blood cells.
2. Name the two types of white blood cell and explain the functions of each type.
3. Make a list of substances carried by the plasma, the liquid part of blood.
4. What important fact about the blood system was first established by William Harvey?
5. Explain the difference between a single and a double circulatory system. What is the advantage of the latter?
6. What is blood pressure, and why is it frequently measured by doctors?
7. What is a pressure point?
8. Write down three important facts about the rate of heartbeat.
9. What is the function of the lymph nodes?
10. Explain, briefly, how blood clots.
11. Why is a person whose blood is group O called a universal donor? What is a person whose blood is group AB called?
12. Why do you think that an expectant mother, whose blood is Rhesus negative, is not usually allowed to give birth to the baby at home, but is given a bed in a maternity home or hospital?

Chapter 4

Getting Rid of Waste: Excretion

4.1. Why is excretion necessary?

Excretion is the removal of the waste products of **metabolism** from the body of an organism. Metabolism is the sum total of the chemical reactions occurring within the body. As well as giving rise to useful products, these chemical reactions also give rise to waste products. Certain of these waste products are toxic and so, if allowed to accumulate, would poison the body. Hence, excretion is necessary to remove them promptly and efficiently.

4.2. The origin and nature of the excretory products

In Chapter 1 we learnt that carbohydrate digestion results in the production of simple sugars, such as glucose; protein digestion results in amino acids; and fat digestion results in fatty acids and propane – 1, 2, 3 – triol (glycerol). These products are able to diffuse into the cells where they are needed. What happens to them if they are not needed? Excess glucose can be removed from the blood stream by the liver, where it is condensed into **glycogen** or animal starch, an insoluble storage carbohydrate. When glucose is required, the glycogen is hydrolysed to glucose, which passes back into the blood stream for distribution. Excess fatty acids and glycerol can be re-converted to fats, and stored around the kidneys and beneath the skin. Excess amino acids, however, cannot be stored unless the nitrogen-containing part of the amino acid is removed. This process is called **deamination** and occurs in several tissues, in particular the liver. The amino acid is split into the nitrogen-containing portion, which is converted to ammonia, and the other portion, which is converted to glycogen. This glycogen is stored in the liver until it is needed to produce energy, in exactly the same way as the glycogen derived from excess glucose is stored. Ammonia, however, is soluble and very poisonous, so it is combined with carbon dioxide (in the presence of enzymes) to form urea, which is not poisonous (see Figure 4.1). The urea is then carried by the blood stream from the liver to the kidneys, which

70

remove most of the nitrogenous waste from the body. In addition to urea, various mineral salts have to be excreted.

Other excretory products are carbon dioxide (from respiration) and water. It should also be remembered that, although not excretion, waste not used by the body is removed from the large intestines, a process known as **defaecation**.

4.3. The organs of excretion

a. The *lungs* excrete carbon dioxide gas and water vapour, as explained in Chapter 2.

b. The *skin* is an excretory organ because water, salts and a minute amount of urea are lost in perspiration (see Chapter 5).

c. The *kidneys* are the principal organs for excreting waste nitrogenous material, and help to maintain the fluid balance of the body.

Investigation 4a. To examine the excretory organs of a dissected rabbit

Examine a rabbit from which the alimentary canal has been removed. Notice the pair of dark-red, bean-shaped organs on the dorsal wall of the abdominal cavity, possibly embedded in fat. These are the kidneys. Notice their position in relation to the ribs. The dorsal region of the lower ribs gives some protection to the kidneys. Kidneys are enclosed in tough membrane of transparent connective tissue. You can probably peel it off. From the inner side of each kidney, a muscular duct called the **ureter** passes close to the dorsal wall of the abdominal cavity into the **bladder**, a muscular sac nestling in the basin of the pelvis. The bladder opens to the exterior through a tube known as the **urethra**.

Examine carefully the blood supply to the kidneys. From the dorsal aorta, the main artery, with whitish walls and pinkish contents,

Biological

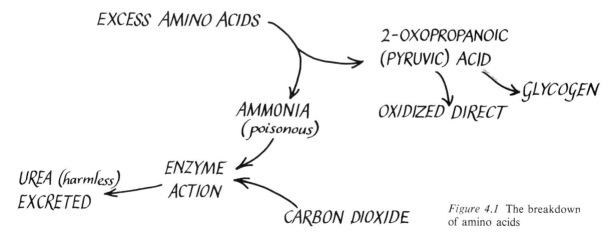

Figure 4.1 The breakdown of amino acids

arises a renal artery to each kidney. Leaving each kidney is a vessel with thinner walls, making it appear deep red in colour. This is the renal vein, which returns the filtered blood to the inferior vena cava.

If you have difficulty in identifying any of the organs, compare the dissection with Figure 4.2.

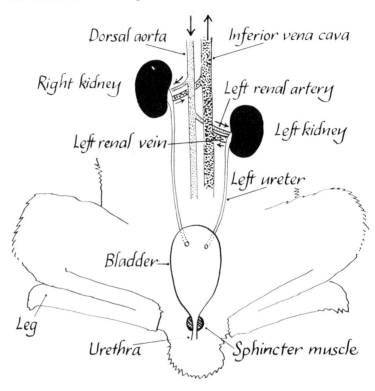

Figure 4.2 The urinary system in a rabbit

Investigation 4b. To examine a mammalian kidney

Biological

Obtain a lamb's or pig's kidney from the butcher. Peel the tough membrane from it and try to identify the stump of the ureter and also of the renal artery and vein. With a sharp scalpel, cut the kidney vertically into two. The incision should be made parallel to the flat surface to produce two similar halves. Examine the cut surface carefully with a lens. In the centre is the **pelvis**, where the urine collects before dripping into the ureter. If you look carefully at the tissue, you may be able to distinguish between the outer region called the **cortex** and the inner region called the **medulla**. Compare your dissection with Figure 4.3, which shows a similar vertical section through a human kidney.

4.4. The fine structure of the kidneys

The kidney is composed of a vast number of tiny tubules held together by connective tissue. Each tubule has a cup called **Bowman's**

72

capsule, whose wall is one cell thick. The capsule opens into a coiled tubule known as the **first convoluted tubule**. This lies in the cortex of the kidney. The tubule continues as the **loop of Henle** which occupies the medulla, returning to the cortex to become the **second**

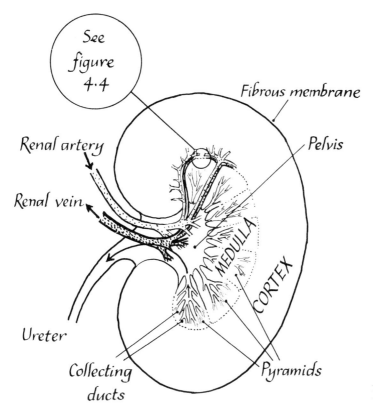

Figure 4.3 A human kidney in vertical section

convoluted tubule. This second convoluted tubule connects with one of the collecting ducts which opens into the pelvis of the kidney. The Bowman's capsule surrounds a knot of blood capillaries called the **glomerulus** (see Figure 4.4).

4.5. The functioning of the kidneys

The diameter of the branch of the renal artery entering the glomerulus is considerably greater than that of the branch leaving it. This imposes a considerable pressure on the contents of the capillaries of the glomerulus and results in the blood being filtered under pressure. Sugars, salts, urea and even quite large molecules like proteins pass through the semi-permeable wall in solution into the cavity of the Bowman's capsule. The solution then passes through the first convoluted tubule into the loop of Henle, where much of the water and all of the glucose and other useful substances are re-absorbed. In this way, the composition of the blood is regulated. The urine then

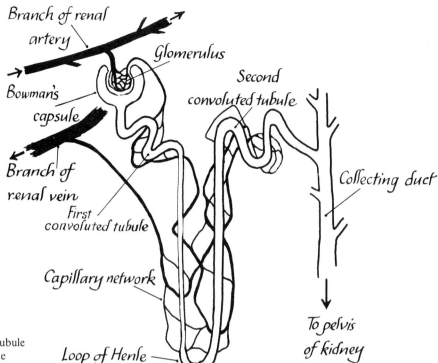

Figure 4.4 A kidney tubule showing the path of the urine formation

passes through the second convoluted tubule and the collecting duct into the pelvis of the kidney. Day and night, urine drips down the ureter into the bladder where it collects. The wall of the bladder is composed of muscular and elastic tissues. The urethra is kept closed by the contraction of the sphincter muscle at the neck. As urine accumulates in the bladder, the elastic walls are stretched until it contains about half a litre. Eventually, the sphincter muscle, which is a semi-voluntary muscle, relaxes and the muscle fibres in the bladder wall contract, expelling the urine through the urethra.

4.6. The composition of urine

A man normally excretes about one and a half litres of urine per day. It consists of about 96% water, 2% urea, 0·2% other nitrogenous substances, 1% sodium chloride and 0·8% other mineral salts. It should not contain sugars or proteins. The amount of urine and its composition may vary with the climate, and the activity and habits of the person. On a hot day, the body's cooling mechanism will result in a great deal of water being lost as perspiration, so that only a relatively small amount of concentrated urine will be passed. On a cold day, however, the pores of the sweat glands will be tightly closed and little water will be lost through them, so a relatively large volume of dilute urine will be passed. Similarly, if a person is very active, he will lose a great deal of water as perspiration and hence a relatively small amount as urine. If, however, a person is sedentary, a larger quantity of urine will be produced. Obviously, if large quantities of fluid are consumed, then proportionately larger amounts of dilute urine will be produced.

Investigation 4c. To test a sample of urine for urea

Add some alkaline sodium bromate (i) solution to a sample of urine. A vigorous fizzing indicates the presence of urea. Alkaline sodium bromate (i) may be prepared by dissolving 9·2g of sodium hydroxide in 23 cm^3 of water and then adding 1·1g of bromine.

★ WARNING. *Care should be taken when adding bromine to sodium hydroxide solution.*

Toxic

Corrosive

Investigation 4d. To test a sample of urine for the presence of glucose

Impale a small piece of yellow 'Tes-tape' on a mounted needle and dip it for one second into a sample of urine. (Tes-tape is paper impregnated with special chemicals. It should be available from the chemist.) If the colour of the Tes-tape changes from yellow to dark green, the presence of glucose in the urine is shown.

Test your understanding

Copy and complete the following paragraphs:

Excretion is necessary to get rid of the . . . .[1] products of . . . .[2] which would . . . .[3] the body if they were allowed to accumulate. The main excretory organs are the . . . .[4] Excess glucose in the blood is converted to . . . .[5] which is stored in the liver. Amino acids are broken down to poisonous . . . .[6] which is then converted to harmless . . . .[7] Urea, water, salts and sugars are filtered from the blood in the . . . .[8] capsule of the kidney tubule. Water and . . . .[9] are re-absorbed in the loop of . . . .[10] The remainder is . . . .[11] which passes down the . . . .[12] into the . . . .[13] where it is stored until expelled through the . . . .[14] to the exterior.

Normal urine contains . . . .[15] % of water, ...[16] % of urea, together with small quantities of salts.

1. Explain why excretion is necessary.
2. Explain how the body deals with excess amino acids.
3. Draw a kidney in vertical section and describe briefly how it functions.
4. How might temperature and activity influence the composition and quantity of urine excreted?
5. Describe how a single kidney tubule functions.

Chapter 5

The Skin and Temperature Control

5.1 The functions of the skin

The skin covers the entire surface of the body, and extends into the mouth, nose and ears. It even covers the front surface of the eyeball, where, of course, it is transparent. The main functions of the skin are as follows:

a. Protection

The surface layer of the skin is tough and horny, being composed mainly of dead cells. This layer serves to protect the more delicate tissues beneath from damage. Being waterproof, the skin also protects the body from desiccation. It also forms a barrier against the entry of disease organisms, such as bacteria. Once the skin is broken, germs are able to enter the body through the wound.

b. Temperature regulation

We shall learn in the second half of this chapter that the skin plays a major role in the control of body temperature. Hairs, sweat glands and blood capillaries are all involved in this regulation.

c. Sensitivity

The skin is the largest of the body's sense organs, and through it we have the sensations of touch, pain, heat and cold (see Section 6.4).

d. Excretion

In the last chapter we learnt that some water, urea and salts are lost from the body in sweat.

e. Production of vitamin D

When the skin is exposed to sunlight, certain substances called sterols are converted into vitamin D. This vitamin is essential for the healthy growth of bones and teeth (see Section 1·7).

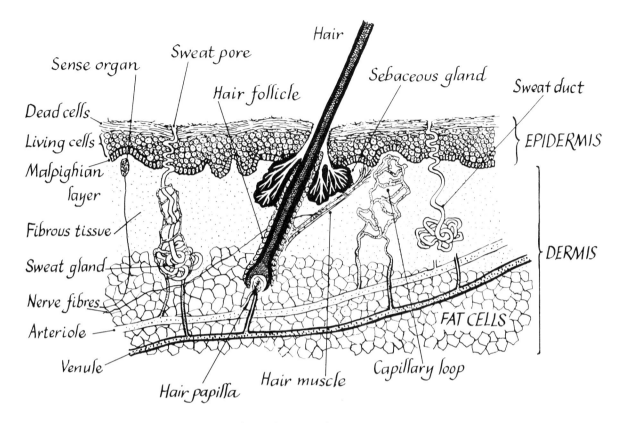

Labels on figure:
Sense organ
Sweat pore
Hair
Hair follicle
Sebaceous gland
Sweat duct
Dead cells
Living cells
Malpighian layer
EPIDERMIS
Fibrous tissue
Sweat gland
DERMIS
Nerve fibres
Arteriole
FAT CELLS
Venule
Hair papilla
Hair muscle
Capillary loop

5.2. The structure of the skin (see Figure 5.1)

The ridged surface of the skin can easily be seen under a binocular microscope. These ridges enable the skin to be elastic and supple. The skin is composed of two layers, the outer epidermis and the inner dermis.

The **epidermis**, or outer skin, is the protective layer, and is many cells thick, especially in those parts of the body which are exposed to wear. Examples of such areas are the palms of the hands and the soles of the feet. The innermost layer of the epidermis comprises cells which are constantly dividing, giving rise to new cells. This is the **malpighian layer**, after the same Marcello Malpighi who discovered blood capillaries. As new cells are formed at the malpighian layer, the older ones are pushed towards the surface. As this happens, they lose contact with the blood which nourishes them and die, becoming flattened and horny scales. Whenever something rubs against the skin, some of these scales fall away, exposing those underneath. Thus the surface of our body is constantly being worn away, and renewed. The more the surface is rubbed, the more cells are produced by the malpighian layer. Eventually, thick layers of dead skin are built up on the outside of the body. This is the body's natural protection against wear. No doubt you have had the painful experience of

Figure 5.1 The structure of the human skin, as seen in vertical section (diagrammatic)

77

blisters developing on skin which has been subjected to heavy wear before this thick layer of dead skin has been allowed to build up.

Hairs are produced by the epidermis. The malpighian layer sinks in to form a **hair follicle**, at the base of which special cells produce the protein **keratin**. The hair grows from the base and gradually extends out of the follicle. Fingernails and toenails are other horny products of the epidermis.

The **dermis**, or inner skin, contains the more delicate structures, which are embedded in fibrous, elastic tissue. These fibres keep the skin taut. In old age, the fibres become weak, like over-stretched elastic bands, and the skin sags into wrinkles. In the dermis are many blood vessels and nerves, and attached to the base of each hair follicle is a **hair-erecting muscle**, the contraction of which brings the hair into a more upright position. Hairs are kept supple and waterproof by a greasy substance called **sebum**, which is produced in the **sebaceous glands**, opening into each hair follicle. Some of this sebum covers the surface of the skin, giving it its shiny appearance. The shiny nose is a reminder that hair follicles and sebaceous glands exist in areas of skin where there may be no actual hairs. The amount of sebum produced determines whether we have a 'dry' or 'greasy' skin. If sebum is allowed to accumulate in confined spaces, such as under the armpits, it may become a breeding medium for bacteria and other germs, and an unpleasant smell (body odour) may result. Regular washing and the use of deodorant will prevent 'B.O.', which even one's best friends do not like to mention!

Other structures in the dermis are the **sweat glands**, of which there are about three million in the whole body. Each gland is a long, coiled tube from which a duct runs to the surface where it opens at a **sweat pore**. The coiled inner end of the tube is in close contact with a knot of blood capillaries.

The inner layer of the dermis is a layer of fatty or **adipose tissue**, which serves both as a store of fat and as an insulation against heat loss or gain.

5.3. Skin colour

If you look around the class, you will see that skin colour varies from brown, through pale yellow, to pink. The various races of man have different skin colours. What causes these differences? There are really four factors which affect skin colour:

a. The thickness of the epidermis. If the epidermis is thick, as in Asiatic races, the skin appears yellowish, for the blood cannot be seen through it.

b. The blood capillaries. If the blood capillaries are close to the surface of the skin, and contain much blood, the skin will appear pink.

c. The amount of melanin. Melanin is a brown pigment contained in special cells in the epidermis. Dark-skinned races have abundant melanin cells, whilst fair-skinned races have few. 'Moles' and 'freckles' are due to local patches of melanin cells.

d. The presence of other substances. Sometimes during illness other substances find their way into the skin. Thus, in jaundice a waste product from the liver, called bilirubin, causes the yellow coloration of the skin.

BODY TEMPERATURE

5.4. Cold-blooded and warm-blooded animals

Animals which are unable to control their body temperature are said to be cold-blooded. The temperature inside these animals rises and falls with changes in the external temperature. Thus they are warmer during the day than during the night, and warmer during the summer than in the winter. All invertebrates are cold-blooded. Among the vertebrates, the fishes, amphibians and reptiles are cold-blooded. During cold conditions, the body processes of these animals are slowed down. You have probably noticed that insects and other cold-blooded animals become sluggish in the autumn. In the winter in cold countries, cold-blooded animals must become inactive, or **hibernate**.

Warm-blooded animals, on the other hand, are not dependent on external temperature, but their body temperature is constant, usually in the region of 38 °C (100 °F). Only birds and mammals are warm-blooded. This means that they are able to be active, if they wish, both day and night, summer and winter. This advantage has enabled birds and mammals to be world-wide in their distribution and to become the most advanced of all animals.

5.5. The regulation of body temperature in man

Our body temperature varies a little during the day, but is normally within the range 36–37 °C (97–99 °F). At this temperature, the body enzymes are most active, and the body metabolism is most efficient. In order to maintain this constant temperature, the body must be able to retain its heat when the outside temperature is lower, and to lose heat to the surroundings when it becomes overheated. Let us examine this process in more detail.

The source of body heat

We have learnt that in the process of cellular respiration glucose is oxidized to carbon dioxide and water, yielding energy. Some 75% of this energy is immediately released as heat. All cells respire and release heat, but the most heat is released in muscle cells, especially during exercise. Of course, should the external temperature rise above 37 °C, the body will gain heat from its surroundings.

Factors causing heat loss

Any object that is hotter than its surroundings will lose this extra heat. Some of the heat will be conducted to colder objects with which it is in contact. Some will be lost to the air, or water, around the object, by the process of convection. Finally, the object loses heat as heat rays (radiation). After a while, therefore, the object will assume the same temperature as its surroundings.

Like any other hot object, the human body will tend to lose heat by conduction, convection and radiation. It also loses heat through the evaporation of sweat. That evaporation causes cooling can be demonstrated by a simple investigation.

Figure 5.2 To show the cooling effect of evaporation

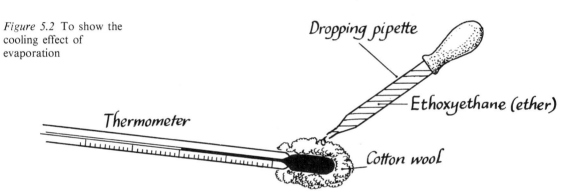

Investigation 5a. To show the cooling effect of evaporating ether

★ *Replace the stopper of the ethoxyethane (ether) bottle immediately after use. Do not breathe the vapour or allow near a naked flame.*

Wrap a light packing of cotton wool round the bulb of a thermometer (− 10 °C to 110 °C). Record the temperature shown on the thermometer. Then, using a dropping pipette, drop a little ethoxyethane (ether) on to the cotton wool and allow it to evaporate (see Figure 5.2). Observe the effect on the temperature shown on the thermometer. Continue adding ethoxyethane, drop by drop, allowing time between each drop for evaporation to occur. You may speed up the evaporation by blowing on the ethoxyethane. What do you now observe on the surface of the cotton wool? Where has this come from? Record the lowest temperature achieved in your investigation. Then unwrap the cotton wool from the bulb, and use the thermometer to measure the temperature of the ethoxyethane in the bottle. How does the temperature of the liquid ethoxyethane compare with that of the room? What do you think you would feel if you were to place a drop of ethoxyethane on to your skin? Try this (use the palm of your hand) and see if your reasoning is correct.

80

We see, then, that evaporation causes cooling, and that evaporation of sweat cools the body. The degree of cooling will depend on the rate of evaporation, which, in turn, depends on the humidity of the surrounding air and the extent to which air is moving across the skin surface. Can you now see why we feel so uncomfortably hot on a humid summer's day, and why the use of a fan will relieve our discomfort?

We do not only sweat when the body is overheated. A certain amount of sweating occurs at all times, though we are not conscious of it (insensible perspiration). Evaporation also occurs from the inner surfaces of the lungs, and this also has a cooling effect on the body.

The effect of overheating

During strenuous exercise much heat is released in the muscles. The blood system delivers this heat to all parts of the body, causing the general body temperature to rise. However, the body immediately begins to lose heat in the following ways:

a. The skin capillaries dilate (enlarge) so that more blood is carried to the surface of the skin, from where heat is lost by conduction, convection and radiation. This rush of blood to the skin makes the person look hot and flushed.

b. The sweat glands produce more sweat, the evaporation of which cools the body.

c. Rapid breathing causes more heat to be lost from the surface of the lungs.

d. Fewer and lighter clothes are worn, so that the heat loss from the skin is not restricted.

The effect of cooling

When the outside temperature is very low, or after a cold swim, the body temperature tends to fall, and the following reactions take place:

a. The skin capillaries contract, thus reducing the blood flow to the skin, and the person looks pale. Heat is conserved, as less is lost from the skin surface.

b. Thicker clothes are worn, thus insulating the skin against heat loss.

c. The tiny muscle attached to the base of each hair contracts, raising the hairs and trapping a thicker layer of warm air around the body. We have so little hair on our bodies that this does not have very much effect on heat loss. However, in more hairy mammals and in birds (who fluff out their feathers) this is an important heat-control mechanism. All that really happens in our case is that the contracting muscles produce depressions in the skin, forming the familiar 'gooseflesh' or 'goose pimples'.

d. Shivering occurs; in other words the skeletal muscles are caused to contract and relax rapidly, without us willing them to do so. More heat is therefore generated in the muscles.

The regulator

The question arises as to how the body knows when it is overheated or cooled, and how the control mechanisms are operated. We are far from knowing the full answers to these questions, but it is known that the brain houses a **heat-regulating centre**. This acts, in some way, like a thermostat which may be used to regulate the temperature in an aquarium or house. The centre is affected by blood temperature, and by 'information' from the nerve endings in the skin. Sweat glands and skin capillaries are under the control of the autonomic nervous system (see Chapter 7).

Figure 5.3 Diagrammatic representation of the factors affecting body temperature

As shown in Figure 5.3, the heat-regulating centre must achieve a balance between the heat gained by the body and the heat lost to the surroundings.

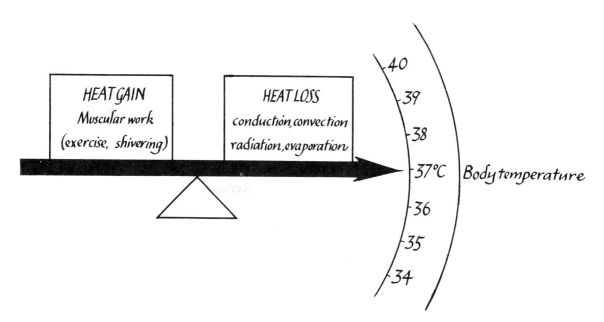

5.6. Illness and body temperature

During illness, the body temperature may rise above normal, and may remain at the new high level; this condition is called a **fever**. The patient feels very hot, but this is not because more heat is being produced in the body, but because the mechanisms of heat loss have been affected. In some cases, the poisons from the disease organisms may directly affect the heat-regulating centre in the brain. At the onset of a fever, a patient often feels intense cold, and shivering occurs and the teeth chatter, even though the mouth temperature is found to be high. If the body temperature of an adult reaches 41 °C life is endangered, and the temperature must be brought down by sponging with cold water and by the use of anti-fever drugs (aspirin, etc.).

A person who is subjected to extreme heat while undergoing physical exercise may suddenly become unconscious, due to a **heatstroke**. The body temperature may rise as high as 42 °C, due to the inability of the person to sweat. Sunstroke is a form of heatstroke.

Heat exhaustion comes on less dramatically, but causes dizziness, weakness and abdominal cramps. Such heat exhaustion may occur in tropical countries, should a person fail to replace the large amount of salt lost in sweat.

Test your understanding

1. Name three things against which we are protected by our skin.
2. What is the connection between the skin and vitamins?
3. What is a fingerprint a record of?
4. Why do you think that badly fitting shoes cause corns?
5. What have hair and fingernails in common?
6. Why is regular washing with soap necessary for a healthy skin?
7. Although there are no hairs on the nose, it still becomes shiny. Suggest a possible reason for this.
8. How do you think a 'blackhead' might be caused?
9. Of what advantage to people of tropical countries is their darker skin?
10. Explain the difference between cold- and warm-blooded animals.
11. Although mammals are warm-blooded, some do become inactive in winter. Suggest reasons for this.
12. List the main ways in which the body loses heat to its surroundings.
13. Why does ethoxyethane (ether) feel cold when placed on the skin?
14. A dog has no sweat glands. From which parts of its body does it lose heat by evaporation?
15. When we are embarrassed why do you think that we feel 'hot and bothered'?
16. How would you treat a feverish patient?

Chapter 6

The Senses of the Body

6.1. The collection of information

The activities of the body are controlled and co-ordinated by the brain. The brain sends instructions in the form of nervous impulses along the motor nerves to the 'doing' or **effector** organs, such as muscles or glands, which bring about the body's response. How does the brain know what instructions to give? If the brain is to give the correct instructions, it must be able to collect information about the surrounding conditions. This is done by the sense or **receptor** organs, such as the eyes, the ears, the nose and the sense organs of the skin. Sense organs are also found in the internal organs, such as the muscles and the gut; they keep the brain informed about internal conditions of the body, such as fatigue and hunger. A change in conditions, internal or external, is a **stimulus**, and is transmitted to the brain by the appropriate sense organ.

6.2. A simple sense organ—the taste buds on the tongue

On the upper suface of the tongue are little projections. Around the base of these projections are grooves which contain groups of sensory cells called **taste buds** (see Figure 6.1). These sensory cells are sensitive to chemicals in solution. The sensory cells are attached

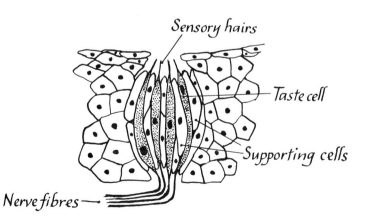

Figure 6.1 Section through a taste bud

to sensory nerve fibres which carry impulses to the brain to be interpreted as the sensation of taste. There are four types of taste bud, each sensitive to a different flavour, namely sweet, sour, salt and bitter.

Investigation 6a. To discover the distribution of the different types of taste bud on the tongue

You need (a) sugar solution to stimulate sweet-sensitive taste buds, (b) lemon juice to stimulate the sour-sensitive taste buds, (c) salt solution to stimulate the salt-sensitive taste buds and (d) quinine solution to stimulate the bitter-sensitive taste buds. With a clean dropper or glass rod, place a drop of each solution on (a) the tip, (b) the right side, (c) the left side, (d) the back and (e) the middle of your tongue. Record the sensations accurately, draw the outline of a tongue and then plot the distribution of the taste buds which are sensitive to different flavours.

6.3. The sense of smell

The sense of **smell** is similar to that of taste. Within the nose occur simple sense organs which are stimulated by chemicals which become dissolved in the moisture within the nose. These chemicals must travel to the nose as gases or in droplet form. Thus substances which vaporize readily (for example ether, petrol, certain oils, etc.) have strong odours.

6.4. The sense organs of the skin

The sense organs in the skin enable the body to feel touch, pressure, temperature changes and pain (see Figure 6.2). Touch is felt

Figure 6.2 Sense organs of the skin

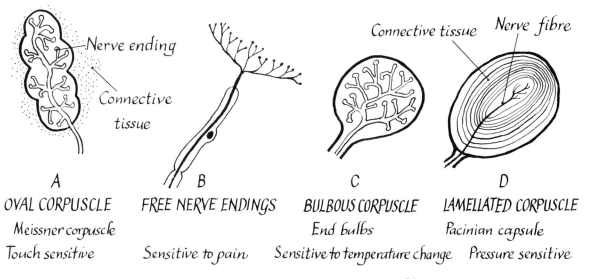

A	B	C	D
OVAL CORPUSCLE	FREE NERVE ENDINGS	BULBOUS CORPUSCLE	LAMELLATED CORPUSCLE
Meissner corpuscle		End bulbs	Pacinian capsule
Touch sensitive	Sensitive to pain	Sensitive to temperature change	Pressure sensitive

by **Meissner corpuscles** near the surface of the skin, which consist of the ends of nerve fibres surrounded by sheaths of connective tissue. Pressure is perceived by **Pacinian corpuscles**, which are situated in the fatty tissue deeper down in the skin. Concentrations of these receptors occur on the hands and feet. Pain is perceived by **free nerve endings**, which lie amongst the cells of the skin. They are more concentrated in some parts of the skin than others, making these regions more sensitive to pain. Temperature changes are thought to stimulate receptors called **end bulbs**.

Certain types of skin receptor are concentrated in particular regions of the skin. Meissner corpuscles are, for example, concentrated in the finger tips, which are therefore particularly sensitive to touch.

Investigation 6b. To compare the sensitivity of the skin to touch in different parts of the body

Biological

Blindfold a volunteer, and take a pair of dividers with the points about 25 mm apart. (Alternatively, stick two pins about 25 mm apart through a piece of card.) Place the points of the dividers on the subject's skin and ask him whether he feels one prick or two. Occasionally, use just one point so that he cannot be sure that you are using two points. Discover which are the more sensitive regions where two pricks are felt and which are the less sensitive regions where only one is felt. Then reduce the distance between the divider tips by stages, and plot out the varying degrees of sensitivity exhibited by different areas of skin.

6.5. The sense of sight

The organs of vision are the eyes, which lie in sockets called **orbits** in the front of the skull. The eyes are protected by the muscular eyelids. At the upper outer edge of the eyeball is the **lachrymal** or tear gland (see Figure 6.3). The lachrymal gland secretes a solution containing sodium chloride and sodium hydrogen carbonate, which is distributed over the eyeball by the eyelids to keep the surface moist and clean. The lachrymal gland can be compared with the screen washers of a motorcar and the eyelid with the windscreen wiper. The tear fluid also acts as a mild disinfectant which kills any bacteria on the eye.

6.6. The muscles of the eye

The eye is held in its socket by six muscles which originate on the orbit and insert on the outermost coat of the eye, the **sclera**. Attached to the top of the eye is the **superior rectus** muscle, and to

86

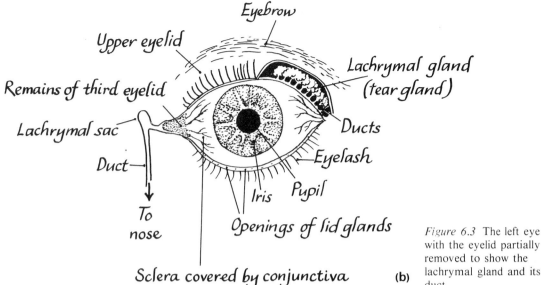

Eyebrow

Upper eyelid

Lachrymal gland (tear gland)

Remains of third eyelid

Lachrymal sac

Ducts

Duct

Eyelash

To nose

Iris   Pupil

Openings of lid glands

Sclera covered by conjunctiva   **(b)**

Figure 6.3 The left eye with the eyelid partially removed to show the lachrymal gland and its duct

the bottom the **inferior rectus** muscle. These two muscles move the eye up and down. The **internal rectus** muscle is attached to the inner side of the eye and the **external rectus** muscle to the outer side. The eye is moved from side to side by these two muscles. The **superior oblique** muscle, attached across the top of the eye, and the **inferior oblique** muscle, across the bottom of the eye, rotate the eye (see Figures 6.4 and 6.5).

Figure 6.4 (left) The attachment of muscles to the right eye as seen from the front

Figure 6.5 (below) The attachment of muscles to the right eye as seen from the side

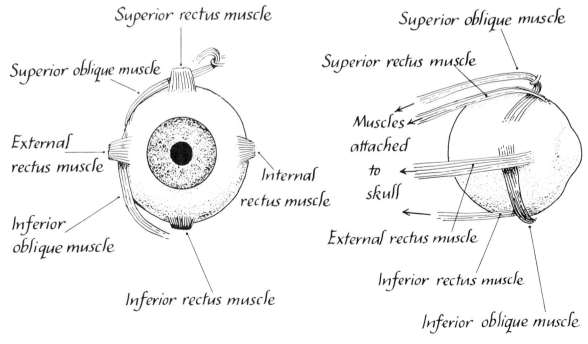

Superior rectus muscle

Superior oblique muscle

External rectus muscle

Internal rectus muscle

Inferior oblique muscle

Inferior rectus muscle

Superior oblique muscle

Superior rectus muscle

Muscles attached to skull

External rectus muscle

Inferior rectus muscle

Inferior oblique muscle

87

6.7. The structure of the eye

Investigation 6c. To examine the structure of a bullock's eye

Biological

Ask your butcher to get you a bullock's eye. Two eyes between two pupils is ideal. You will also need a pair of sharp scissors, a small cork mat and a few pins.

Working with a partner, remove any fat from the eye, taking care to leave the muscles intact. Try to decide if you have a left eye or a right eye; the positions of the muscle insertions will help you. Notice the tough, outer coat of the eyeball to which the muscles are attached. It is called the **sclera**. At the front of the eye it becomes the transparent **cornea** through which light passes into the eye. At the back of the eyeball, notice the white **optic nerve** which carries impulses to the brain.

Take one of the bullock's eyes, pierce the sclera with the tip of a pair of sharp scissors and cut the eye vertically into two halves, the right side and the left side.

Inside the eye, look for the **choroid**, a layer containing many tiny blood vessels which supply the eye with food and oxygen. Look carefully at the choroid around the margin of the cornea. You may just be able to detect a ridge of muscle, the **ciliary body**. Suspended from it by the inelastic **suspensory ligaments**, you will find the **lens**.

The coloured diaphragm between the cornea and the lens is the **iris**. In the centre is a hole, the **pupil**. The iris consists of two layers of muscle, circular and radial, which behave antagonistically and control the size of the pupil, thereby regulating the amount of light entering the eye; when the circular muscles contract, the radial muscles relax and the pupil becomes smaller, reducing the amount of light entering the eye. The fluid in the space between the cornea and the lens is the **aqueous humour**, and the jelly-like substance found behind the lens is called the **vitreous humour**. They help to bend the light so that an image is formed on the retina and also help to maintain the shape of the eye. The sense cells of the eye form the very delicate innermost layer of the eyeball called the **retina**. This is the photosensitive part of the eye.

Use Figure 6.6, a vertical section through a human eye, to help you to identify the different parts. Pin out the dissected eyes on cork mats.

With the second eye, make the incision at right angles to the incision in the first one, cutting the eye vertically into a front half and a back half. This leaves intact certain structures damaged in the first section. If a deep-freeze is available, the eyes can be frozen and then sawn into two with a junior hack-saw.

6.8. The formation of an image

The light-sensitive cells of the retina are the actual receptors.

88

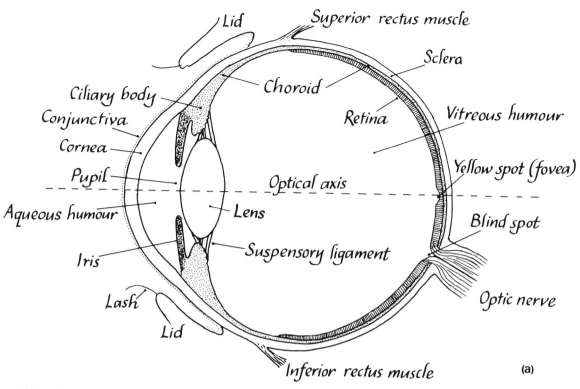

Although many times more sensitive, they are the equivalent of the film used in a camera. The main structure of the eye is equivalent to the camera itself, and is concerned with causing images of objects seen to fall on the retina. Light from an object outside the eye enters through the pupil and is brought to a focus by means of the curved surface of the cornea, the lens and the humours. The image of the object formed on the retina is inverted and laterally transposed (back-to-front), as shown in Figure 6.7.

Figure 6.6 The human eye in vertical section

Figure 6.7 The formation of an image on the retina of the eye

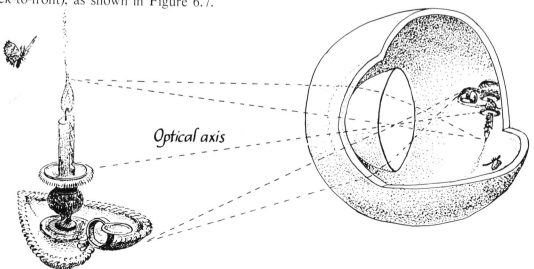

Optical axis

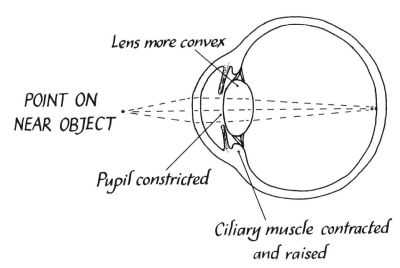

Lens more convex

POINT ON
NEAR OBJECT

Pupil constricted

Ciliary muscle contracted
and raised

Figure 6.8 The eye
accommodated for near
vision

6.9. The accommodation or focusing of the eye

The lens is elastic and has a natural tendency to become spherical and focused on near objects. The lens, however, is suspended from the ciliary body by the inelastic suspensory ligaments. In the relaxed eye, the suspensory ligaments are held taut by the fluids within the eye pressing out on the sclera. When the suspensory ligaments are taut, the lens is pulled into a thinner shape and the eye is focused for distant vision. The ciliary body contains muscle fibres running in a circular direction around the edge of the choroid.

a. Near vision

When the eye is focused on a near object, the muscle fibres in the ciliary body contract, thus reducing its diameter and causing it to stand slightly proud from the wall of the eyeball. The tension in the suspensory ligaments is thus reduced, allowing the lens to become more spherical and powerful, thus bringing the near object into focus (see Figure 6.8).

At the same time, the circular muscles of the iris contract and the radial ones relax, causing the pupil to become smaller. This admits

Figure 6.9 The muscles
of the iris

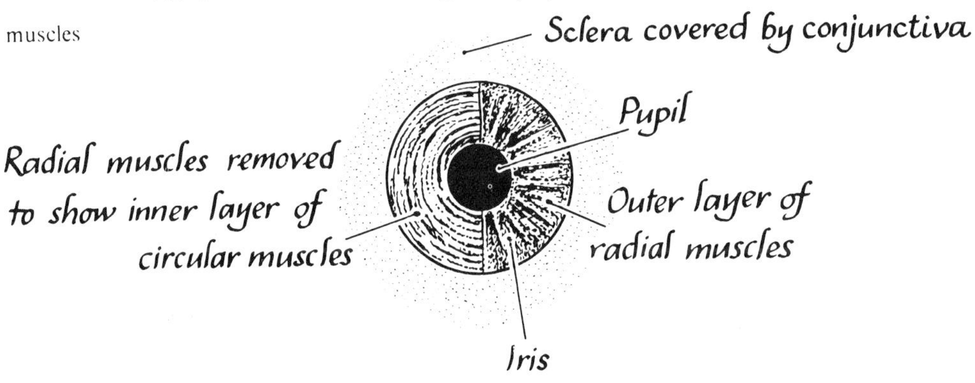

Sclera covered by conjunctiva

Pupil

Radial muscles removed
to show inner layer of
circular muscles

Outer layer of
radial muscles

Iris

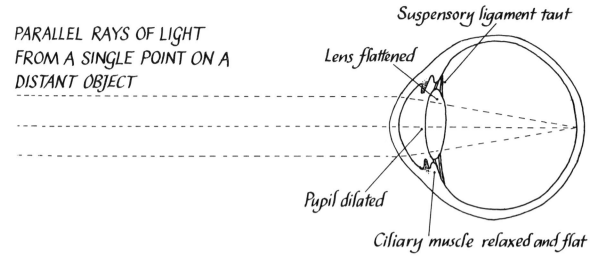

PARALLEL RAYS OF LIGHT
FROM A SINGLE POINT ON A
DISTANT OBJECT

Suspensory ligament taut

Lens flattened

Pupil dilated

Ciliary muscle relaxed and flat

a narrower cone of light into the eye and increases the depth of focus (see Figure 6.9).

Figure 6.10 The eye accommodated for distant vision

b. Distant vision

When the eye focuses on a distant object, the circular muscle fibres in the ciliary body relax, allowing the ridge of muscle to flatten along the side of the eyeball. This puts tension on the suspensory ligaments which pull the lens against the vitreous humour, causing it to flatten and enabling it to focus on distant objects. At the same time, the circular muscles of the iris relax and the longitudinal muscles contract, making the pupil larger and allowing it to admit more light (see Figures 6.10 and 6.11).

Figure 6.11 Diagram to explain the accommodation of the eye: (a) for near vision and (b) for distant vision

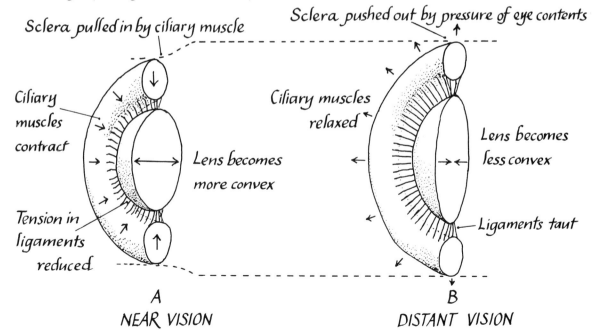

Sclera pulled in by ciliary muscle

Sclera pushed out by pressure of eye contents

Ciliary muscles contract

Lens becomes more convex

Tension in ligaments reduced

A
NEAR VISION

Ciliary muscles relaxed

Lens becomes less convex

Ligaments taut

B
DISTANT VISION

6.10. The retina

The receptor cells of the retina are stimulated by light and produce an image. It is now thought that the retina analyses the image before transmitting it, in the form of impulses, to the brain. The image on the retina of the eye is inverted and back-to-front, but it is interpreted correctly by the brain. Once a retinal receptor has been stimulated it becomes inactive for a while, so it is necessary to keep moving the eye slightly to stimulate more receptor cells. If this is not done the image will disappear.

Black and white vision

The retina contains two types of photosensitive receptor cells, the **rods** and the **cones** (see Figure 6.12). The rods are concentrated around the edge of the retina and perceive a black, white and grey image only. As they are sensitive to low-intensity light, they are particularly valuable in dim light. The rods contain a dye called **visual purple**. In very bright light, the visual purple contained by rod cells is bleached. They become relatively inactive and the eye then

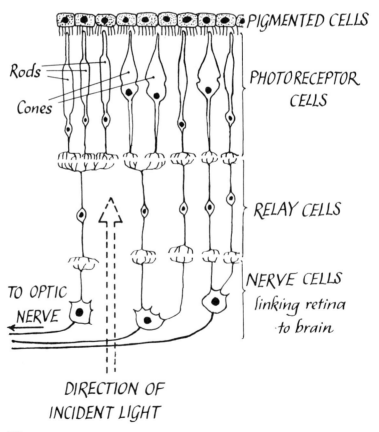

Figure 6.12 The structure of the retina

depends upon the cones. In dim light, the visual purple is gradually restored and objects can again be seen.

Colour vision

The cones are concentrated in the central region of the retina. These receptors are sensitive to bright light and are able to perceive colours. It is *thought* that there are three types of cone cell. Each type contains a substance which is sensitive to light of a particular wavelength or colour. One type of cone is stimulated by red light, one type by green light and the third type by blue light. Both the red cones and the green cones are stimulated by yellow light, as it is a mixture of red and green light.

Colour-blindness

About one man in every twelve and one woman in every two hundred is colour-blind. There are two types of human colour-blindness. The first type is total colour-blindness when there are no cones in the retina, only rods, so that the person can only see in black and white and tones of grey. In the more common type of colour-blindness, partial colour-blindness, it is thought that one of the three types of cone is missing. In this case, the person is unable to distinguish between certain colours—often red and green.

The blind spot

At the point where the retina enters the optic nerve, there are no rods or cones. This means that the image formed at this point is not transmitted to the brain.

Investigation 6d. To demonstrate the blind spot

Position this book about two feet away. Close your left eye and with the right eye concentrate on the cross shown in Figure 6.13. Slowly bring the book closer to the face. When the image of the spot is focused on the blind spot, it will seem to disappear. Find out the distance of the book from the right eye when this happens. Normally, however, the image is not focused on the blind spot.

Figure 6.13 Demonstration of the blind spot

The yellow spot or fovea

The yellow spot, or fovea, is the part of the retina which lies on the optical axis of the eye; in other words, it is the place on the retina directly behind the exact centre of the lens. It is hollow and contains only cones. On this part of the retina the most accurate image in both form and colour is formed, and it is the normal focus point for close vision.

6.11. Defects of vision and their correction

a. Short-sightedness or myopia

Short-sightedness occurs when the light rays from a distant object are focused in front of the retina, as in Figure 6.14. This can be caused by the eyeball being too long or by the lens being too fat and therefore too powerful. The effect is that the person has difficulty in focusing on distant objects.

Figure 6.14 (left) Short-sightedness

Figure 6.15 (right) Short-sightedness corrected

Short-sightedness can be corrected by wearing spectacles with concave lenses which make the light rays diverge, enabling the lens to focus them on the retina, as in Figure 6.15.

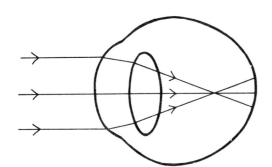
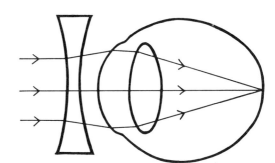

b. Long-sightedness or hypermetropia

Long-sightedness occurs when the light rays from an object do not focus on the retina, but would come into focus behind it as in Figure 6.16. This can be caused by the eyeball being too short or the lens being too thin and therefore too weak. The effect is that near vision is not possible without spectacles, and accommodation is necessary for distant vision.

Long-sightedness can be corrected by wearing spectacles with convex lenses which make the light rays converge before reaching the eye, so that they come into focus on the retina, as in Figure 6.17.

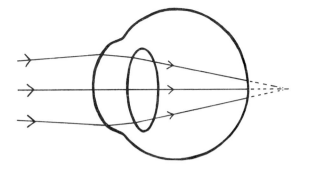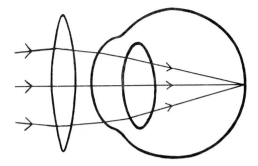

c. Old sight or presbyopia

This condition occurs when the lens hardens in old age and will not accommodate. This is a cause of long-sightedness, so spectacles with convex lenses may help. Often, however, two pairs of spectacles may be necessary, a pair with convex lenses for close vision and a pair with concave lenses for long vision. The two types of lens may, however, be combined into one pair of **bifocal** spectacles.

d. Astigmatism

This condition is caused by a deformed cornea which lacks a true spherical surface. The person is unable to focus simultaneously on lines at right angles to each other. When he focuses on one set of lines the others are out of focus, and vice versa. Astigmatism can be corrected by wearing spectacles with specially ground cylindrical lenses.

6.12. The sense of hearing

Sound is perceived by the ears, which are able to convert sound waves into nervous impulses and transmit them to the brain. The brain is able to interpret these impulses as meaningful signals. Sound travels as waves, which are disturbances of the molecules in the air. Sound waves are produced by vibrating objects such as guitar strings, vocal cords and clanking pieces of metal.

6.13. The structure of the ear

There are three main regions of the ear: the outer ear, the middle ear and the inner ear. The outer ear consists of the **pinna** which collects the sound waves and channels them into the ear passage, or **external auditory meatus** (see Figure 6.18). The design of the pinna enables us to detect the direction of a sound without moving the head.

The outer ear is separated from the middle ear by the eardrum, or **tympanic membrane.** The middle ear is an air-filled cavity within

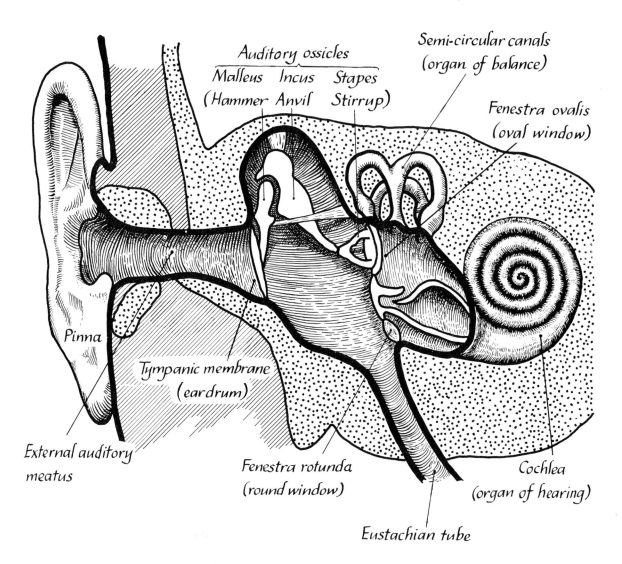

Figure 6.18 Diagram of the human ear (the middle ear and the inner ear are drawn much larger in proportion to the outer ear)

the bone of the skull. It is linked to the throat by the **Eustachian tube** which ensures that the air pressure inside the ear is equal to the atmospheric pressure, thus enabling the eardrum to vibrate freely. Sound waves are transmitted across the middle ear by a lever system composed of the **ear ossicles**, the three smallest bones in the body. Attached to the eardrum is the hammer bone, or **malleus**, which articulates with the anvil bone, or **incus**. This, in turn, articulates with the stirrup bone, or **stapes**, which transmits vibrations to the fluid of the inner ear through the oval window, or **fenestra ovalis**.

The inner ear consists of two main parts, the **semi-circular canals** and the **cochlea**. The semi-circular canals are concerned with the sense of balance, changes in direction, acceleration and deceleration.

96

The coiled cochlea converts sound waves to nervous impulses which are transmitted to the brain by the auditory nerve. It has been shown that very high-pitched sounds over a long period of time destroy that part of the cochlea which perceives the high notes (as in 'boiler-maker's disease'). The ear is a very delicate organ and must be treated with respect.

6.14. The working of the ear

a. Hearing

Sound waves collected by the pinna strike the eardrum, causing it to vibrate. The hammer bone attached to the eardrum vibrates with it. The hammer bone articulates with the anvil bone, and as the hammer is one and a half times the length of the anvil, the force of the vibration is amplified by that magnitude. The vibration is transmitted across the middle ear to the stirrup bone which causes the oval window to vibrate. As the area of the eardrum is twenty times greater than that of the oval window, the force of the vibration is amplified tremendously, even though a certain amount of this increased force is lost in transmission. The vibrating oval window sets up oscillations in the fluid of the inner ear. This fluid is not compressible, so acts as a medium to pass the vibrations to the cochlea. This movement stimulates the receptor cells in the cochlea lining, which then send nervous impulses to the brain. The brain interprets these impulses as sounds.

b. Balance

The semi-circular canals consist of three fluid-filled tubes arranged at right angles to one another. From the lining of these canals project the nerve endings of receptor cells. As the head changes its position, movement is produced in the fluid in the canals. This movement is detected by the nerve endings of the receptor cells, which send nervous impulses to the brain, informing it about the change in position of the head.

6.15. Causes of deafness

The causes of deafness fall into three categories:

a. **Blockage** of the external auditory meatus caused by the excessive secretion of wax, or blockage of the Eustachian tube by mucus during a heavy cold.

b. **Transmission deafness** may be caused by damage to the eardrum or the ear ossicles as a result of accident or disease. Sometimes the stapes may become fixed to the oval window, preventing the transmission of vibrations.

c. **Perceptual deafness** cannot be helped by hearing aids. It may be caused by the failure of the auditory nerve to develop or by a loss of function of the part of the brain that perceives the sensation of sound.

Test your understanding

Copy and complete the following paragraphs:

The five senses are ....[1], ...[2], taste, ...[3] and touch. The sense organs collect information about the ....[4] and transmit it in the form of ....[5] impulses along ....[6] nerves to the brain. Such information may be called a ....[7], which often evokes a response by an ....[8] organ such as a muscle or a ....[9]

The eye is moved by ....[10] attached to the outer coat of the eyeball, which is called the ....[11] The choroid is the middle layer of the eyeball and is well supplied with ....[12] The inner, photosensitive layer is called the ....[13] It contains two types of light-sensitive receptor cells: rods which perceive ....[14] light and ....[15] which perceive colour. It is thought that there are three types of cones: one which is sensitive to ....[16] light, another sensitive to ....[17] light and the third sensitive to ....[18] light. Short-sightedness is caused by an eyeball which is ....[19] ....[20] can be corrected with spectacles with convex lenses.

The ....[21] of the ear collects the sound waves. The sound is passed down the external auditory meatus and causes the ....[22] to vibrate. These vibrations are transmitted across the ....[23] ear by the ....[24] bone, the anvil bone and the ....[25] The inner ear consists of the semi-circular canals which are concerned with ....[26] and the ....[27] which is concerned with hearing. Deafness may be caused by wax in the ....[28], damage to the ....[29] or by the failure of the ....[30] to develop.

1. What is the difference between receptor and effector organs?
2. How many kinds of taste bud have we, and to what flavours are they sensitive?
3. Name the muscles that move the eye.
4. What are the functions of the lachrymal secretions (tears)?
5. Explain the changes which occur in the eye as you walk out into the street, buy a newspaper and begin to read it.
6. What causes 'long sight', and how might it be corrected?
7. How is it thought that we appreciate colour?
8. How does the body maintain its balance?
9. Explain how the sound is transmitted from the pinna to the inner ear and what happens to it.
10. Explain the main causes of deafness. Why do more elderly people tend to be deaf?
11. Is a great deal of loud 'pop' music good for your sense of hearing?

Chapter 7

Co-ordination: The Nervous System

7.1. The need for co-ordination

In the last few chapters, we have learnt about some of the major body systems, the functions of which are as follows:

TABLE 7.1

System	Function
Skeletal system (see Chapter 10)	Support and protection of organs and for attachment of muscles.
Digestive system	Breakdown and absorption of food.
Respiratory system	Provision of energy.
Blood system	Transport of materials.
Excretory system	Removal of waste.

Each of these body systems comprises a number of different organs. Thus, for example, the digestive system includes such organs as the tongue, oesophagus, stomach, intestine and pancreas. Within the system, each of these organs has its own particular part to play in the working of that system. However, this does not mean that each organ is 'a law unto itself'. No organ can work without regard for the working of the other organs in the system, or there would be chaos. Thus, for example, it would be no use for the stomach to start to churn and secrete its digestive juice, if the oesophagus had not done its part to deliver the food to the stomach.

It follows, therefore, that organs need to be controlled in such a way that they work properly together. We say that the organs need to be **co-ordinated**. Systems, as well as organs, have to be co-ordinated. Let us consider an example of this co-ordination of systems.

Suppose that while you were asleep a fire was to break out in your house. The first of your body organs to be involved would be your sense organs. Your nose would smell the fumes and your ears would hear the crackling of the fire. The 'information' from these sense organs would wake you up. As your eyes opened, they would sense the bright light of the fire and would inform you of its direction. Automatically, your body systems would take up 'action stations'. Your heartbeat would quicken and more blood would be pumped to the skeletal muscles. Less blood would be sent to the intestines, and digestive processes would slow down. Deep, rapid breathing would supply the blood with abundant oxygen, enabling the muscle cells to release the maximum amount of energy. As you moved into action, your muscles would move the limbs rapidly and efficiently, so that you could escape from the burning house quickly. All these body actions seem so obvious and sensible that we accept them without thinking about how well they are controlled and co-ordinated.

Two controlling mechanisms are involved, namely the **nervous**

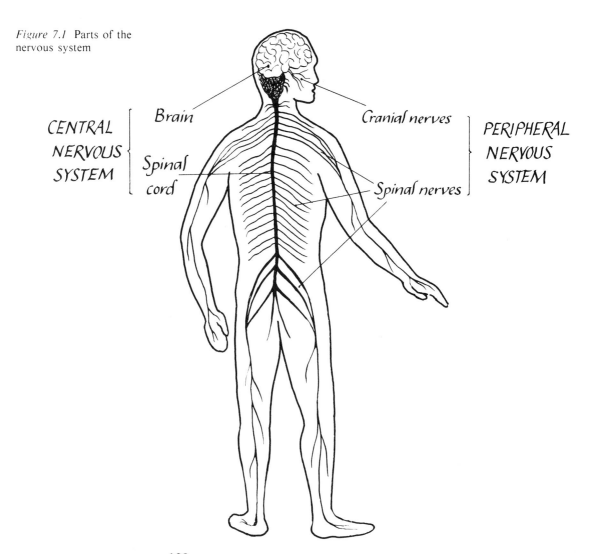

Figure 7.1 Parts of the nervous system

CENTRAL NERVOUS SYSTEM

Brain

Spinal cord

Cranial nerves

Spinal nerves

PERIPHERAL NERVOUS SYSTEM

system and the **endocrine system**. The nervous system comprises the brain, spinal cord and nerves, and is the main controlling system for body actions, such as movement (see Figure 7.1). The endocrine system comprises a series of organs which produce chemical substances called **hormones**. These hormones are dispersed all over the body by the blood stream, and have important effects in controlling the rate of metabolism and of growth. We shall consider the endocrine system in more detail in the next chapter.

7.2. Receptors and effectors

In the example given in Section 7.1 we have seen that the sense organs have a vital role to play. Only through them are we able to know what is happening around us. Sense organs such as the eyes, ears and nose are called **receptor organs**, because they receive 'information' from our surroundings. Can you think of any other sense organs?

Actually, not all of our sense organs are concerned with the outside world, for some are able to sense changes within the body. Try this little test. Close your eyes. Are you able to say what position your feet are in? If your feet are in contact with the floor, the sense of touch will tell you this. What about the position of your head and arms? Can you tell the position of a part of the body which is not in contact with a surface? The ability to do this suggests that we have internal sense organs. Our muscles, for instance, contain **stretch receptors**, which tell us whether the muscle is contracted or relaxed. Therefore, if we are aware that the biceps muscle is contracted, we know that the lower arm is raised. Information about the position of our limbs is important if movement is to be co-ordinated.

Of course, it would be a waste of time for the body to have a system of receptor organs if the information from them was not to be used to the body's advantage. Merely for the body to 'know' that the house is on fire is useless, unless the body *reacts* in some sensible way. Organs which bring about reactions are called **effectors**. Muscles are the body's main effector organs, and the reaction that they produce is movement. Glands are also effector organs; they react by secreting a juice. Thus, for instance, the sight and smell of strawberries and cream causes the salivary glands to react by secreting saliva (the mouth 'waters').

In simple animals such as the hydra, the receptors (sense cells) are very close to the effectors (muscle cells). These cells are linked by small nerve cells. However, in higher animals, the receptor cells are usually some distance from the effectors, and the nerve cells connecting them have to be very long. In the next section, we shall see how the receptor, nerve cell and effector all contribute to a simple action.

101

7.3. Reflex actions

Investigation 7a. The knee-jerk reflex

For this investigation you will need to work in pairs. One of the pair should sit on a chair, with the right leg resting across the left thigh and hanging limply. The other member of the pair should now strike the right leg of the seated partner just below the knee-cap. Use the edge of the hand or a thin book, and make the blow sharp and quick. Notice how the leg reacts to this stimulus. Is this reaction, which is called the 'knee jerk', a conscious, voluntary movement? Do we decide to do it or is it involuntary?

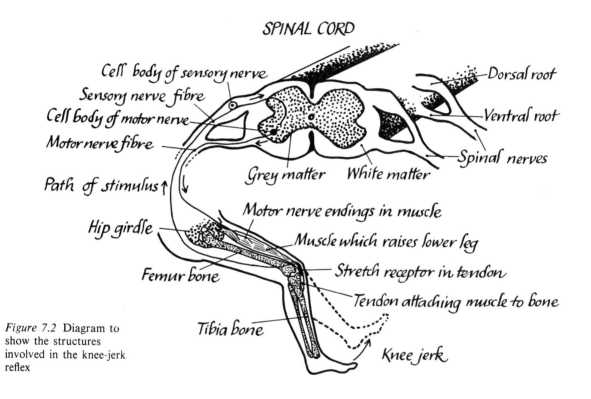

Figure 7.2 Diagram to show the structures involved in the knee-jerk reflex

A response such as the knee jerk, which is quick, automatic and given on receipt of a definite external stimulus, is called a **reflex action**. Further examples of reflex actions are given in Table 7.2.

If you think about the examples of reflex actions, you will realize how important some of them are to the body. Some reflexes control routine, everyday actions over which we do not need to have conscious control, such as the movement of food through the alimentary canal. Others provide an immediate, protective response in times of danger, as in coughing. In simple, invertebrate animals, such as the amoeba and hydra, reflex actions account for almost all of the animal's behaviour. Thus, for example, both of these organisms show

TABLE 7.2. EXAMPLES OF REFLEX ACTIONS

Reflex	Stimulus	Response
Coughing	Dust or food particles entering the respiratory tract.	Violent contraction of muscles causing exhalation of air from lungs.
Swallowing	Arrival of food in the pharynx.	Raising of the glottis (Adam's apple), closing the entrance to the trachea.
Pupil reflex	Bright light striking the eye.	Contraction of the circular muscles in the iris, reducing the size of the pupil.
Withdrawal reflex	Hand touching very hot object.	Contraction of muscles, causing immediate withdrawal of the hand.
Foot reflex	Stroking the sole of the foot with a pencil.	Big toe bends towards sole.

withdrawal reflex: the amoeba withdraws its pseudopodia and the hydra its tentacles. What stimuli cause these reflexes?

7.4. The reflex arc

Since reflex actions are so important, it is necessary for us to examine more fully the mechanism behind them. Let us again use the knee jerk as an example. It will be useful if, when following this description, the reader refers back to Figure 7.2.

In the knee-jerk reflex, the receptor for the stimulus is located in the tendon which joins the muscle of the front of the thigh to the tibia, or shinbone. The stimulus is the blow struck with the hand or with the book. The effector organ is the thigh muscle itself (the quadriceps femoris). When this muscle is stimulated to contract, it exerts a sudden pull on the tibia, causing the knee to jerk.

We must now consider how the stimulus passes from the receptor (in the tendon) to the effector (in the muscles). This is achieved by the stimulus passing through a **reflex arc**, formed by two nerve cells, or **neurons**. These are known as the **sensory** neuron, and **motor** neuron. The structure of these nerve cells is shown in Figure 7.3.

When the knee tendon is struck, the receptor is stimulated, or excited. The axon of the sensory neuron conducts the stimulus to the spinal cord, located within the vertebral column of the back. Here the stimulus is passed to the motor neuron, down whose axon it passes to the thigh muscle. Each of the fine endings of the motor axon stimulates the contraction of the group of muscle fibres to which it connects.

The passage of the nervous impulse round this reflex arc is very

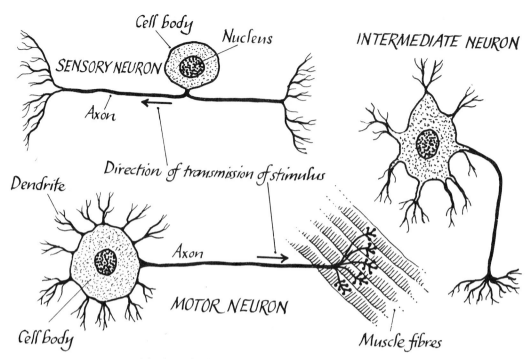

Figure 7.3 Types of nerve cell (neurons)

rapid, the whole conduction taking less than one-fiftieth of a second. It should be noted that the brain is not involved in this reflex, although the stimulus and effect are registered by the brain after the event. Indeed, the reflex is still shown by a decapitated animal.

In most reflex areas a third neuron is involved. This is located in the spinal cord, serving to link the sensory and motor neurons. It is known as the **intermediate** or connector neuron.

Investigation 7b. The 'all or nothing' law

We may use the knee-jerk reflex to illustrate another feature of nervous conduction. With your partner sitting as before, strike the knee tendon gently. Is there a knee jerk? Gradually increase the strength of the blows. Are you able to get a 'half' response, or do you achieve 'all or nothing'?

We may compare the result with trying to switch on an electric light. If we gradually move the switch we get no reaction until the pressure exerted suddenly becomes enough to throw the switch and cause the light to come on. It is not possible to have the light 'half on'. The 'all or nothing' law therefore applies in this case, as it does to nervous conduction.

7.5. Conditioned reflexes

The reflexes that we have been considering do not have to be learnt, but are inborn. Much of our behaviour, however, results

104

from another type of reflex which is built up from past experience and training. Such learnt reflexes are called **conditioned reflexes**. Let us consider an example of such a reflex.

We learnt in Chapter 1 that the saliva in our mouths is secreted by salivary glands. Although some saliva is normally required in the mouth to keep it moist, more is required when food is being chewed. It follows that salivary glands must become more active at this time. The control of salivary secretion is an inborn reflex. Thus, for instance, a puppy will produce more saliva just after birth if the taste buds on its tongue are stimulated by milk. Unless food is actually in the mouth, increased salivation does not occur. However, as the puppy grows older, it learns to recognize the appearance and smell of milk, and associates these with the pleasure of drinking milk. Milk does not now have to be present in the mouth for saliva to flow, the mere sight and smell being a stimulation to the glands. The inborn reflex has become a conditioned reflex. In humans, the conditioning may be taken to an extreme degree; our mouths may 'water' at the sight of a coloured picture of strawberries and cream!

We owe much of our knowledge of conditioned reflexes to a Russian scientist, **Ivan Pavlov**, who towards the end of the last century investigated the salivary secretion of dogs. In one experiment, each time he gave food to a hungry dog, he also rang a bell. Eventually, the dog produced saliva if the bell alone was rung, no food being offered. The dog had become conditioned to associate the bell with food. If you have a pet, you may be able to think of reflexes that you have conditioned in it; a dog may learn to associate 'going for a walk' with his master putting on his shoes.

Whilst inborn reflexes do not necessarily involve the brain, conditioned reflexes always do; for their establishment requires learning.

7.6. The central nervous system

In a telephone system all the telephones in a particular area are linked to a central exchange, through which all incoming and outgoing calls are fed. There are many such exchanges in the country. They are linked by cables to form a national network.

In some ways, the nervous system in our bodies resembles such a telephone system. Our receptors and effectors are linked to local nervous centres, which are, in turn, all linked together. These nervous centres lie in the **spinal cord** and the **brain**, and form the central nervous system.

Although the comparison between our nervous system and a telephone system helps our understanding, the analogy should not be carried too far. Whereas a telephone switchboard can only make connections, our brain is able to judge, make decisions and direct our actions.

a. The spinal cord

This lies in the vertebral canal and extends from the brain to the first lumbar vertebra.

Investigation 7c. To examine the structure of the spinal cord

Examine a slide of a transverse section of the spinal cord of a mammal under the low power of the microscope. Identify the various tissues by comparing the slide with Figure 7.4.

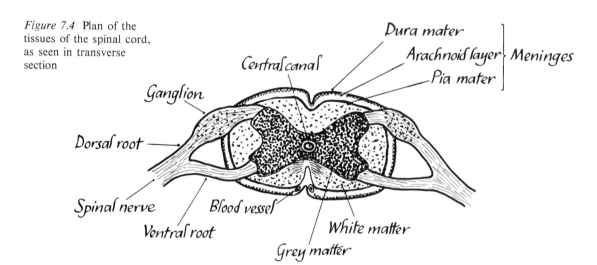

Figure 7.4 Plan of the tissues of the spinal cord, as seen in transverse section

The core of the spinal cord contains the cell bodies of nerve cells (neurons) together with their axons, embedded in a mass of neuroglial cells. The cell bodies are confined to a central, H-shaped area, known as the **grey matter**. Surrounding this is the **white matter**, consisting mainly of nerve axons. Some of these axons extend outwards from the cord into the spinal nerve, whilst others extend lengthwise along the cord, and may reach as far as the brain. A third type of axon connects one side of the spinal cord with the other. The total number of nerve axons in the cord is very large indeed, and their connections are far from fully understood. The number of axons extending from the hand, alone, is believed to be over 100 000.

The spinal cord probably serves four main functions:
a. To act as a relay centre for spinal reflexes (see Section 7.3).
b. To link the nerves of one region of the body with those of adjacent regions.
c. To carry sensory impulses from sense organs (for example, the skin) to the brain.

d. To carry motor impulses from the brain to the skeletal muscles.

Accidental displacement of an intervertebral disc ('slipped disc') or distortion of the vertebral column by bad posture may lead to pressure being exerted on the delicate spinal cord. This can be very painful, the pain being experienced in those regions to which the sensory axons of the affected part of the spinal cord connect. Thus a slipped disc in the lumbar region may lead to the experience of pain in the legs.

b. The meninges

Surrounding the nervous tissues of the brain and spinal cord are three layers known as meninges. The outermost is a tough, fibrous **dura mater**. This separates the nervous tissue from the enclosing bone and generally protects it from damage. The innermost layer, closely applied to the nervous tissue, is the **pia mater**, which is rich in blood vessels. The nervous tissue itself contains no blood capillaries, not even in the brain, all exchange of food, oxygen and waste materials being by diffusion with the blood in the pia mater. Separating the dura and pia mater is a spongy **arachnoid layer**, which may have a shock-absorbing function.

Inflammation of the meninges is known as **meningitis**, a condition which may be caused by a number of different disease-causing bacteria.

c. The brain

The brain is completely enclosed in the skull. At birth it weighs about 350 grams ($\frac{3}{4}$ lb), and reaches almost full size at the age of six. The adult brain weighs 1 300–1 400 grams (about 3 lb), and contains some 10 000 000 000 nerve cells, together with an even greater number of neuroglial cells.

The parts of the brain and its position in the head are shown in Figure 7.5.

The main core of the brain is called the **brain stem**. It mainly contains bundles of nerve axons linking the higher centres of the brain with each other and with the spinal cord. The region where the brain stem connects with the spinal cord is called the **medulla oblongata**. Here lie the reflex centres controlling vital 'everyday' processes such as breathing, heartbeat, movement of food along the gut, and the control of body temperature.

Surrounding the brain stem are important outgrowths. At the back, the crinkly-surfaced **cerebellum** serves the important function of the co-ordination of muscular movement. Although it does not actually cause muscles to act, it does exercise control over the

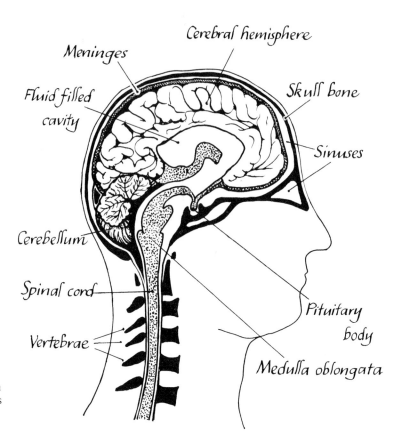

Figure 7.5 Section through the head, showing the parts of the brain

pattern of their action when several need to co-operate for one end, as, for example, when riding a bicycle or walking. We are not conscious of this control, but in cases where the cerebellum is damaged by disease the patient is unable to walk and use limbs properly. The cerebellum also assists muscle tone and the sense of balance.

By far the largest and most important part of the brain is the **cerebrum**, which comprises two **cerebral hemispheres**. These considerably overhang the front and sides of the brain stem, obscuring all other parts of the brain stem except the medulla and cerebellum. The surface area of the hemispheres is much increased by folding; the surface is seen to bear grooves (fissures) and crinkles (sulci). An inner core of white matter (mainly fibres) is surrounded by the grey matter of the cerebral **cortex**, the layer which contains most of the brain's nerve cells. The cerebral cortex is the part of the brain where we experience consciousness. Medical research has led to the mapping of the parts of the cortex according to their functions (see Figure 7.6).

The **motor area** controls the voluntary muscles, or those over which we have conscious control. The different parts of this area control the muscles of different regions of the body. Just behind the motor area is the **sensory area**, where we experience the sense of

108

touch. Each region of the body has fibres connecting to its own part of this area. The senses of sight, hearing and smell have their own areas of the cortex, whilst another area controls the movement of the eyes. Can you think why a blow on the back of the head may cause one to 'see stars'?

Large areas of the cortex remain unmapped, for their functions are still unknown. These are important areas, for somewhere here lie the seats of **learning** and of **memory**. It is the ability to memorize information and to learn from past experience that distinguishes man and the higher mammals from all other creatures. By placing electrodes on to the surface of the cortex in these unmapped areas, it can be shown that they are regions of continual, spontaneous, electrical activity, even when we are asleep.

Investigation 7d. To test reaction time

Ask all the members of the class to stand in a ring, leaving one gap in the ring. Stand in the gap, holding a stop-watch in your left hand. Tell the class that, with your right hand, you are going to squeeze the left hand of the person on your right. As soon as he feels the squeeze, he must squeeze the left hand of the person on his right. In this way the squeeze must be 'passed on' round the circle.

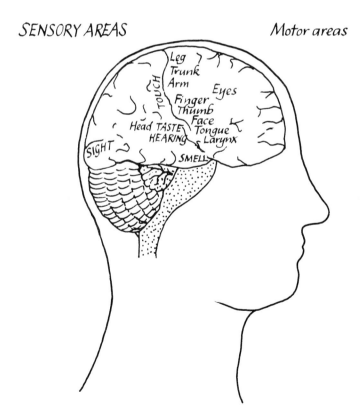

Figure 7.6 Map showing the functions of the parts of the cerebral cortex

109

Now, start the squeeze going and start the watch simultaneously. While the squeeze is passing from person to person, change the watch to your right hand, releasing your left hand to receive the squeeze from the person on your left. When you feel this squeeze, stop the watch. Divide the total time taken by the number of pupils in the circle, so calculating the average reaction time. Repeat the exercise four or five times. Does the reaction time remain the same? How do you account for this?

7.7. Nerves

Every organ of the body has many nerve axons connecting it with the central nervous system, just as a housing estate has many electric wires connecting it to the generating station. Such wires do not run separately, but are bound into cables. For the same reason, nerve axons are bound into nerves (see Figure 7.7).

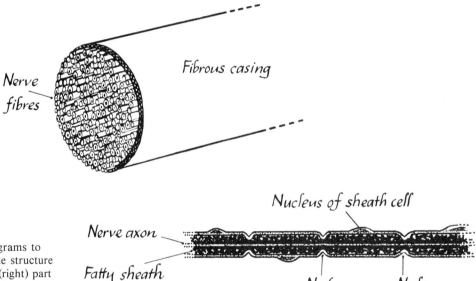

Figure 7.7 Diagrams to show (above) the structure of a nerve and (right) part of a nerve fibre in section

Each axon is separated from its neighbours by a fatty sheath, enclosed in a cellular membrane. It may be that this sheath serves to insulate the axon, just as electric wires have rubber or plastic insulation around them. An axon, together with its sheath, constitutes a **nerve fibre**. The sheath may not complete its development until after birth. Thus the nerve fibres to the legs, for instance, are not fully developed until the second year. Since this is about the time that a child begins to walk, it would appear that the sheath is essential for the proper functioning of the nerve fibre.

A **sensory nerve** carries only sensory fibres—fibres linking the central nervous system with the sense organs. A **motor nerve** carries

110

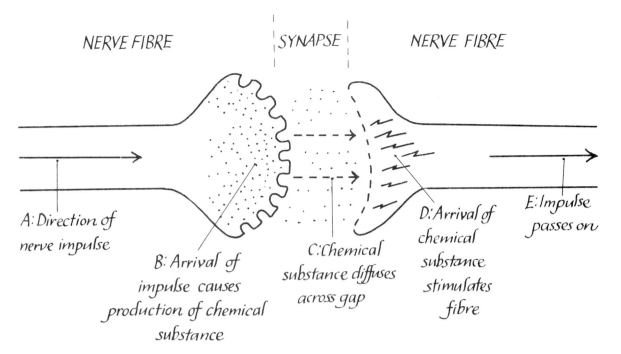

NERVE FIBRE   SYNAPSE   NERVE FIBRE

A: Direction of nerve impulse

B: Arrival of impulse causes production of chemical substance

C: Chemical substance diffuses across gap

D: Arrival of chemical substance stimulates fibre

E: Impulse passes on

only motor fibres—fibres linking the central nervous system with the muscles and glands. Many nerves are **mixed**, carrying both sensory and motor fibres. Can you think of an example of a mixed nerve that we have already encountered?

Nerves which connect directly with the brain are called **cranial nerves**, and include the optic nerve, auditory nerve and the nerves to the face and jaw. The number of nerve fibres in a nerve varies according to its size, but even small nerves carry several hundred.

Figure 7.8 The passage of a nerve stimulus across a synapse

7.8. The synapse

In this chapter we have compared the nervous system with an electrical circuit. However, in one sense, there is a difference. If in an electrical circuit we wish electricity to pass from one wire to another, we connect the ends in some way. The end of a nerve fibre, on the other hand, does not come into direct contact with the end of another fibre. Instead, the stimulus has to be transmitted across a small gap, known as a **synapse**. It is believed that the end of the stimulated fibre releases a chemical which diffuses across the gap and excites the delicate endings of the other fibre, so that the stimulus passes on (see Figure 7.8). How many synapses will occur in the reflex arc shown in Figure 7.2?

7.9. The autonomic nervous system

Many of the routine activities of the body are not under our conscious control. Thus, for instance, we cannot change the rate of our heartbeat or increase the amount of blood to our skin. The unconscious part of the nervous system is called the **autonomic system**. This is a dual system, each controlled organ having two sets of fibres. One set acts as an accelerator, speeding the action of the organ, whilst the other set decelerates, or slows the organ. Thus, in the case of the heart, stimulation of one set of fibres increases the rate of heartbeat, and stimulation of the other set decreases it. Just as the speed of a horse depends on how much the whip (or spurs) and reins are used by the rider, so, also, the rate of heartbeat depends on the balance between the two sets of fibres. Can you think of any other organs which are controlled by our autonomic nervous system?

Test your understanding

1. What is meant when we say that the action of the body organs must be co-ordinated?
2. Name the two co-ordinating systems of the body.
3. Explain what is meant by (a) receptor organs, (b) effector organs.
4. What is a reflex action?
5. Give an example of a reflex action not included in Table 7.2.
6. What does a reflex arc comprise?
7. What is meant by the 'all or nothing' law?
8. What is a conditioned reflex?
9. From your own experience, give an example of a conditioned reflex.
10. What contribution did Ivan Pavlov make to science?
11. Where are grey and white matter found, and what is the difference between them?
12. What are meninges and what is their purpose?
13. If you were able to examine the brain of a fish, which region would you expect to be less developed than in our brain? Give reasons for your answer.
14. Distinguish between a nerve axon, a nerve fibre and a nerve.
15. Explain what is meant by a synapse.
16. How do you think that the presence of the synapse affects the rate of nervous conduction? Give reasons for your answer.

Chapter 8

Chemical Control: Endocrine Organs and Hormones

8.1. Chemical co-ordination

If the testes, the reproductive organs, are removed from young male poultry, the birds do not develop fine plumage, spurs or the ability to crow, which are characteristic of the adult cockerel. Instead they develop into fine, fat birds with plumage more like that of a hen. These birds are called **capons** and are ideal for eating.

The operation of removing the testes is called **castration**, and it has been performed on male domestic animals for many centuries. Only the best male cattle and sheep, the bulls and rams, are allowed to breed; the others are castrated at an early age. The castrated males become bullocks and fat lambs, which are more docile and become heavier, with a higher ratio of flesh to bone. In previous centuries, the operation was sometimes carried out on young boys; these boys grew up into **eunuchs**, with high-pitched voices and no facial hair. The eunuchs were in demand as harem guards in the East because they were large, strong men, and also as choristers because they retained their high-pitched, boyhood voices throughout their lives.

What could be causing these changes? In 1848, A. A. Berthold, a German physiologist, experimented with cockerels and made the following observations:

a. The intact, male chick grows up into a cockerel with fine plumage and spurs, and proudly struts around and crows.

b. If the testis is completely removed, then the chick grows into a capon.

c. If the nerves and blood vessels to the testis are cut, the nerve does not grow again but the testis does develop a fresh blood supply and the chicken grows up into a normal cockerel.

d. If the testis is removed but replanted elsewhere in the chicken's body, the testis soon acquires a new blood supply but not nerves. The male chicken develops into a normal-looking cockerel.

What do these experiments tell us about the control of growth and development in poultry? If the testis is completely removed, then the male characteristics do not develop. The testis, therefore, is not solely concerned with the production of sperm, but also influences the development of the male characteristics of the bird. How can the testis influence the growth of the bird? If the nerve supply to the testis is cut, it does not regenerate, but the bird still develops the male characteristics. This suggests that these changes are not under the control of the nervous system. If the blood supply is cut, a new blood supply develops. If would appear that an intact blood supply is essential for the testis to affect growth.

In addition to producing sperm cells, testes contain the male **endocrine organs**, or ductless glands, which secrete 'chemical messengers' called **hormones**. Many of the activities of the body are influenced by hormones. It is particularly the slow, permanent changes associated with growth and development which the hormones control.

8.2. Endocrine organs, or ductless glands

Unlike the secretions associated with digestion, hormones do not usually act at the place where they are secreted. For example, hormones secreted by the testis of the cockerel affect its comb, its plumage, its voice and its behaviour. Ducted glands have ducts leading into the organ which receives the secretion, but ductless glands have no ducts through which their products pass (see Figures 8.1 and 8.2). They are enveloped in a rich supply of blood capillaries. The *blood stream* carries the hormone directly from the gland to its place of action.

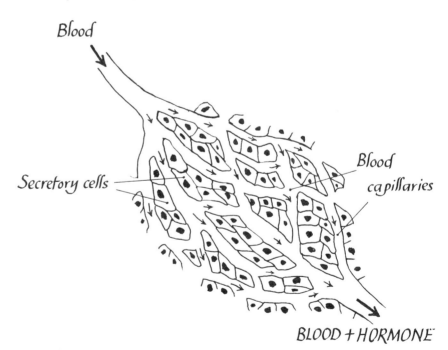

Figure 8.1 A ductless gland: thyroid

114

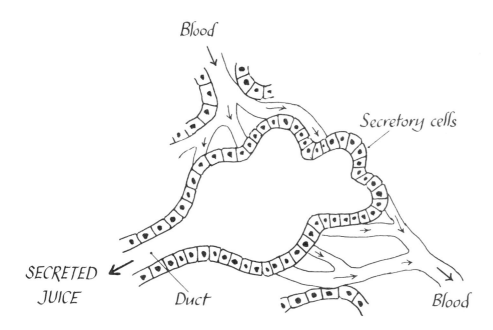

Figure 8.2 A ducted gland: salivary gland

8.3. The pituitary gland

The pituitary gland is often called the master ductless gland, or the 'conductor of the endocrine orchestra', because several of the hormones it secretes in turn control the secretion of other ductless glands. If the pituitary gland is removed, an animal will survive, but all the other endocrine organs will shrivel up and their secretions will be much reduced and inadequate. The pituitary gland lies in the base of the skull and consists of two parts, the **anterior lobe** and the **posterior lobe** (see Figure 8.3).

The anterior lobe secretes a hormone which regulates growth. Over-secretion of this **growth hormone**, phyone, before maturity causes rapid elongation of the bones and results in **gigantism**. Over-secretion after maturity causes **acromegaly**, in which the bones of the face and limbs become enlarged. Under-secretion of the growth hormone in very young babies results in stunted growth and retarded mental development. In older children, a lack of the growth hormone causes **dwarfism**, but mental development is normal.

The anterior lobe also secretes **gonadotrophin** which controls the menstrual cycle in the female and sperm production in the male. The female's anterior pituitary also secretes **prolactin**, which stimulates the secretion of milk in the mother's breast after the birth of a child. **Thyrotrophin** controls the hormone output of the thyroid gland. This, together with other hormones which influence the activity of the adrenal glands and pancreas, is also secreted by the anterior lobe of the pituitary gland.

The posterior lobe of the pituitary secretes two hormones. One of these controls urine production and the contraction of blood-vessel

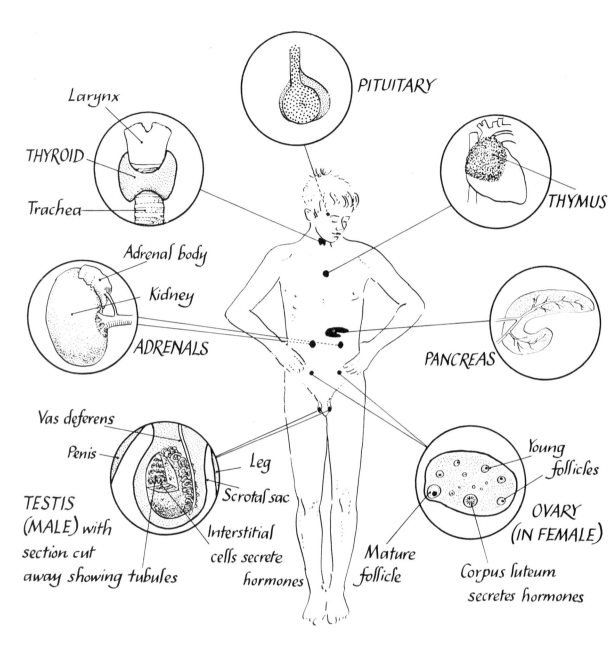

Figure 8.3 The endocrine organs in man

walls. Hence it influences the blood pressure. The other posterior pituitary hormone causes muscle contraction, particularly in the uterus, and is therefore concerned with birth.

8.4. The thyroid gland

The thyroid gland consists of two lobes, situated one on either side of the trachea at the base of the throat. It produces the hormone called **thyroxin**, which regulates the metabolic activities and the general growth rate of the body. Thyroxin contains iodine, which is

116

normally obtained from drinking water. A young child lacking thyroxin becomes a **cretin**, stunted in both physical and mental growth. Adults lacking thyroxin suffer from **myxoedema**, having slow speech and pulse, baldness and a dry, thickened skin. Such a patient recovers if fed with thyroxin.

A person with an enlarged thyroid gland, or **goitre**, receives too much thyroxin, with the result that his metabolic rate becomes too rapid. The person becomes thin and very excitable, and has a high pulse rate—the whole body overworks. A goitre may also be caused by a lack of iodine in the drinking water. The gland grows larger in an attempt to make up for the lack of iodine (and hence thyroxin). In some areas, iodine is added to the drinking water in order to prevent this type of goitre. Iodine is also added to table salt for the same reason. Goitre may give rise to protruding eyeballs and a massive enlargement of the thyroid gland, sometimes called 'Derbyshire neck'. Why do you think the disease is given this name?

8.5. The thymus

This gland is situated in the chest above the heart. The hormone it secretes inhibits the attainment of sexual maturity. It gradually diminishes in size until it disappears completely at about the age of thirteen, allowing the development of full sexual maturity.

8.6. The pancreas

The pancreas lies in the loop of the duodenum. It consists of two distinct types of secretory cells (see Figure 8.4). In addition to the normal tissues which produce the enzymes of the pancreatic juice, there are patches of cells quite different in appearance. These are called the 'Islets of Langerhans', after the German scientist who first observed them. If the pancreas is removed, the secretion of pancreatic juice is lost, but, in addition, a familiar condition develops known as **sugar diabetes**, in which the blood sugar rises to an abnormally high level and sugar is lost in the urine. If, however, the pancreas is left in position but its duct is tied up tightly, most of the gland degenerates, but not the 'Islets of Langerhans'. Moreover, the animal does not develop sugar diabetes. This suggests that these 'Islets of Langerhans' play some part in the control of sugar in the blood stream. Thus the pancreas consists of both a ducted gland producing the digestive enzymes in pancreatic juice, and ductless glands, the 'Islets of Langerhans'.

Insulin is the hormone produced by the ductless glands of the pancreas. If insulin is injected into the blood stream of an animal which has no pancreas and is suffering from sugar diabetes, the blood sugar falls to a low and healthy level and the animal survives.

117

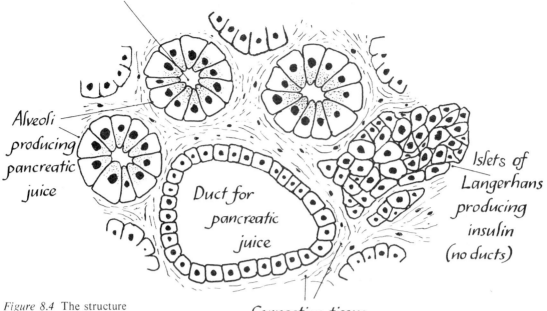

Small duct down centre of alveolus

Alveoli producing pancreatic juice

Duct for pancreatic juice

Islets of Langerhans producing insulin (no ducts)

Connective tissue

Figure 8.4 The structure of the pancreas

Diabetes is recognized by the presence of a large amount of glucose in the urine, as normal urine contains no glucose. Insulin controls the level of sugar in the blood by maintaining a balance between the amount of glucose obtained from food and the amount used for respiration and storage. If too little insulin is available, then the level of sugar in the blood rises. Insulin lowers the level of sugar in the blood, either by reducing the conversion of protein to glycogen or by increasing the rate of glucose utilization. It is probably a combination of the two, the latter being the most important, but despite intensive research, it is not clear how the insulin affects the glucose metabolism.

If the pancreas produces no insulin, then the body cannot make use of glucose. As a result, glucose accumulates in the blood stream to as much as three times its normal level. The kidneys cannot re-absorb this amount, so it is lost in the urine. As the body cannot make use of carbohydrate in the absence of insulin, it gets its energy from the breakdown of proteins and fat. This results in the production of substances like propanone which the body cannot dispose of in large quantities. Propanone gives the breath and urine a characteristic odour. If the production of these substances is not checked the tissues become increasingly acid and a coma will result. Unless treatment is available, death will finally occur.

Diabetes cannot be cured, but it can be successfully controlled by regular injections of insulin. Frequent injections can be unpleasant, but insulin is a protein and if taken orally is promptly digested. Some patients can be treated by a related substance, **tolbutamine**, which can be taken in tablet form. Whichever method is used, the diabetic can lead a perfectly normal life, provided that sugary foods and violent exercise on an empty stomach are avoided.

8.7. The adrenal glands

The adrenal glands lie directly on top of the kidneys. The glands consist of two regions, the outer **cortex** and the inner **medulla**. If the cortex is removed from an animal it dies within a week, but if the medulla of the gland is destroyed the animal appears to suffer no ill effect. The cortex of the adrenal glands secretes hormones, called **steroids**, such as cortisone. The hormones affect carbohydrate metabolism and the permeability of membranes to sodium and potassium. Under-secretion by the adrenal cortex results in **Addison's disease**, which is characterized by loss in weight and vigour, tiredness, low blood pressure and a peculiar bonze colouring of the skin. In children over-secretion speeds up and exaggerates their sexual development, whilst in adults it may cause a reversal of sexual characteristics.

The medulla of the adrenal glands secretes **adrenalin**, particularly in moments of stress. The effect of adrenalin secretion is to alert the body, preparing it for 'fight or flight'. It increases the pulse rate; increases the respiratory rate; causes constriction of the blood vessels in the skin and gut; and increases blood flow to the skeletal muscles and heart. Adrenalin secretion causes a rise in the level of blood sugar and boosts the rate at which glucose is oxidized to produce energy. The startled feeling, due to a sudden and unexpected noise, or the 'butterflies in the stomach' before an examination or special date, is probably due to adrenalin passing into the blood stream.

8.8. The gonads

In addition to producing sperms and ova, the sex organs (the testes and ovaries) act as endocrine organs and secrete sex hormones into the blood stream. These glands become active at puberty and control the secondary sexual characteristics. These obviously vary with the sex.

The human *testes* secrete the sex hormone, **testosterone**, which stimulates the growth of hair on the face, chest and legs, under the armpits and in the pubic region, and stimulates muscular development, broadening of the shoulders and deepening of the voice. These changes are accompanied by normal sexual behaviour, and the development and functioning of the sex organs.

The *ovaries* secrete the sex hormones, **oestradiol** and **progesterone**.

TABLE 8.1. THE ACTION OF SOME OF THE

Name of Gland	Location	Hormone Secreted	Normal Response to Hormone
Pituitary	Floor of skull	Phyone	Regulates growth of bones
		Gonadotrophin	Regulates menstrual cycle in females and sperm production in males
		Prolactin	Stimulates secretion of milk in mother's breast after childbirth
		Thyrotrophin	Controls hormone output of the thyroid gland
Thyroid	Neck	Thyroxin	Regulates metabolic rate and growth rate
Thymus	Above heart		Delays the onset of maturity in children
Islets of Langerhans	Pancreas	Insulin	Regulates glucose metabolism
Adrenals	Above kidneys	Adrenalin	Controls pulse rate, respiratory rate, constriction and dilation of blood vessels and iris
		Steroids	Carbohydrate metabolism and membrane permeability
Gonads: Testes	Scrotal sac	Testosterone	Development of secondary sexual characteristics
Ovaries	Lower abdomen	Oestradiol	Development of secondary sexual characteristics
		Progesterone	Prepares body for pregnancy

Oestradiol stimulates the development of the breasts, the widening of the hips and the growth of hair under the armpits and in the pubic region. These changes are accompanied by the onset of menstruation and normal sexual behaviour. **Progesterone**, the pregnancy hormone, prepares the body, particularly the uterus, for pregnancy. It also prevents ovulation during pregnancy so that no more ova can be fertilized whilst an embryo is developing in the uterus.

Progesterone is used widely in tablet form as an efficient oral contraceptive. If the 'pill' is taken regularly, there is always progesterone in the blood stream, with the result that the body 'thinks it is pregnant' and stops liberating ova. If ova are not produced, then conception is impossible.

Response to Excessive Secretion	Response to Deficient Secretion
Before maturity—gigantism After maturity—acromegaly	Young children—retarded physical and mental development Older children—dwarfism, but normal mental development
Over-excitability; goitre	Children—cretinism Adults—myxoedema
Rare form of diabetes—deficiency of blood sugar	Common form of diabetes—excess of blood sugar
Children—premature sexual development Adults—tendency to sex reversion	Addison's disease

Test your understanding

Copy and complete the following paragraph:

The ductless glands produce chemical messengers called . . . .[1] These are carried round the body in the . . . .[2] They co-ordinate the activities of the body concerned with . . . .[3] and development. The master ductless gland is called the . . . .[4], and is found in the base of the skull. The main hormone produced by the pituitary is the . . . .[5] hormone. A deficiency of this hormone results in . . . .[6], whilst an excess causes . . . .[7] The . . . .[8] gland is found in the neck and produces the hormone called . . . .[9] A deficiency of this hormone causes . . . .[10] The . . . .[11] gland is found only in young animals. The pancreas has special groups of cells called the . . . .[12], which produce the hormone . . . .[13] An absence of this hormone results in the disease called ....[14] The adrenal glands secrete ....[15], which prepares the body for ....[16] The sex hormones control the secondary sexual characteristics such as ....[17] and ....[18] in boys and ....[19] in girls.

1. What are the differences between the endocrine organs and the glands concerned with digestion?
2. How was the nature of hormone secretion discovered?
3. Why is the pituitary gland particularly important?
4. What is the role of the thyroid gland?
5. What sort of gland is the pancreas?
6. What are the signs of sugar diabetes?
7. Explain the cause and control of diabetes.
8. How do the adrenal glands prepare the body for action?
9. Explain the role of the sex hormones.
10. How can a hormone be used as an efficient contraceptive?

Chapter 9

Having Young: Reproduction

9.1. The purpose of reproduction

Every living thing has a certain life-span. This may be a matter of minutes, as in some bacteria, or several hundred years, as in some trees. Living organisms may, of course, never reach the end of their expected life-span, but have their lives ended earlier. They may be killed or eaten by other organisms, or they may die of starvation or disease. Since the individuals comprising any group, or species, will eventually die, it follows that new individuals must continually be born, to replace them and to ensure that the species survives. The process whereby living organisms give rise to new individuals which are like themselves is called **reproduction**.

Reproduction is usually accompanied by **dispersal**. If new-born individuals were to remain with their parents, they would compete with them and with each other for the essentials of life, such as food and oxygen. To prevent this competition, the young are dispersed in some way, so that they are able to start their lives in new surroundings. In many species the process of dispersal is wasteful, for many of the young fail to reach a suitable home and fall, like the biblical seeds, 'on stony ground'. Moreover, the eggs and young often form the diet of other animals. To compensate for this wastage, many potential offspring are produced. Thus a single cod may lay eight to ten million eggs, of which perhaps only one or two will survive to become egg-layers themselves.

Reproduction usually leads to **variation**. Except in the case of asexual reproduction (see Section 9.2), the offspring are not identical, but have features in which they differ from one another and from the parent. We shall learn in Chapter 14 that this natural variability enables species to change and new species to arise. This process, whereby new species arise from pre-existing species, is called **evolution**.

We see, then, that reproduction normally results in:

a. The production of new individuals to replace those that die, thus ensuring continuation of the species.

b. The dispersal of the species to new surroundings.

c. The evolution of new species.

9.2. Asexual reproduction

The simplest form of reproduction is asexual; in other words, it does not involve more than one individual. We have seen such asexual reproduction in the amoeba (see Book I, Section 4.6). Once the parent cell has grown to full size the nucleus duplicates itself, and the cytoplasm cleaves into two halves, each with a daughter nucleus. Thus the parent cell ceases to exist, but continues as two offspring, each of which eventually becomes a parent cell. Splitting into two, in this way, is known as binary fission, and is common in unicellular organisms.

In multicellular organisms, asexual reproduction is usually accomplished by only part of the parent body; that part becomes detached to form the offspring. We have seen an example of this in the budding of the hydra (see Book I, Section 4.15). This type of reproduction is more common in plants (see Book I, Section 13.13).

The offspring from asexual reproduction are identical to each other and to their parent. Variation is not possible, and any defects in the make-up of the parent will be passed to the offspring, as will any good features. The main advantage of asexual reproduction is that it is simple and rapid: many offspring may be reproduced in a short time. Thus, a single bacterial cell which undergoes fission every twenty minutes will have produced over a million of its kind within seven hours. We shall see the effects of this rapid multiplication in Chapter 16.

9.3. Sexual reproduction

In sexual reproduction the offspring is produced by the fusion, or joining, of two cells, known as sex cells or **gametes**. The process of fusion is called **fertilization** and the product of fusion a **zygote**. In some lower forms of life, such as *Mucor* (pin mould), the gametes that fuse together are identical in appearance, as are the parents that produce them. In most cases, however, the gametes are dissimilar in appearance and behaviour, and the parents can be distinguished from each other. One parent, the female, produces a gamete which is stationary, whilst the other parent, the male, produces a gamete which moves to the female gamete and fuses with it. In animals, the female gamete is the egg, or ovum, whilst the male gamete is the sperm (see Figure 9.1). Animals in which the ova and sperm are produced by separate individuals are said to be **unisexual**, whilst those in which the ova and sperm are produced by the same individual are termed **hermaphrodite**. In hermaphrodite animals there is usually some means whereby fusion of the egg with the individual's own sperm (self-fertilization) is prevented (see the hydra, Book I, Section 4.15).

Sexual reproduction has the great advantage that the offspring

124

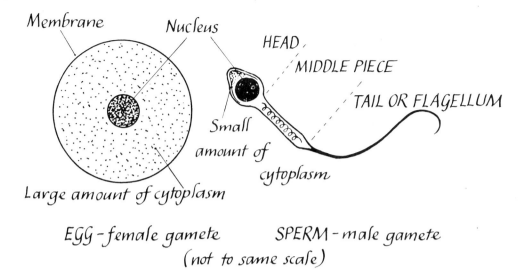

Membrane

Nucleus

Small amount of cytoplasm

Large amount of cytoplasm

HEAD

MIDDLE PIECE

TAIL OR FLAGELLUM

EGG – female gamete

SPERM – male gamete

(not to same scale)

show variation: they differ from each other and from the parents. The gametes differ in the hereditary units, or **genes**, that they carry (see Chapter 15). When ovum and sperm combine, there are many possible combinations of genes. The process of natural selection (see Section 14.8) tends to weed out the poorer offspring, enabling the strong ones to grow up and reproduce. In this way the species is improved, and new species arise.

Figure 9.1 Diagrams to show the parts of typical male and female sex cells (gametes)

Investigation 9a. Microscopic examination of eggs and sperm

In this investigation we are going to examine the eggs and sperm of the marine worm *Pomatoceros*. This is a convenient animal for study, for it is relatively easy to cause the animal to discharge its gametes. The worms are unisexual and inhabit chalky, white tubes which form incrustations on rocks and pebbles of the sea-shore (see Figure 9.2). Rocks encrusted with these tubes may be obtained from

Figure 9.2 Removal of the marine worm *Pomatoceros* from its tube

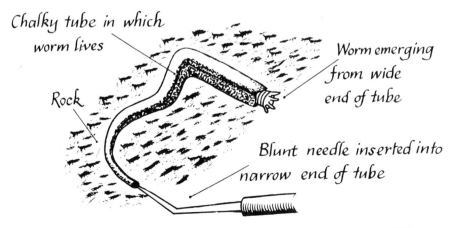

Chalky tube in which worm lives

Rock

Worm emerging from wide end of tube

Blunt needle inserted into narrow end of tube

the Plymouth Marine Laboratory, if you are unable to collect them from the sea-shore yourself. The rocks must be kept in a bucket of sea water through which air is continually bubbled.

The removal of the worm from its tube is effected in the following way:

1. Chip away a little of the tube at its widest end, taking care not to damage the head of the worm.
2. Insert the tip of a blunt needle into the tail end of the tube and 'tickle' the worm, which should now crawl out of the wide end. Males have yellow bodies, whilst those of females are red or violet.

Transfer the worm to a watchglass containing a little sea water. It should immediately release eggs or sperm into the water. Pipette a little of the water from the watchglass on to a clean microscope slide, cover with a cover-slip, and examine under the low power of the microscope. Decide whether you have eggs or sperm. Look at the material under the microscopes of other pupils, so that you are able to distinguish between the two types of gamete.

Fertilization

Sperm are attracted by chemicals given out by eggs of their own species. The sperm surround the egg, and one penetrates the egg membrane. The head of the sperm detaches from its tail and fuses with the egg nucleus. In some way the egg membrane now changes, so that other sperm are unable to enter. The stages in fertilization are shown in Figure 9.3.

Figure 9.3 Stages in fertilization

We may watch this process of fertilization using the eggs and sperm of *Pomatoceros.*

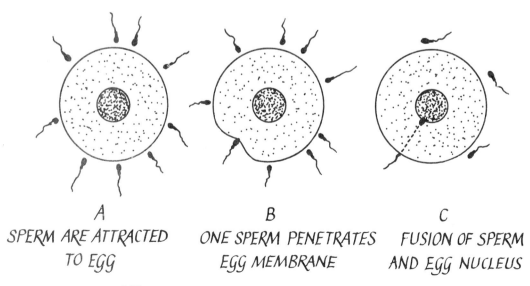

A
SPERM ARE ATTRACTED
TO EGG

B
ONE SPERM PENETRATES
EGG MEMBRANE

C
FUSION OF SPERM
AND EGG NUCLEUS

1. Using a teat-pipette, transfer a little sea water containing a few eggs of *Pomatoceros* on to a cavity slide.
2. Examine the eggs under the low power of the microscope.
3. Using a separate pipette, transfer a drop of sea water containing *Pomatoceros* sperm on to the eggs.
4. Without delay, cover with a cover-slip and re-examine the eggs under the microscope. With a little practice, you will learn to do this fast enough to see the egg become surrounded by sperm and fertilized.
5. Observe the fertilized eggs at intervals during the next few hours. What is happening to them?
6. Observe eggs that have been fertilized for several days. Notice how their appearance has changed.

All eggs begin the process of development by undergoing division, or **cleavage**. Thus a single-celled egg becomes a many-celled **embryo**. At first the cells of the embryo are all alike, but gradually, as the embryo develops, they become **differentiated**, as they take on different forms. Thus cells which are to form part of the epidermis of the skin will become different from those which are to form part of a muscle.

9.4. Sexual reproduction in fishes

Investigation 9c. Examination of the sex organs of a fish

From the fishmonger, obtain a fish such as a whiting, herring or mackerel, making sure that the animal has not been gutted. With a sharp scalpel or scissors, slit open the abdomen along the mid-ventral line (the underside) from the cloaca to just behind the gill cover (see Figure 9.4a).

Biological

Pin back the body wall as shown in Figure 9.4b. Notice the liver and the coiled alimentary canal (digestive tube). Deflect these organs to one side and notice a pair of long organs lying closely applied to the roof of the abdominal cavity. These are the sex organs or 'roe'. Break one of the organs and examine the contents. The presence of distinctly rounded ova indicates that the organ is an ovary, and that the fish is female. A softer roe, without distinctly rounded structures inside, is a testis, the sex organ of the male.

Examine the fish dissected by other members of the class and compare the appearance of the two types of sex organ, or gonad. Would you say that the female fish produces few or many eggs?

The life-history of the salmon

Although most salmon inhabit the seas of the Northern Hemisphere, their eggs cannot be fertilized or develop in sea water. At

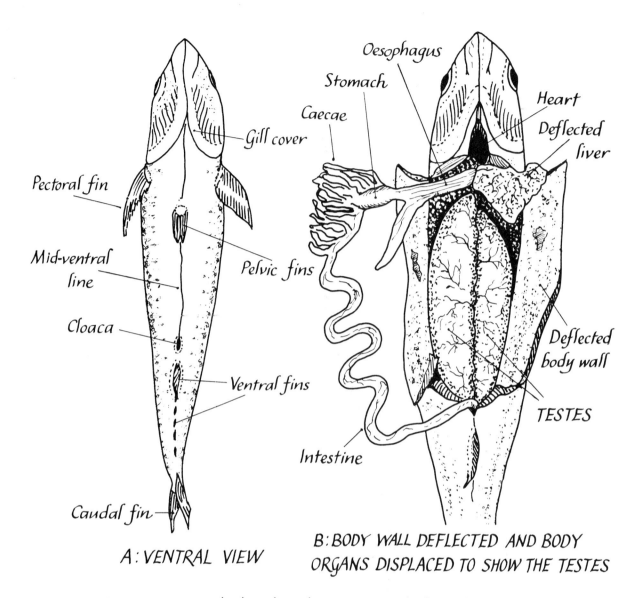

Pectoral fin

Mid-ventral line

Cloaca

Ventral fins

Caudal fin

A: VENTRAL VIEW

Gill cover

Pelvic fins

Oesophagus

Stomach

Caecae

Heart

Deflected liver

Deflected body wall

TESTES

Intestine

B: BODY WALL DEFLECTED AND BODY ORGANS DISPLACED TO SHOW THE TESTES

Figure 9.4 Displaying the sex organs of a fish (a mackerel)

certain times in spring, summer and winter, the adults swim up the rivers against the current, often leaping up waterfalls in their frantic efforts to reach the spawning grounds.

Pairing usually takes place where fresh water runs fast over rough gravel. By flicking her tail, the female makes a trough in the gravel, into which she deposits many thousands of eggs. Immediately, the male releases sperm and fertilization takes place. Apart from being covered with stones by the female, the eggs are not looked after by their parents. Many are devoured by fish such as the trout. Often, the exhausted parents die, particularly the males. Those females that survive, return to the sea.

Meanwhile, the surviving eggs hatch into small **fry**. These live among the stones for six weeks, using the food in the yolk sac attached to the abdomen. Later, they are able to feed on small crustaceans and molluscs. They develop into golden **parr**, with many bright spots on the skin. After two years in fresh water, the parr change to a silvery colour, and are now called **smolt**. The smolt make the long journey downstream to the sea, where they complete their development into adult salmon. Young salmon of three to four years may return to the rivers to breed.

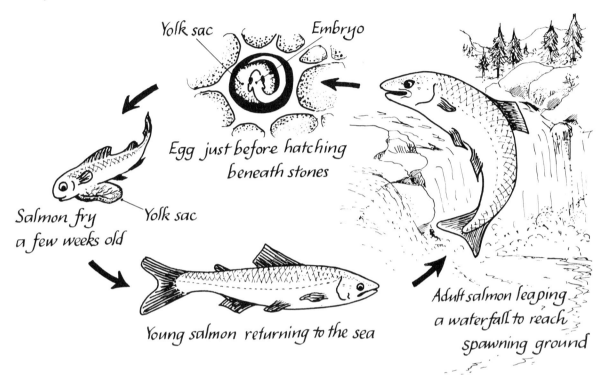

Yolk sac

Embryo

Egg just before hatching beneath stones

Yolk sac

Salmon fry a few weeks old

Young salmon returning to the sea

Adult salmon leaping a waterfall to reach spawning ground

The life-history of the salmon is illustrated in Figure 9.5. Notice three important features of this life-cycle:

Figure 9.5 The life-history of the salmon

    a. There is a strong urge to mate, which ensures that reproduction takes place.

    b. Fertilization is external, that is, it occurs outside the body of the female.

    c. Because there is very little parental care, many eggs have to be laid, to ensure that some survive to become adults.

The life-history of the stickleback

The stickleback is a freshwater fish whose life-history shows advances over that of the salmon. During the mating season, the male builds a tubular nest from water-weed, which is stuck together with a secretion from the kidneys. He will adopt a threatening attitude towards any other male that approaches the territory of his nest.

The belly of the male is red at this time and, should a female approach, he displays this belly to her. The female is attracted and follows the movements of the male as he performs a zig-zag dance (see Figure 9.6). By means of the dance, the male leads the female to the nest and guides her into it. He then prods her tail repeatedly,

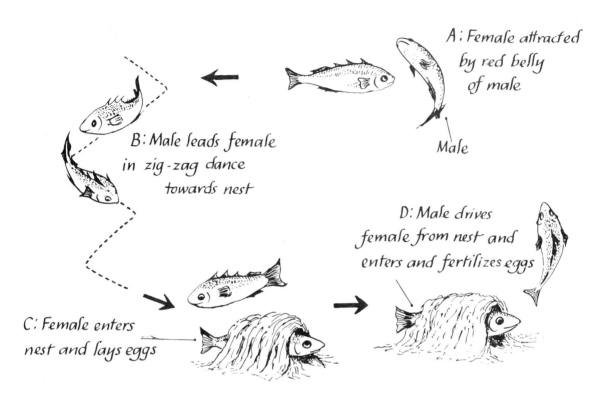

A: Female attracted by red belly of male

Male

B: Male leads female in zig-zag dance towards nest

D: Male drives female from nest and enters and fertilizes eggs

C: Female enters nest and lays eggs

Figure 9.6 Courtship behaviour of the stickleback

stimulating her to lay from about 120 to 150 eggs. The male then bites the female and drives her off, so that he may enter the nest himself and fertilize the eggs with his sperm. During the early development of the young, it is the male that guards the nest, the female playing no further part.

Notice that in this life-history:

a. Reproduction is ensured by a courtship behaviour in which the male plays the dominant role.

b. Because the eggs are laid in a protective nest, guarded by the parent, fewer eggs need to be laid.

9.5. Sexual reproduction in amphibians

Although amphibians, such as frogs and toads, are adapted for life both in water and on land, their reproduction must take place in water or, at least, in a very moist environment. This is because fertilization is external and their eggs cannot survive out of water.

130

Moreover, the creature which hatches from the egg is a minute **larva**, the tadpole, which is completely aquatic. Although the tadpole is very small when it hatches out it is soon able to fend for itself, and grows rapidly. Its life in the water lasts for about three months, during which time the adult structures gradually make their appearance. By this transformation, or **metamorphosis**, the tadpole makes the change of form from an aquatic larva to an amphibious adult.

An example of an amphibian life-cycle, that of the common frog, is illustrated in Figure 9.7.

9.6. Sexual reproduction in reptiles and birds

So far, the animals that we have considered in this chapter have been aquatic in their reproduction; in other words the eggs have been laid in water and the young have spent their development period in water. Reptiles and birds, however, are land vertebrates, and one of the reasons for their success is that they do not need water for their reproduction and are not, therefore, confined to areas where water is abundant.

To be able to develop out of water an egg must have the following requirements:

Figure 9.7 The life-cycle of the common frog

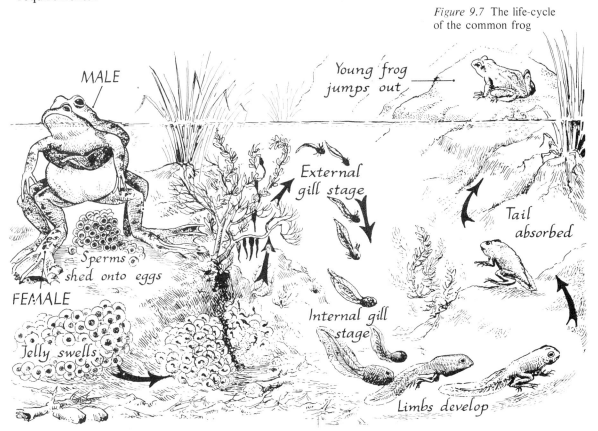

MALE

Young frog jumps out

External gill stage

Tail absorbed

Sperms shed onto eggs

FEMALE

Jelly swells

Internal gill stage

Limbs develop

a. A *shell*, to support the soft egg and to prevent it from drying up.

b. Ample *food* (yolk), to enable the egg to grow fully into the adult form, thus omitting the larval stage.

c. Ample *water*, to supply the needs of the developing embryo and to 'cushion' or buffer it against changes in temperature, etc.

d. A supply of *salts*, which are necessary for healthy growth.

e. A means of *storage of excretory products*.

Investigation 9d. Examination of the egg and embryo of a chicken

Place a fresh hen's egg on a ring of plasticine in a petri dish. With a pencil, mark a line round the side of the shell to indicate where you intend to open up a 'window'. Then, using blunt forceps or small scissors, break through the shell round this line. Be careful that you do not push the points of the scissors or forceps in too far. Eventually, it should be possible to lift the window off in one piece, exposing the contents of the egg. Which part of the egg can be seen?

To examine the egg further it is necessary to tip the contents into a shallow dish of warm salt solution (saline). This has to be done very carefully, otherwise the yolk membrane will be broken and the yolk will be released. You will find it easier if you lower the egg into the saline before tilting it to empty the contents. What additional parts of the egg are you now able to see?

Examine the inside of the shell. Are you able to see the thin lining membrane and the air-space at the blunt end? Look at Figure 9.8, and think of the function of each of the parts of the egg.

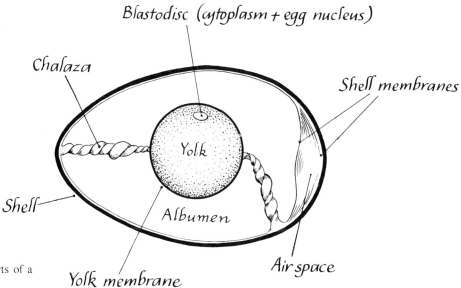

Figure 9.8 The parts of a hen's egg

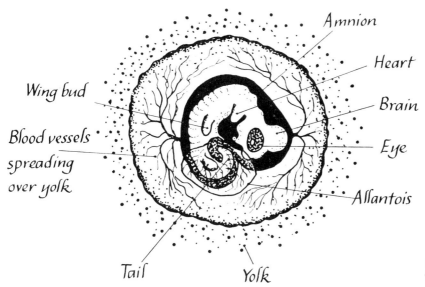

Figure 9.9 A five-day chicken embryo

Labels in figure:
Amnion
Heart
Brain
Eye
Allantois
Wing bud
Blood vessels spreading over yolk
Tail
Yolk

Now examine the contents of an egg which has been fertilized and then incubated for five days (see Figure 9.9). Are you able to see the developing embryo within its delicate membrane (amnion)? Prod the amnion gently. With what does it seem to be filled?

We see, then, that the embryo is actually developing in a watery fluid, just as did the embryos of fishes and amphibians. The land vertebrate develops its own little 'pond' within the egg, enabling development to occur in dry situations.

You should now be able to answer two questions:
1. Will fertilization in land vertebrates be external or internal?
2. Will land vertebrates lay as many eggs as fishes and amphibians?

Parental care

Whilst the eggs of reptiles and birds are similar, these two groups of vertebrates differ considerably in the extent to which the young are looked after by the parents. Some reptiles, such as the common lizard, are **viviparous**. This means that the egg is retained inside the female's body until it is ready to hatch, and the young are then born alive. Most reptiles, however, simply hide the eggs away in a suitable place, and then leave them to hatch on their own. In all reptiles the young are left to fend for themselves after hatching.

Birds, on the other hand, are more advanced. After courtship and pairing, the parents build a nest, in which the eggs are laid. Incubation then occurs, the parent sitting on the eggs to keep them warm. After hatching, the parents remain together, feeding and caring for the chicks during their early life. Thus the birds have improved on the method of reproduction of their ancestors, the reptiles.

9.7. The sex organs in mammals

Investigation 9e. Examination of the sex organs of a male and female rat (or rabbit)

In this investigation you will need to examine a male and female rat or rabbit, which have been dissected to display the organs of reproduction.

In the male, notice the position of the paired testes. How does their position differ from that of the other vertebrates you have studied? Notice the muscular penis between the scrotal sacs which house the testes. Are you able to follow the route taken by the sperm in passing from the testis, where they are formed, to the penis, through which they leave the body? Compare the dissected animal with Figure 9.10, and identify the other structures shown in the diagram.

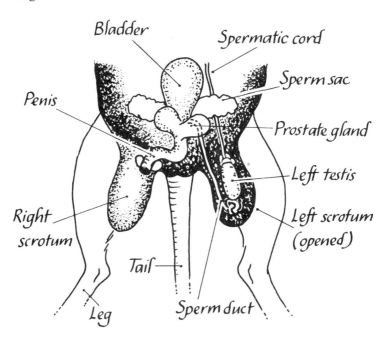

Figure 9.10 The reproductive organs of a male rat

In the female, notice the pair of small ovaries located against the dorsal abdominal wall. From these extend the narrow oviducts, or Fallopian tubes, which broaden on each side into the uterus, or womb. The uteri join at the vagina, a tube which opens to the exterior at the vulva. Compare the dissected animal with Figure 9.11.

Actually, the testes do not develop in the scrotal sacs, but in the abdomen. Just before birth, or just after, they are dragged down into the scrotal sacs by the contraction of a muscular cord, the **gubernaculum**. This movement of the testes explains the peculiar course of the spermatic artery and vein, which pass high into the abdomen before joining the dorsal aorta and posterior vena cava, respectively.

134

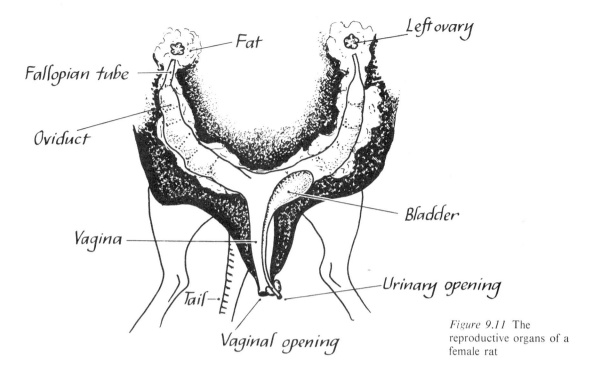

Figure 9.11 The reproductive organs of a female rat

It is considered that the external position of the testes enables the sperm to develop at a lower temperature than would be possible within the body.

Glands such as the prostate secrete a fluid called **semen**, in which the sperm leave the body. Sperm are produced in their millions by the testes, and their production is continuous. Mature sperm accumulate in the mass of coiled tubing adjacent to the testis itself.

In the female human, the ovary is about the size and shape of a walnut. All the ova that are to be developed during life are present in the ovary at birth, there being some 100 000 immature ova at this time. We shall see, in Section 9.14, that mature eggs are released from the ovary only at certain times.

Figures 9.12 and 9.13 show the sex organs of a male and female human. Compare these with the organs of the rat.

9.8. Mating and fertilization

As in reptiles and birds, fertilization in mammals is internal. The sperm meet the egg in the upper part of the oviduct, or Fallopian tube. During mating, the male penis becomes stiffened, or erected, by a rapid inrush of blood. The male then inserts the erect penis into the vagina of the female, and by thrusting movements stimulates the ejaculation of sperm. In this manner, semen, containing as many as 250 000 000 sperm, is shot into the upper part of the vagina. By the lashing movements of their tails, the sperm propel themselves up the

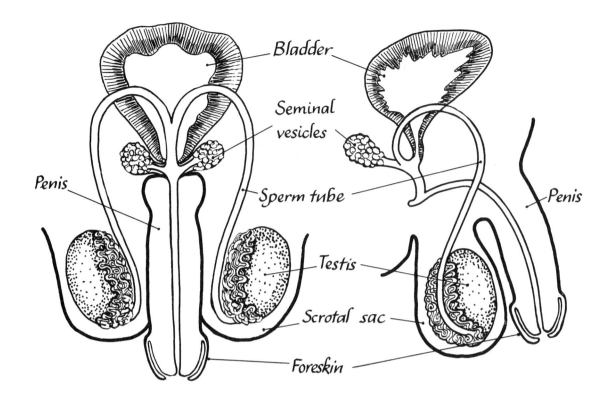

Bladder

Seminal
vesicles

Penis

Sperm tube

Penis

Testis

Scrotal sac

Foreskin

FRONT VIEW

SIDE VIEW

Figure 9.12 Reproductive
organs of a man

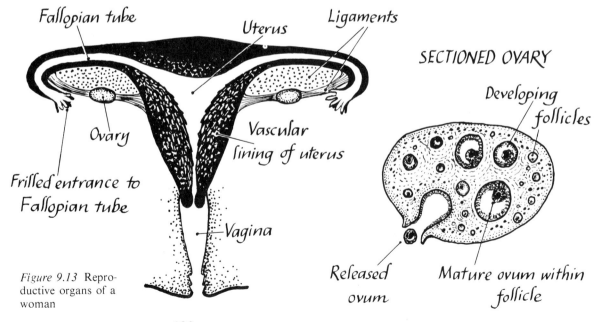

Fallopian tube

Uterus

Ligaments

SECTIONED OVARY

Developing
follicles

Ovary

Vascular
lining of uterus

Frilled entrance to
Fallopian tube

Vagina

Mature ovum within
follicle

Released
ovum

Figure 9.13 Repro-
ductive organs of a
woman

moist inside wall of the uterus and enter the Fallopian tubes. If the time is correct for a mature ovum to have been released from the ovary, fertilization will occur in the Fallopian tube; one sperm penetrates the egg membrane and the two nuclei fuse. Sperm are able to survive for four to five days inside the female oviduct, so fertilization may occur if an ovum is released at any time during this period.

9.9. Development of the embryo

In all except the most primitive of mammals the fertilized egg is retained inside the mother's uterus, where it develops into an embryo and eventually into a foetus, or unborn baby. During its development, the embryo receives nourishment and oxygen from the mother, who also disposes of the embryonic waste products. This intimate relationship between mother and embryo, where the embryo is like a parasite within the mother, is the most advanced form of reproduction developed by animals. We will now follow the stages in human development in a little more detail (see Figure 9.14).

Immediately after fertilization, the human ovum begins to undergo cell division (mitosis) and to travel down the Fallopian tube to the uterus or womb. This journey takes about four days, at the conclusion of which the embryo consists of a cluster of cells (the blastocyst). Preparatory to the arrival of the blastocyst, the uterine wall has increased the thickness of its spongy, inner lining, a layer which is very rich in blood vessels. The tiny embryo, little larger than a full-stop, sticks to the lining of the uterus, which is stimulated to grow so that it comes to enclose the embryo.

The embryo, which is now said to be **implanted**, grows rapidly and soon comes to be enclosed by a double membrane. The innermost membrane, the amnion, encloses a fluid-filled sac in which the embryo is protected. Thus, even in the mammal, the young develops in a watery environment.

The outer membrane, the chorion, together with the maternal tissues with which it is in contact, grows rapidly to form the **placenta**. This organ is responsible for all interchange of materials between the mother and embryo, and here the maternal and embryonic blood circulations come very close to each other. It should be appreciated, however, that there is no mixing of maternal and foetal blood, all exchange taking place by diffusion. Oxygen and digestive products, such as glucose and amino acids, pass from the mother to the embryo, whilst carbon dioxide, urea and other waste products pass from the embryo to the mother. Thus the placenta serves as a nutritional, respiratory and excretory organ for the developing embryo.

As development proceeds, the embryo floats freely in the enlarged uterus, connected to the placenta by the **umbilical cord**. Eventually, the foetus will completely fill the cavity of the uterus.

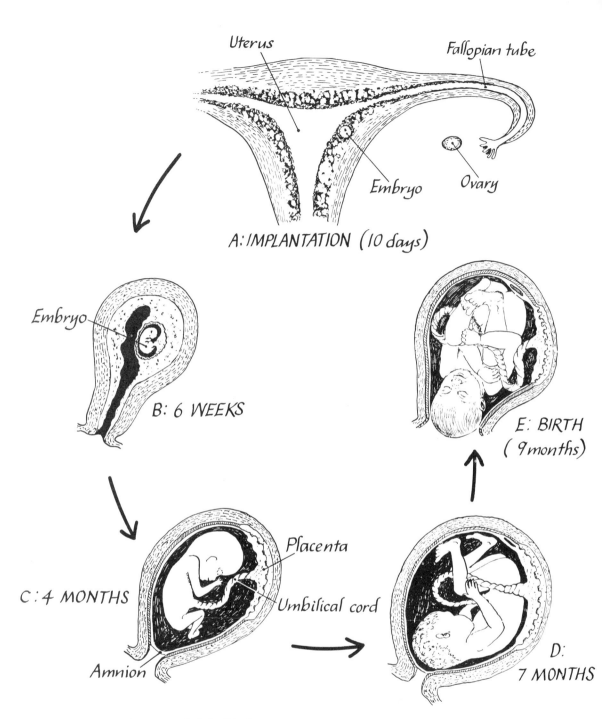

Uterus

Fallopian tube

Embryo

Ovary

A: IMPLANTATION (10 days)

Embryo

B: 6 WEEKS

Placenta

Umbilical cord

C: 4 MONTHS

Amnion

D: 7 MONTHS

E: BIRTH (9 months)

Figure 9.14 Stages in human development

9.10. Birth

The period of growth and development of a baby is called the **gestation period**. The average length of this period in humans is 280 days, or just over nine months. The position of the baby just before birth is shown in Figure 9.14. The mother knows that birth is about to take place when the uterus begins to undergo periodic

138

contractions, perhaps half an hour apart at first, but gradually becoming stronger and more frequent. These contractions burst the membranes surrounding the foetus, causing a discharge of fluid through the vagina (the 'breaking of the water'). Eventually, the cervix and vagina widen sufficiently to allow the contracting uterus to force the baby out, head first. It will immediately take its first breath.

The new-born baby is still attached to the mother by the umbilical cord, but this is severed by the doctor or midwife in such a way as to avoid loss of blood. The short stump of the cord attached to the baby is soon absorbed, leaving only the navel, or 'belly button', as a sign of its existence. About half an hour after birth the mother's uterus contracts again, discharging the remains of the cord and the placenta (the 'afterbirth').

9.11. Early growth of the baby

For the first few months the baby feeds entirely on milk from the mother's breasts or from a bottle. During the time that the mother is carrying the baby (pregnancy), milk glands in the breasts enlarge, the secretion of milk being stimulated by hormones. Mother's milk is better for the baby than bottled milk, for it has the correct composition for the baby's digestion and is at the right temperature. Moreover, breast feeding gives satisfaction to both mother and baby. The sucking action of the baby stimulates the continual production of this ideal food from the mother's breasts. After about six months the baby is 'weaned', the milk diet being replaced by more solid food.

9.12. How twins arise

We have seen that the baby begins to develop when a ripe ovum, released from the ovary, is fertilized by a sperm cell. In Chapter 15, we shall learn that the future characteristics of the offspring depend on certain hereditary factors, or genes, carried in the nucleus of the sperm and ovum.

Occasionally, two eggs are released at the same time, either from the same ovary or one from each ovary. If sperm are present and fertilization occurs, two embryos may descend into the uterus. Each will become implanted and will form its own membranes and placenta. The two babies will be dissimilar twins; they will be no more alike than any other two members of the same family, except, of course, inasmuch as they are the same age.

The so-called 'identical' twins arise when a single ovum is fertilized and, after the first division, separation of the daughter cells occurs. The 'twin' cells develop into embryos which share the same membranes and placenta. Since the embryos have originated from

139

the fusion of the same egg and sperm, they will inherit the same potentialities for character development. As they begin life with only half the normal amount of egg cytoplasm, identical twins are smaller, at birth, than the average normal baby. Why do you think that such twins cease to be identical as they grow up? What can you say about the possible sex of dissimilar and similar twins?

The difference in origin of the two types of twins is illustrated in Figure 9.15.

Figure 9.15 How twins arise

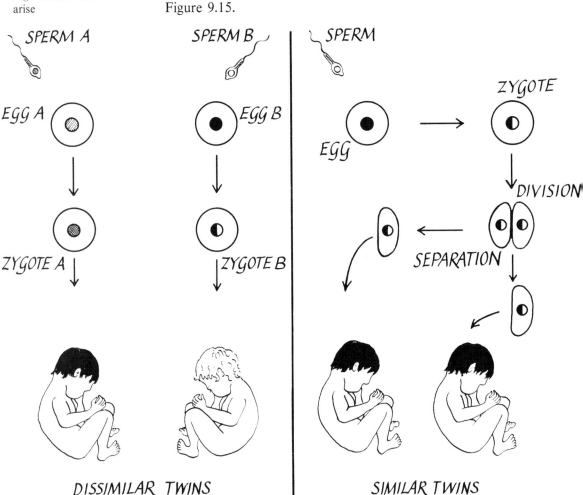

DISSIMILAR TWINS

SIMILAR TWINS

9.13. Growing up: puberty

Human growth is not a steady, even process, but occurs in spurts, separated by periods of slower growth. The first period of rapid growth is during the first few years of infancy. The second occurs during adolescence (about 11 to 17 years), when many changes take place in the body of the male and female. At the onset of puberty the sex organs mature and are able to release sperm or eggs. This

140

maturity is brought about by hormones, released at this time by the pituitary gland (see Chapter 8). In addition to producing sperm or eggs, the testes and ovaries secrete their own hormones, which cause changes in other parts of the body. Thus, in boys, hair grows under the armpits, on the face, chest and legs and in the pubic region, the physique becomes more manly and the voice breaks. In girls, hair develops under the armpits and in the pubic region, the breasts develop and the hips widen.

These changes in the physical appearances of boys and girls are accompanied by emotional changes, each becoming more interested in members of the opposite sex.

9.14. Menstruation

We saw in Section 9.9 that there is a build-up of the lining of the uterus in preparation for the arrival of the embryo. This increase in blood tissue takes place over a period of about fourteen days. If, after a further period of five days, an embryo has not become implanted, the uterine lining rapidly breaks down, and is shed from the female's body over a period of about five days. This loss of blood and other tissue is called the **menstrual flow**, or menstruation. It is followed by a period of repair and then of re-building of the lining. This process of build-up and breakdown is repeated continually, only to be interrupted if pregnancy occurs. The whole cycle of events, from the commencement of one menstrual flow to the next, takes about twenty-eight days. The cycle is illustrated in Figure 9.16.

Figure 9.16 The menstrual cycle

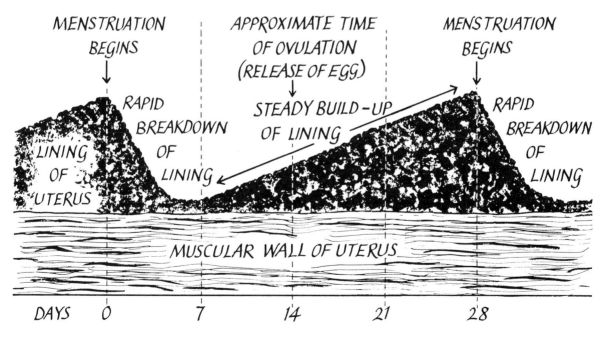

The first menstrual cycle commences at puberty (from about eleven years), and such cycles continue throughout the female's life until the age of about forty-five to fifty (the 'change of life') when the release of ova ceases.

Test your understanding

1. Explain the meaning of the terms asexual and sexual reproduction.
2. What is the main advantage of asexual reproduction? What are its disadvantages?
3. Explain the precise meaning of the following terms: sperm, egg (ovum), fertilization, external fertilization, internal fertilization, zygote, embryo, foetus, hermaphrodite.
4. What is the main advantage of sexual reproduction?
5. Give reasons why most fish produce a large number of small eggs.
6. What advance does the reproduction of the stickleback show over that of most fishes?
7. What part is played by the tadpole in the life-cycle of an amphibian?
8. Draw a simple diagram to show the parts of a chicken's egg. On your diagram indicate the functions of each part.
9. In what respects can birds be said to have improved on the reproduction of reptiles?
10. Suggest three important ways in which mammals, such as rabbits and humans, are more advanced in their reproduction than any other vertebrate.

Chapter 10

The Skeletal System

10.1. Movement

Movement is one of the characteristic activities of living organisms. Most animals are able to move under their own power. Movement enables an animal to select, collect or capture the food it likes; to escape from its enemies; to find a suitable site for its nest or home; and to search for a suitable mate so that it can reproduce and continue the species.

Movement is usually brought about by a muscle, whose fibres are able to contract and so exert a force on a rigid part of the body. This rigid structure is part of the skeleton, comprising either an external shell or internal bones.

There are two main types of skeleton:

a. An **exoskeleton**, as found in such animals as the lobster and crab, is composed of hard plates, which cover the animal rather like a suit of armour. In a small animal, an exoskeleton has the advantage of lightness and strength, yet does not hamper movement as there is plenty of room inside the shell. An exoskeleton is unsuitable for larger animals for its weight hinders movement. We may imagine the difficulty in movement experienced by a knight in a suit of armour!

b. An **endoskeleton** is found in all vertebrates, including man (see Figures 10.1 and 10.2). It consists of a framework of bones embedded within the body. As the animal grows, so do the bones of the skeleton. Such a skeleton provides large animals with support without being so heavy as to hinder movement.

10.2. Why is a skeleton necessary?

a. Support

The skeleton gives the body support and shape. Imagine the body without any bones. Like the jelly-fish which has been washed up on the beach and has lost the support of the water, it would be a shapeless mass. Organs would crush one another and would be unable to carry out their functions.

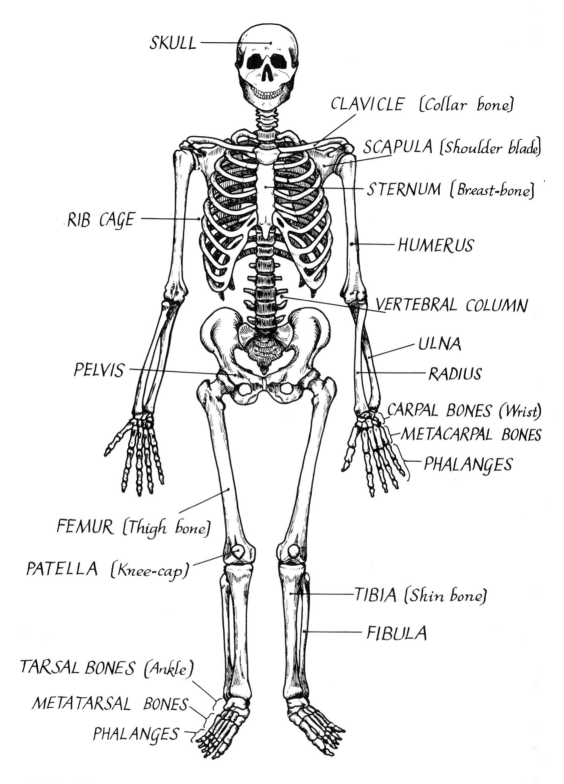

SKULL

CLAVICLE (Collar bone)

SCAPULA (Shoulder blade)

STERNUM (Breast-bone)

RIB CAGE

HUMERUS

VERTEBRAL COLUMN

ULNA

PELVIS

RADIUS

CARPAL BONES (Wrist)

METACARPAL BONES

PHALANGES

FEMUR (Thigh bone)

PATELLA (Knee-cap)

TIBIA (Shin bone)

FIBULA

TARSAL BONES (Ankle)

METATARSAL BONES

PHALANGES

Figure 10.1 The skeleton
of man

144

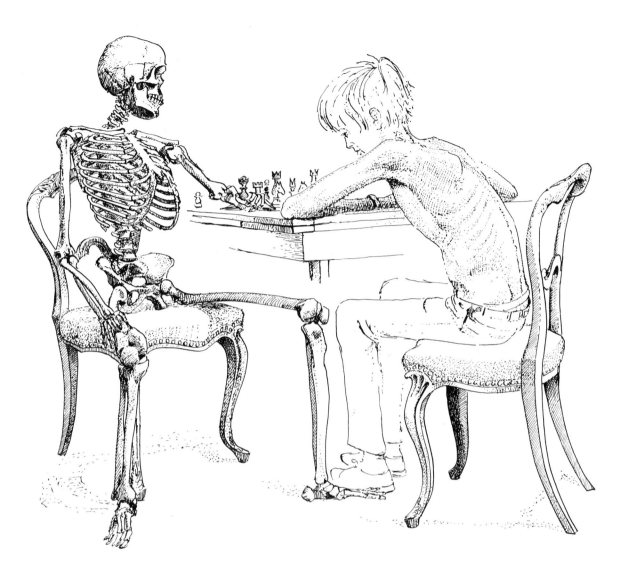

Look at Figure 10.2 and notice how the shape of the body is determined by the shape of the skeleton.

When building a model aircraft, you construct the frame of the model first. This determines the shape of the model and provides a foundation on which you can attach the working parts, such as the motor and the controls. Finally, the model is covered and painted. Similarly, the shape of the human body is largely determined by its framework, the skeleton.

Figure 10.2 The skeleton determines the shape of the body

b. Protection

The skeleton protects delicate and vital organs from damage. In the head, the skull protects the brain and houses the sense organs in protective sockets or capsules. The protective sockets of the eyes are called **orbits**, whilst the delicate hearing mechanism is enclosed by the bones forming the **auditory capsules**. The rib cage protects the vital lungs and heart. The pelvis supports the contents of the abdomen and protects the lower gut and reproductive organs.

c. Movement

In addition to giving shape and support to the body, the skeleton allows movement. The skeleton consists of a series of bones, held together at joints. Most of these joints allow the bones to move in relation to each other. The skeleton has numerous ridges and processes to which the muscles are attached. These muscles provide the effort or force to move the bones and hence the body.

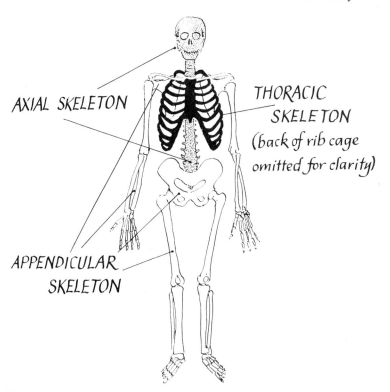

Figure 10.3 A diagram showing the regions of the skeleton

10.3. The regions of the skeleton

The skeleton has three regions, as shown in Figure 10.3:

a. The **axial skeleton**, which consists of the skull and the vertebral column (backbone or spine). The axial skeleton gives support to the main axis of the body.

b. The **appendicular skeleton**, which consists of the four limbs, or appendages, of the body and the girdles which support them.

c. The **thoracic skeleton**, the skeleton of the thorax or chest.

146

10.4. The axial skeleton—the skull

The skull is the skeleton of the head. Its main job is protection. The main part of the skull is a bony box called the **cranium**, which houses and protects the body's most important and delicate organ, the brain. In several places in the cranium are circular holes called **foramina** (singular: foramen), through which pass nerves and blood vessels. The largest foramen is in the base of the cranium, and is called the **foramen magnum**. An extension of the brain, the spinal cord, passes through this hole into the spinal canal which is a space inside the vertebral column or backbone. Can you suggest why the

Figure 10.4 (left) The under-surface of a human skull showing the foramen magnum and the occipital condyles

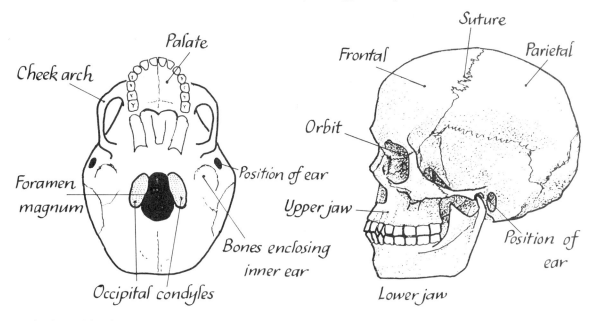

Figure 10.5 (above) Side view of a human skull

spinal cord is situated inside the backbone? On each side of the foramen magnum is a smooth, roundish knob of bone called an **occipital condyle** (see Figure 10.4). The occipital condyles connect by means of a movable joint to the **atlas**, the first bone of the vertebral column. This enables the head to nod backwards and forwards.

In most animals, the major sense organs are situated in the head. Can you suggest why? The skull houses and protects these sense organs. The eyes are sunk into the orbits and are protected by the ridges of the eyebrows (see Figure 10.5). The delicate sheets of bone, which support the sensitive cells of the nose, are protected by the **nasal capsule** and the cartilage of the nose. The external ears are simply to collect sound waves; the delicate mechanism which converts the sound waves into nerve impulses (electrical messages) is embedded in the bony auditory capsules in the side of the head.

The bones of the skull and the capsules of the sense organs are fused together by immovable joints called **sutures**. The upper jaw bone is also fixed, but the lower jaw bone articulates with the skull

147

to allow the mouth to open and close for eating, chewing and talking. The jaws are armed with teeth, which enable man to break up his food into pieces small enough to be swallowed. Many animals, however, also use their jaws or teeth for capturing, holding and killing their prey, and also as weapons of offence and defence.

In a very old person the bones of the skull have fused completely, and it may not be possible to discern the joints at all. In the skull of a child, however, some of the bones are not fully fused, and a gap called the **fontanelle** is left on the top of the head, covered by a cartilaginous membrane. This cap is gradually closed during the first year or so of life. Although immovable, there is a certain amount of 'give' between the bones of the skull of a young person, which will absorb some of the energy in a severe impact, and may prevent the bones from fracturing.

10.5. The vertebral column—the backbone or spine

Although the vertebral column acts as a girder supporting the main axis of the body, it is also concerned with movement. For this reason it cannot be absolutely rigid and inflexible. To allow movement backwards and forwards and from side to side, the vertebral column is not composed of a single bone, but comprises thirty-three bones called **vertebrae** (see Figure 10.6). Each vertebra has the same functions as the skeleton as a whole, namely support, protection and movement.

The basic structure of a vertebra may be seen best by examining a vertebra from the **lumbar** region, or the region of the lower back (see Figure 10.7). The most obvious structure is the thick solid piece of bone. This is the **centrum**, and is the part of the vertebra which supports the weight of the body. Can you suggest why the centra of the lumbar vertebrae are much stouter than those in the neck (**cervical**) region? Between the centra of adjacent vertebrae are discs of cartilage with soft centres, which make the vertebral column flexible and allow movement. From the dorsal surface of the centrum arises the **neural arch**, from the centre of which rises the **neural spine**. The neural arch encloses a cavity, in which lies the spinal cord. From the sides of the vertebrae project the **transverse processes** which, together with the neural spine, serve for the attachment of muscles.

To enable each vertebra to articulate freely with the one in front and the one behind, there are a pair of processes on the anterior surface which face upwards and inwards. These processes are called the **prezygapophyses**, and articulate with the downward and outward-facing **postzygapophyses** of the vertebra in front.

Of the thirty-three vertebrae, the first twenty-four are separate, but the last nine are fused together in groups of five and four. The vertebrae are grouped into five regions. We shall note how the vertebrae from each region are modified from the typical vertebra

148

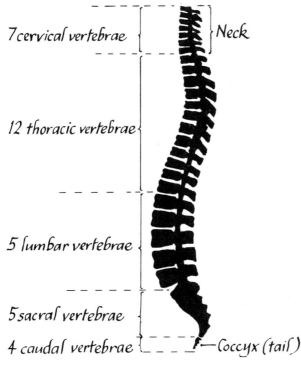

7 cervical vertebrae { } Neck

12 thoracic vertebrae {

5 lumbar vertebrae {

5 sacral vertebrae {

4 caudal vertebrae { ⌐—Coccyx (tail)

Figure 10.6 The vertebral column of man as seen from the side

described above, and how this modification suits them for their particular function.

Investigation 10a. To discover how the vertebrae in the various regions of the vertebral column are adapted to perform their own tasks

1. We have examined in some detail the structure of a typical vertebra. Examine an entire skeleton. If one is not available, refer to Figures 10.2 and 10.6. The first vertebra in the cervical region is called the **atlas**. Examine an atlas vertebra (or if it is not possible to handle· one, study Figure 10.8 carefully). Compare the

Figure 10.7 (left) A typical vertebra from the lumbar region

Figure 10.8 (below) Anterior view of the atlas vertebra

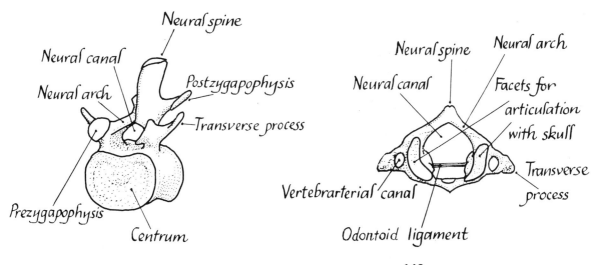

Neural spine

Neural canal

Neural arch

Prezygapophysis

Postzygapophysis

Transverse process

Centrum

Neural spine   Neural arch

Neural canal

Facets for articulation with skull

Vertebrarterial canal

Odontoid ligament

Transverse process

149

atlas with the typical vertebra in Figure 10.7. Notice the large flattened surfaces on the anterior side of the atlas. What is their function? If you are not sure, examine the base of the skull. Can you see any complementary surfaces on the skull which might articulate with the surface of the atlas? Try to articulate the atlas with the skull. What type of movement does this joint allow? What component of the typical vertebra appears to be missing from the atlas? Can you suggest a function for the **odontoid ligament**, which separates the neural canal from the space left by the missing component?

Figure 10.9 (below) Side view of the axis vertebra

2. The second cervical vertebra is called the **axis**. Examine it carefully or study Figures 10.9 and 10.10. Try to articulate the axis

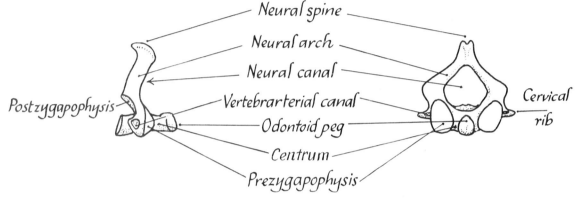

Neural spine

Neural arch

Neural canal

Postzygapophysis

Vertebrarterial canal

Odontoid peg

Cervical rib

Centrum

Prezygapophysis

Figure 10.10 (right) Anterior view of the axis vertebra

with the atlas. Can you see the peg-like **odontoid process** projecting from the anterior surface of the centrum? Can you see where it fits in the atlas? Perhaps now the function of the odontoid ligament is apparent. What sort of movement can the head make at the joint between the atlas and the axis?

3. The remaining five cervical vertebrae are all similar and resemble the structure of the typical vertebra, except for one feature peculiar to all the cervical vertebrae, including the atlas and the axis. Examine a cervical vertebra or study Figure 10.11, and see if you can spot this feature.

4. The **thoracic** vertebrae of the chest region are all similar. There

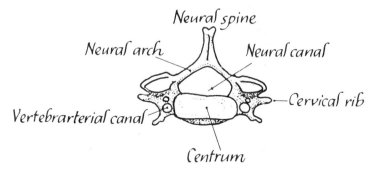

Neural spine

Neural arch

Neural canal

Vertebrarterial canal

Cervical rib

Centrum

Figure 10.11 Anterior view of a typical cervical vertebra

150

are twelve, and they can be recognized by their prominent neural spine. Examine two thoracic vertebrae and try to articulate them. Notice how the upward- and inward-facing prezygapophyses articulate with the downward- and outward-facing postzygapophyses of the vertebra in front.

Examine a thoracic vertebra, or Figure 10.12, carefully. Look

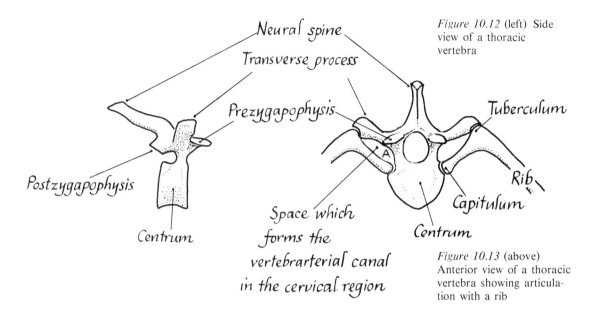

Figure 10.12 (left) Side view of a thoracic vertebra

Figure 10.13 (above) Anterior view of a thoracic vertebra showing articulation with a rib

first of all at the transverse processes. Can you see the smooth, shiny, articulating surfaces? What do these surfaces articulate with? On either side of the centrum you will see more of these articulating surfaces. Try to fit a rib to the thoracic vertebra, or study Figure 10.13. Can you see the two articulating surfaces on the rib? The surface which articulates with the centrum of the vertebra is called the **capitulum** ('C' goes with 'C'), and the surface which articulates with the transverse process of the vertebra is called the **tuberculum** ('T' goes with 'T'). Notice the space (A) between the rib and the transverse process of the vertebrae. This is important because a blood vessel, the vertebral artery, passes through it.

The cervical vertebrae also have ribs, but these are very short cervical ribs, which instead of being jointed are fused to the transverse process of the vertebrae. Look at a cervical vertebra, or Figure 10.11. Can you see the short ribs? Can you see also that the space referred to in Figure 10.13 has been retained to form the vertebrarterial canal through which runs the vertebral artery. The canal is characteristic of cervical vertebrae.

5. There are five vertebrae in the **lumbar** or lower back region. They have no special features. Examine one carefully, or see Figures

151

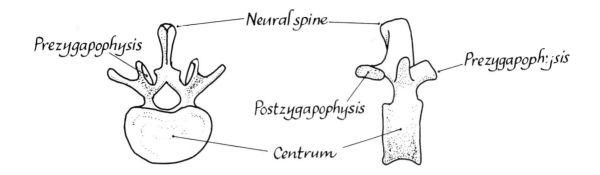

Figure 10.14 (above) Anterior view of a lumbar vertebra

Figure 10.15 (right) Side view of a lumbar vertebra

10.14 and 10.15. Compare the size of the different parts with those of cervical vertebrae. Can you account for any differences in size and strength?

6. The **sacral** region consists of five vertebrae which are fused together to form the sacrum (see Figure 10.16). The sacrum is fused to the pelvic girdle to form the **pelvis**, and through this the weight of the body is transferred to the legs. The pelvis also protects the main organs of the abdomen.

7. The last four vertebrae in the vertebral column are the **caudal** vertebrae of the 'tail'. They have become so much reduced and simplified that only the four centra remain. These are fused together to form the **coccyx**, or the bone of the tail of man (see Figure 10.17).

8. Examine either an articulated skeleton or Figure 10.2. Can you see the intervertebral discs between the centra of adjacent vertebrae? These cartilaginous discs are important as they allow movement between the vertebrae, particularly as the body turns or bends. To some extent they are all compressible, being fairly rigid around the outside, but soft in the centre. (The effect is thus like squeezing a sachet of shampoo.)

Figure 10.16 (below) The five sacral vertebrae fused together to form the sacrum

Figure 10.17 (right) The four fused caudal vertebrae forming the coccyx

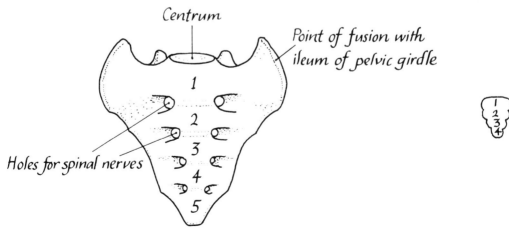

10.6. Summary of the functions and adaptations of the vertebral column

We have seen that the vertebral column is composed of thirty-three bones called vertebrae, articulating to provide the body with an axial stiffener which still allows movement. The vertebral column is divided into regions. The cervical region consists of seven vertebrae, the first two of which are specialized. The first cervical vertebra is the atlas, having large prezygapophyses which articulate with the occipital condyles of the skull, forming a joint which enables the head to nod. The atlas is the only vertebra without a centrum. In its place is a space into which fits the odontoid process, a forwardly pointing projection from the centrum of the axis, the second cervical vertebra. This forms a pivot joint between the atlas and the axis, around which the head can turn. The odontoid ligament of the atlas prevents the odontoid process from damaging the spinal cord. The other five cervical vertebrae are similar to each other and typical in that a very short cervical rib is fused to the transverse process. The space enclosed between the rib and vertebra is the vertebrarterial canal.

There are twelve thoracic ribs, characterized by their long neural spines and the fact that each one articulates with a pair of ribs. The tuberculum of the rib articulates with the transverse process of a vertebra, and the capitulum with the centra of two adjacent vertebrae. Part of the articulating surface of the capitulum fits into the centrum of one vertebra, and the rest with the centrum of the vertebra behind. The lumbar vertebrae are large and strong for the attachment of powerful body muscles; otherwise they are relatively unspecialized. The lower parts of the vertebral column have to support an increased weight, so the vertebrae (particularly their centra) become larger and stronger, and in the sacral region are fused.

10.7. The structure of long bones and flat bones

Bones have to withstand a great deal of stress and strain and yet, at the same time, they must be moved easily by the muscles acting upon them. Can you suggest two properties that bones must therefore possess? The bones of the limbs are called the long bones. The girdles of the skeleton and the bones of the skull are flat bones.

Investigation 10b. To investigate the structure of a long bone

Obtain two limb bones from your butcher's shop. Ask the butcher to cut one in section. He *might* be able to cut the other lengthways for you. Is the bone solid right through? Is the hard **compact** bone

★ *Do not attempt this yourself as the bone may splinter.*

153

the same thickness in the **shaft** of the bone as it is in the **head** of the bone? Does the head of the bone consist of the same type of bone as the shaft? Compare your bone with Figures 10.18 and 10.19.

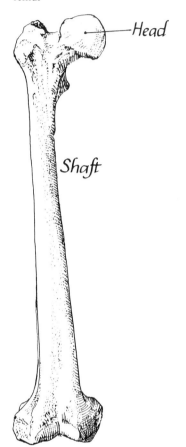

Figure 10.18 (below)
A human long bone—the femur

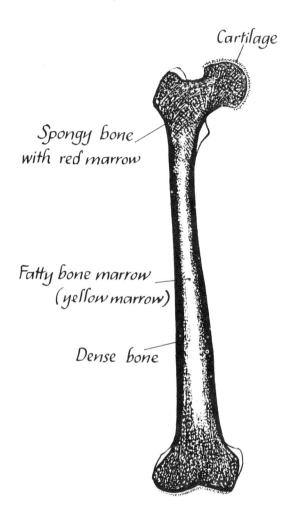

Cartilage

Spongy bone with red marrow

Fatty bone marrow (yellow marrow)

Dense bone

Figure 10.19 (right)
Femur in vertical section

Investigation 10c. To investigate the structure of a flat bone

From your butcher, obtain a piece of shoulder blade or, better still, a hip bone of an ox. Allow it to dry out and then cut it through with a saw. Study the cut surface with a hand lens. Where in the long bone did you find this type of structure?

Investigation 10d. To remove the inorganic material from bone

Get a good bone from the butcher and clean off any remaining muscle, cartilage or ligament. Soak the bone for several days in hydrochloric acid. The acid will dissolve away the inorganic portion such as the calcium salts.

After several days, wash the bone well and examine it carefully. Write down any other changes you notice in the bone, such as changes in size, colour, shape, rigidity, etc. Try to break it.

Harmful

Investigation 10e. To remove the living material from a bone

Remove the muscle, etc., from a bone and place it in an open tin over a fierce bunsen burner in a fume cupboard for an hour or two. Allow the bone to cool and make observations as before. Try to break the bone.

Hard bone consists of a rubbery protein called **collagen**, which is hardened by the deposition of inorganic calcium salts. The organic portion can be removed by burning, and the inorganic portion by soaking in acid.

You will have discovered that the shaft of the long bone is hollow. The cavity is filled with a soft, fatty material—**marrow**. Certain regions are well supplied with blood vessels. In these regions, the marrow is known as the **red bone marrow**. It is here that the red blood cells and white, granular blood cells are formed. The shaft consists of hard, compact (or dense) bone. Inside the head of the bone, the bone is not compact but has a structure like a honeycomb, and is called **spongy bone**. Flat bones have a layer of dense bone on the outside, but consist of spongy bone inside, thus giving maximum strength with least weight.

10.8. The appendicular skeleton

The appendicular skeleton consists of the bones of the limbs or appendages, together with the girdles that support them. Man is an animal whose ancestors inhabited the woods rather than the plains, so his limbs are adapted for climbing rather than for running very fast. He lacks the visible tail which some of his forerunners used for balance and for clinging to branches. Instead he has an opposable thumb which enables him to grip branches and other things in his hand.

The pectoral appendages, or fore-arms, are supported by the **pectoral girdle** which consists of the shoulder blade, or **scapula**, and the collar bone, or **clavicle**. The scapula is a flattened bone bearing a ridge for the attachment of muscles, and bears at its end a hollow cavity, the **glenoid cavity**, into which the head of the upper arm bone, the **humerus**, fits to form a ball-and-socket joint. The clavicle articulates with the scapula at one end and with the breast-bone, or **sternum**, at the other. The fore-arm consists of two bones, the **radius** and the **ulna** (see Figure 10.20). Beyond the elbow the ulna projects as the **olecranon process** to which muscles are attached. When the wrist turns the position of the ulna remains fixed whilst the radius swings over it.

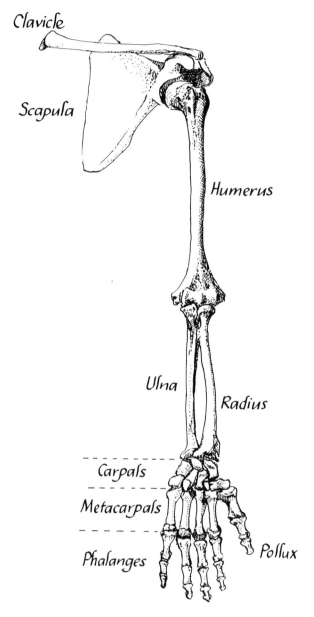

Figure 10.20 The skeleton of the arm of man

The bones of the hand consist of eight small wrist bones called **carpals** which are arranged in two rows, five palm bones called **metacarpals** and fourteen finger bones, or **phalanges**. Each finger contains three phalanges, but the **pollux**, or thumb, contains only two.

The pelvic appendages, or legs, of man are supported by the

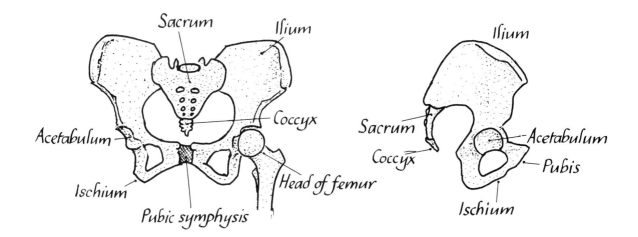

Figure 10.21 The male pelvic girdle: (left) front view and (right) side view

pelvis, or pelvic girdle (see Figure 10.21). In addition to transferring the weight of the body to the legs, the pelvic girdle helps to support the contents of the body cavity and protects the urinary and reproductive organs. In the female, the pelvis is larger and more basin-shaped, to enable it to support and protect the developing foetus. The pelvic girdle is composed of three pairs of bones fused in mid-line.

Each side of the pelvic girdle consists of the **ilium** (hip bone), and the **ischium** and the **pubis** which meet at the **acetabulum**, a cup-shaped cavity into which fits the head of the **femur**, or thigh bone (see Figure 10.22). At the back, the ilia fuse with the sacrum and at the front the pubic bones fuse at the pubic symphysis. The bones of the pelvic girdle are thus not capable of independent movement. Between the two pubic bones of the female pelvis is a pad of cartilage which does allow slight movement during childbirth.

The femur is the largest and strongest bone in the body. It articulates at the knee with the two bones of the lower leg, the thick inner **tibia** and the thinner outer **fibula**. The knee is a hinge joint which is protected by a small bone, the patella or knee-cap, formed in the tendon.

The foot, like the hand, consists of three sets of bones. The **tarsus**, or ankle, is composed of seven bones called **tarsals**. The middle of the foot is composed of five longer **metatarsal** bones. The bones of the toes are called phalanges, two in the inner 'big toe', or **hallux**, and three in each of the four outer toes.

10.9. The thoracic skeleton

The bones of the thorax or chest provide support, protect the heart, lungs, liver and kidneys, and help bring about the breathing movements which ventilate the lungs. The thoracic skeleton consists

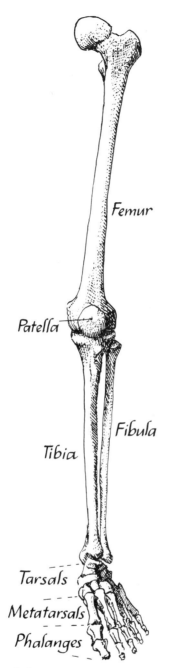

Femur

Patella

Fibula

Tibia

Tarsals

Metatarsals

Phalanges

Figure 10.22 Skeleton of the left leg of man

of the **sternum**, or breast-bone, and twelve pairs of ribs (see Figure 10.23). On the dorsal side, each rib articulates with two thoracic vertebrae. On the ventral surface, the first seven pairs of ribs, the true ribs, articulate by means of their costal cartilages with the sternum. The false ribs (pairs eight, nine and ten) articulate by means of their costal cartilages with the seventh pair. The last two pairs (eleven and twelve) are called floating ribs as they do not articulate at all on the ventral surface.

158

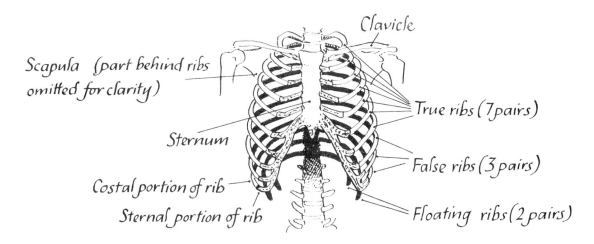

Scapula (part behind ribs omitted for clarity)

Clavicle

True ribs (7 pairs)

Sternum

False ribs (3 pairs)

Costal portion of rib

Sternal portion of rib

Floating ribs (2 pairs)

Test your understanding

Figure 10.23 Ventral view of the rib cage of man

Copy and complete the following paragraphs:

The main functions of the skeleton are to give the body ....[1] and support, to ....[2] the delicate organs and to provide rigid attachments for the ....[3] which move the body. Large animals, such as vertebrates, have an ....[4] since this type of skeleton provides ....[5] without hindering ....[6]

The human skeleton comprises axial, ...[7] and thoracic regions. The axial skeleton includes the ....[8] and ....[9] In the base of the skull is a hole called the ....[10] through which passes the ....[11] On either side of this hole are the bony knobs called the ....[12], which articulate with the ....[13]

The vertebral column is composed of a total of ....[14] vertebrae. In the ....[15], or neck, region there are ....[16] vertebrae, the first of which is called the ....[17] The turning movement of the head occurs at the joint between this vertebra and the ....[18] The twelve ....[19] vertebrae each articulate with a pair of ribs. The largest vertebrae in the column occur in the ....[20] region.

1. Give reasons why long bones (a) have a tubular structure and (b) have spongy bone at their ends.
2. Why does a bone become (a) brittle when heated strongly and (b) rubbery when left in acid for several days?
3. In which region of the skeleton would you find (a) fused vertebrae, (b) floating ribs, (c) scapulae and clavicles, (d) phalanges and (e) tarsals?
4. Give three examples of the protective function of the skeleton.
5. List the main regions of the skeleton (skull, vertebral column, etc.) and, against each, write down the approximate number of bones. Your total should be around two hundred bones.

Chapter 11

Movement: Muscles and Joints

In the last chapter, we have seen that the skeleton comprises some two hundred bones which must be linked together to provide support and protection for the body.

The place where two or more bones meet is referred to as a **joint**, at which place the bones are said to **articulate**. Most joints are movable, and the type of joint determines the type of movement which can take place at that joint.

11.1. Types of joint

a. The **ball and socket joint** permits universal movement (movement in all directions). Examples of such joints are shown in Figure 11.1.

In the shoulder joint, the ball-shaped head of the humerus fits into the glenoid cavity of the scapula. The socket is fairly shallow to allow a high degree of mobility. For this reason, dislocation of the shoulder is quite common.

Figure 11.1 Ball and socket joints of (left) the shoulder and (right) the hip

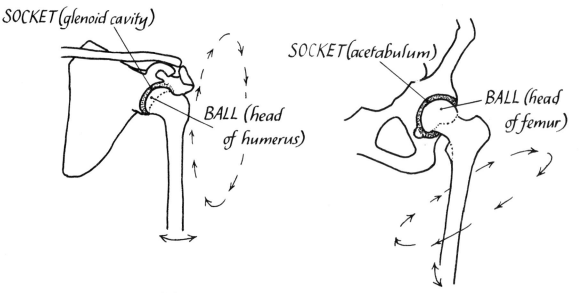

160

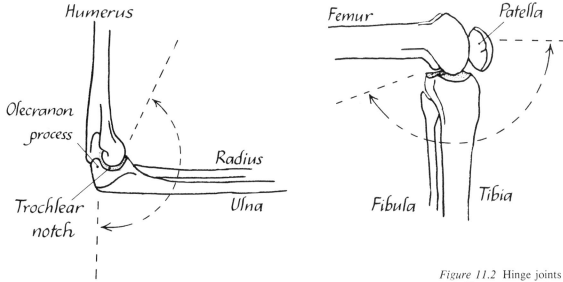

Figure 11.2 Hinge joints at (left) the elbow and (right) the knee

At the hip joint, the ball-shaped head of the femur fits into the cavity, or acetabulum, of the pelvic girdle. The socket is fairly deep, so accidental dislocations of the hip joint are far less common. Occasionally, in babies, the head of the femur does not develop in its proper position within the acetabulum, and orthopaedic treatment is necessary.

b. The **hinge joint** enables a limb to bend in one plane only. The knee and elbow joints are good examples (see Figure 11.2).

c. **Gliding joints** occur between adjacent vertebrae, allowing a small degree of movement (see Figure 11.3).

d. A **pivot joint** occurs between the atlas and axis vertebrae, allowing the head to rotate.

e. **Immovable joints** are found between the bones of the skull, pelvic girdle and sacrum.

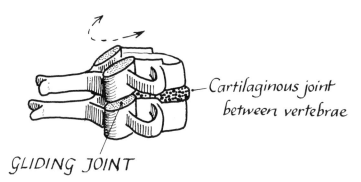

Figure 11.3 A gliding joint between two adjacent vertebrae

11.2. Joint structure

The structure of a movable, or synovial, joint is shown in Figure 11.4. The surfaces of the bones which move over one another are covered with a thin layer of very smooth cartilage (articular cartilage). The bones are held together by **ligaments** whose fibres allow a certain amount of flexibility. The ligaments enclose the joint in a **capsule**, within which is a cavity. Lining the cavity is a membrane which secretes a lubricating fluid, reducing friction between the bone surfaces and ensuring smooth movement.

In the disease arthritis, the joint structure undergoes harmful changes which lead to severe pain and restriction of movement.

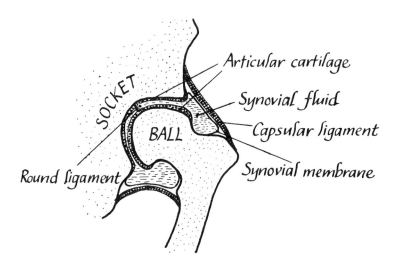

Figure 11.4 A synovial joint, seen in section

Investigation 11a. Examination of ball and socket and hinge joints

When your mother next cooks a leg or shoulder of lamb, rescue the joint after the meat has been eaten. Remove all remaining traces of flesh and examine the joint structure. Whichever joint you have, you should be able to recognize a hinge joint or a ball and socket joint. Can you name the bones? Remove the ligaments and examine the articular cartilages at the ends of the bones.

11.3. Types of muscle

Muscles provide the effort which enables the body to move. There are three types.

a. Voluntary muscles

These are sometimes called skeletal muscles, as it is these muscles which are attached to the skeleton and cause movement. They are under the direct control of the will. The voluntary muscles form the flesh of the body. They comprise bundles of **muscle fibres**, held together by connective tissue (see Figure 11.5). Each muscle fibre is composed of a number of elongated cells without distinct boundaries. At each end of the muscle are one or more **tendons**—stiff, non-elastic cords which serve to attach the muscle to bones. Muscles appear red in colour because of the many tiny blood vessels between the fibres. Why is it necessary for muscle fibres to be so well supplied with blood?

Muscle fibres have the peculiar property of contracting and becoming shorter (and fatter) when stimulated by a nervous impulse. Each individual fibre is in contact with a nerve ending and is, at any one time, either completely contracted (short and fat) or completely

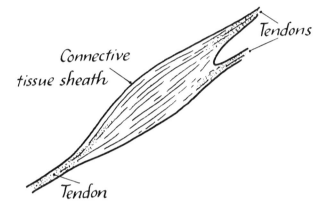

Figure 11.5 A voluntary muscle

relaxed (long and thin). The state of the whole muscle will depend upon the state of the fibres in it. If most of the fibres are contracted then the muscle will be contracted, but if most of the fibres are relaxed, then the muscle will be relaxed. Even in a relaxed muscle a few fibres are contracted. This gives the muscle a certain degree of firmness, known as **muscle tone.**

Voluntary muscles contain stretch receptors from which sensory nerve fibres pass information to the brain about the state of contraction of the muscle. This enables us to know, for example, the positions of our arms or legs without conscious thought.

b. Involuntary or smooth muscles

These, as their name suggests, are not under conscious control. They form sheets of muscle in the walls of the alimentary canal, blood vessels, etc. Unlike voluntary muscles, they can contract even if their connection with the nervous system is severed. The movement of food along the gut, by peristalsis (see Section 1.12), is brought about by involuntary muscle.

163

c. Cardiac muscle

This is found only in the walls of the heart. Its fibres resemble those of voluntary muscle, but are not under conscious control. They are also unique in that they do not suffer fatigue, even though they contract and relax continually.

11.4. Muscles and movement

Muscles are attached to bones on either side of a joint, so that the bones act as levers. The joint is the fulcrum and the muscle provides the effort. At one end the muscle is usually attached to a fixed bone, which does not move (the **origin** of the muscle), whilst the other end of the muscle attaches to a movable bone (the **insertion** of the muscle).

A muscle can contract or relax; it cannot expand. Thus a muscle which has pulled a bone in one direction cannot return it to its former position. This must be done by a counteracting or **antagonistic muscle**. Thus muscles work in pairs, and the position of the joint bones depends on the amount of pull exerted by each of the pair, just as whether a horse moves to the left or to the right depends on the amount of pull exerted by the left and right reins.

Muscles which bend the limbs at a joint are called **flexor** muscles, whilst those which straighten the limb are called **extensors**. As the flexor contracts, the extensor relaxes, guiding and steadying the bending of the joint. The roles of the muscles are reversed when the limb is straightened.

The paired action of muscles is illustrated in Figure 11.6. One of the flexor muscles of the arm is the **biceps**, attached at one end to the scapula and at the other to the movable radius. The extensor muscle is the **triceps**, attached at one end by three tendons, two to the scapula and one to the head of the humerus. At the other, the triceps inserts on the olecranon process of the ulna.

When the fore-arm is raised, a nervous impulse is sent from the brain to the biceps, which then contracts, becoming shorter and fatter and exerting a pull on its tendons. The tendons are inelastic and the pull is, therefore, transmitted to the bones. The shoulder is held rigid by other muscles, whilst the radius is free to move. Thus the fore-arm is raised. During this action the triceps is largely relaxed, steadying the movement.

When the fore-arm is straightened, the triceps contracts and the biceps is largely relaxed. The tendons of the triceps pull on the shoulder and on the end of the ulna, the latter being movable (see Figure 11.7).

Hold your left arm straight and grip the biceps firmly with the right hand. Now bend your arm. Can you feel what happens to the biceps?

164

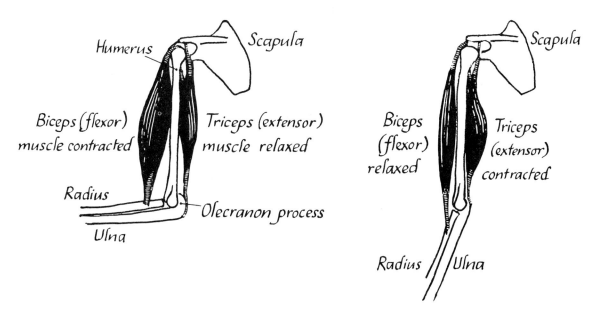

Frequently, groups, rather than pairs of muscles, are involved in delicate movements. The actions of voluntary muscles are, at all times, co-ordinated by the nervous system (see Chapter 7).

Figure 11.6 (left) The action of bending the fore-arm

Figure 11.7 (above) The action of straightening the fore-arm

11.5. Posture

Correct posture

We have seen that the position of the movable bones is determined by the pairs of muscles attached to them. For each joint, there is a position of the bones where the muscles are balancing each other and are least likely to suffer strain and fatigue. When the whole body is in this state, with its joints held in the most relaxed position, we say that it has correct posture (see Figure 11.8). Thus there is a correct posture for standing, sitting, walking, etc.

The chief muscles concerned in posture are as follows:

a. The neck muscles, which hold the head in an erect position and prevent it pitching forward under its own weight.

b. The muscles attached to the vertebrae, holding the spine in the correct position (see Figure 11.9a).

c. The hip muscles, supporting the pelvis.

d. The muscles at the front and back of the thigh, bracing the legs in a straight position at the knee.

e. The leg muscles, supporting the ankle and the arch of the foot.

Bad posture

Whenever a pair of muscles acting at a joint ceases to work in concert, a defect of posture will result. Thus, if the muscles on one

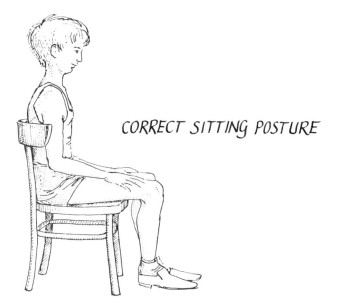

CORRECT STANDING POSTURE

CORRECT SITTING POSTURE

Figure 11.8 Correct posture for standing and sitting

side of part of the spine are permanently more contracted than those on the other side, the spine will be distorted (see Figure 11.9b). Such a postural defect will tend to throw the body off balance and, to compensate for this, the muscles in another region will pull the bones into an abnormal position, to restore the balance. An increased forward curvature of the lumbar region of the spine will tend to throw the body's weight forward and will be balanced by an increased backward curvature of the thoracic and cervical regions. Severe distortion of the spine may result.

What causes bad posture? There are several causes, including:

a. Badly designed furniture (chairs, school desks, etc.) which does not support the body properly.

b. Poor ventilation and lighting, leading to the body being held in bad positions.

c. Lack of exercise, so that some muscles become weak through insufficient use.

d. Unsuitable clothing.

e. Carrying weights for long periods on one side of the body (for example, school satchel with shoulder strap).

f. Bad habits, such as standing with the weight on one foot, slumping forward in a chair, etc.

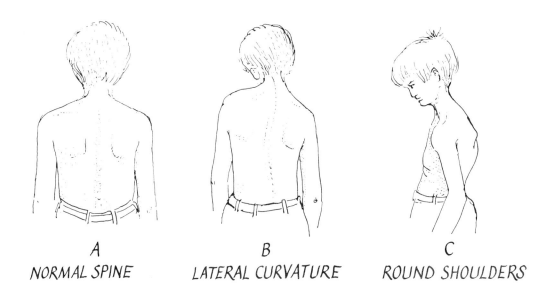

A	*B*	*C*
NORMAL SPINE	LATERAL CURVATURE	ROUND SHOULDERS

g. Malnutrition.

h. Disease, such as rickets (see Table 1.5).

Figure 11.9 (a) Correct posture of the spine and (b and c) defects of spinal posture

Remedying bad posture

Once the cause of the bad posture has been removed (for example, by improvement of habits), the fault itself may frequently be remedied by special exercises which strengthen the weakened muscles and restore the bones to their correctly balanced position.

Severe postural defects may need an operation or some structural appliance to brace the deformed region.

Test your understanding

Copy and complete the following paragraphs:

Bones meet at ....[1] The shoulder is an example of the type of joint called a ....[2], whilst the ....[3] is an example of a hinge joint. Immovable joints are found in the ....[4] and ....[5] The fibrous structures which hold bones together at joints are called ....[6], the fibres of which allow a certain amount of ....[7] Bones glide easily over one another at a joint because of the smooth layer of ....[8] covering their surfaces and because of the lubricating ....[9] Joint deformity occurs in the disease called ....[10]

Muscles which move bones are called ....[11] muscles. They are composed of long ....[12], bound together by ....[13] Muscles attach to bones by ....[14] whose fibres differ from those of ligaments in that they are ....[15] The point where a muscle attaches to a movable bone is called its ....[16] Muscles can contract and relax, but not ....[17] When slightly contracted, a muscle is said to have ....[18] The antagonistic muscle which works with a flexor is called an ....[19] and its action is to ....[20] a limb.

1. List the main types of joint and give as many examples of each as possible.
2. Explain the functions of the various components of a synovial joint.
3. Make a table to show the differences between the three types of muscle.
4. Explain the meaning of the following terms: muscle contraction, origin of muscle, insertion of muscle, antagonistic muscles, correct posture.
5. Make a critical examination of the furniture in (a) your classroom and (b) your home, from the aspect of posture. Draw examples of both well-designed and badly-designed furniture.

Chapter 12

Teeth and Dentition

12.1. Tooth structure

Teeth are derived from the skin rather than from bone, but they do contain a high proportion of non-living material.

A tooth has three regions: the **crown** is the part projecting above the gum, the **neck** is embedded in the soft gum and the **root** is out of sight, anchoring the tooth in its bony socket (see Figure 12.1). Inside the tooth is a fairly hard material which contains some living cells; this is the **dentine**. The dentine cannot withstand wear, so in the crown and neck it is covered with a layer of hard, non-living **enamel**. The dentine in the root is covered with a substance called **cement**, which helps to fix the tooth in its socket. Inside the dentine, in the

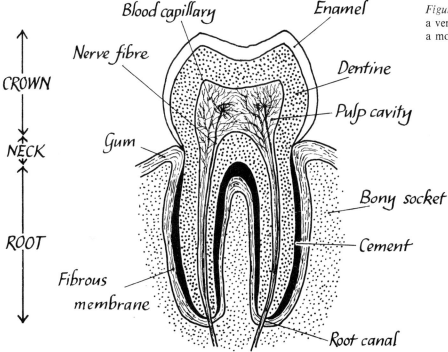

Figure 12.1 A diagram of a vertical section through a molar tooth

centre of the tooth, is a hollow **pulp cavity** containing nerves, a small artery and a small vein.

The teeth are not, however, set immovably in their sockets. If this were the case, we should frequently break our teeth when biting on something unexpectedly hard. Instead, they are suspended by fibres, extending from the dentine to the jaw socket. When we bite, these fibres have a cushioning effect, preventing damage.

Our teeth stop growing when they are fully formed, and the openings at the base of the roots close. In gnawing animals, such as rabbits, these openings do not close and the teeth continue to grow as they are worn away by gnawing.

Figure 12.2 The various types of teeth

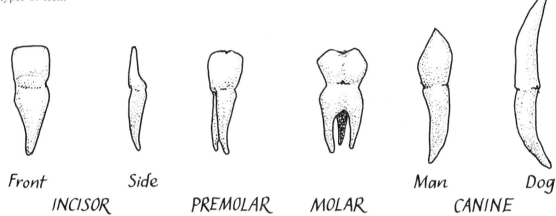

Front   Side   Man   Dog

INCISOR   PREMOLAR   MOLAR   CANINE

12.2. Types of teeth

The adult human has thirty-two teeth in a complete set but, unlike those of fishes, amphibians and reptiles, they are not all similar. Each type of tooth is adapted for a particular function, such as biting, chewing or tearing. The four types of teeth found in mammals are shown in Figure 12.2.

a. **Incisor** teeth are flattened, with a sharp cutting edge for biting. Man has eight incisors at the front of the mouth, four in the upper jaw and four in the lower jaw. Gnawing animals, such as mice, have particularly well-developed incisors.

b. **Canine**, or 'eye', teeth are strong pointed teeth on either side of the incisors and are used for tearing flesh. The four canines of man are not as well developed as those of animals such as the dog, where they are long, curved and sharply pointed. Can you suggest why this is so?

c. **Premolar** teeth are much flatter than the incisors and canines but their top surfaces are furrowed so that, when rubbed across similar surfaces on another tooth, they form a grinding mechanism.

Premolars are broad teeth with two roots. Man has four such teeth in the upper jaw (two on each side) and four in the lower jaw.

d. **Molar** teeth are at the back of the mouth and, like premolars, are used for chewing and grinding. The complete adult set of teeth contains a total of twelve molars, six in each jaw, three on each side. The four molars at the extreme back of the mouth often do not erupt until the late teens or early twenties, and for this reason are often referred to as 'wisdom teeth'. Wisdom teeth often have difficulty erupting, and decay quickly. Can you suggest why this is so?

12.3. Milk and permanent teeth

Man, in common with many mammals, has two sets of teeth during his lifetime. The baby, or milk, teeth appear between the ages of four months and two years. A complete set of milk teeth has no molars and contains only twenty teeth (see Figure 12.3). Milk teeth are small, for they have only to cope with the soft foods of infancy.

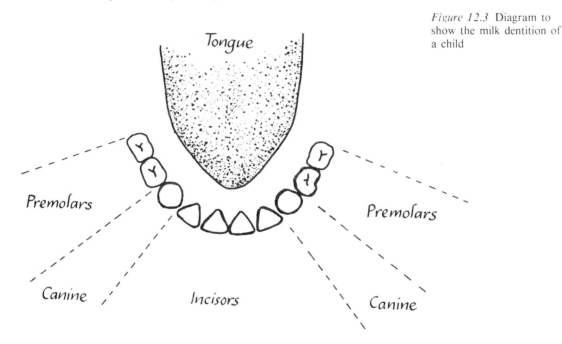

Figure 12.3 Diagram to show the milk dentition of a child

Between the ages of five and ten the milk teeth are lost, one or two at a time, as their roots are dissolved away. Beneath each is a permanent tooth, ready to erupt in its place. The permanent set is shown in Figure 12.4.

12.4. Care of the teeth

Sound, healthy teeth not only make you look more attractive and keep your breath free from odour, but also enable you to eat all

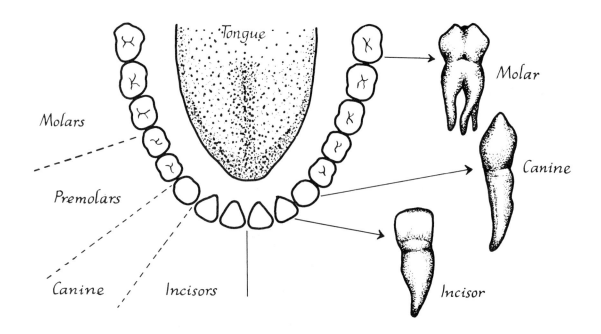

Tongue

Molars

Premolars

Canine

Incisors

Molar

Canine

Incisor

Figure 12.4 Diagram to show the permanent dentition of an adult

foods and reduce the chance of infection spreading to the mouth and chest. Unfortunately, very few school children, let alone adults, have a perfect set of teeth. Probably only one young person out of every hundred leaving school has a perfect set of permanent teeth, although all the teeth may not yet even be through. Tooth decay (see Figure 12.5) is common today amongst children—more so than it was many years ago. Can you suggest a reason for this?

Decay is caused by particles of sugary food, which become trapped in the cracks and crevices between the teeth. If these food particles are not promptly removed by regular brushing, bacteria in the mouth will convert them to acids which attack the tiny cracks or blemishes in the enamel. Once the enamel has been penetrated, bacteria feeding on the decaying food will multiply rapidly and attack the softer dentine inside the tooth. If this is not halted by the dentist, all the dentine may be eaten away, leaving a cavity which eventually reaches the pulp cavity and exposes the nerve. This causes severe toothache. If this condition is ignored, an abscess may form under the tooth. This is extremely unpleasant and may need hospital attention.

12.5. Prevention of tooth decay

The obvious remedy is to remove the particles of food from between the teeth by brushing regularly after meals. With a fairly firm brush and a reliable toothpaste, the teeth should be cleaned with an up-and-down action. Merely brushing the teeth from side to side

172

can push the food particles deeper into the crevices between the teeth. Do not forget to give the teeth a second brushing with clean water. Finally, rinse the mouth to get rid of the particles brushed from between the teeth. Brushing the gums will improve them, but do not use a toothbrush which is too hard, or brush so vigorously that the gums bleed. This gives bacteria the opportunity of entering the wound and infecting the gum.

Investigation 12a. To discover if acid is produced in the mouth

Chew a piece of toffee during the lesson. At the end of the lesson, remove the debris from around the teeth and add a few drops of 0·02% (water-soluble) methyl red indicator to it. Note any colour change. Methyl red changes from red to yellow as acidity increases.

Investigation 12b. To discover the effect of acid on teeth

Take some extracted human teeth (ask your dentist for them) and dip them in molten wax. When the wax has solidified, scratch it away from certain areas to expose the enamel and leave the teeth in dilute hydrochloric acid for about a week. Examine them at the end of that time.

Harmful

Investigation 12c. To discover if bacteria are present on your teeth

You should have your toothbruth and paste with you for this investigation. First of all, cover your lips with vaseline to prevent them from becoming stained. Now chew a tablet containing Erythrosin and look carefully at the teeth, noting their appearance. Now clean your teeth well, chew another Erythrosin tablet and re-examine.

Figure 12.5 The stages in decay of a tooth

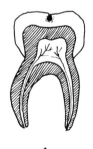

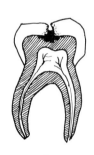

A
Enamel attacked
- NO PAIN

B
Dentine penetrated
- OCCASIONAL TWINGES

C
Pulp cavity penetrated
- nerve exposed
- PAINFUL

D
Abscess forms
- EXCRUCIATING

173

The Erythrosin in the tablets stains any bacteria present. Did cleaning them make any difference? Try different methods of cleaning the teeth and test to see how effective they are.

Toffee is chewed before Investigation 12a to ensure that there is plenty of sugary debris for the teeth bacteria to convert to acid. Sweet, sticky foods are the biggest danger to teeth, so do not eat too many sweets, and when you eat any, make sure you clean your teeth well and rinse out your mouth immediately afterwards.

You may say that all this tooth-cleaning is rather a 'fag', and anyway you may not want to take your toothbrush to school every day. This is not necessary; some foods are good for the teeth and clean them for you. Hard fruits and vegetables, such as apples and carrots, are ideal. After lunch at some schools, all the children are given an apple or carrot to chew. A visit to the dentist will hold less discomfort if you eat an apple or raw carrot after every meal. Even so, regular six-monthly visits to the dentist for a check-up are vital, so that any trouble can be stopped before it becomes serious and painful.

Calcium salts are necessary for the building-up of healthy bones and teeth. It is important, therefore, to see that the diet contains milk, eggs, cheese and green vegetables, for such foods contain calcium.

12.6. Fluoridation of water

Another substance that has been found to help prevent tooth decay is fluorine, which hardens the enamel. The teeth of people in certain parts of America are mottled brown in colour, but they seldom decay. It was discovered that the drinking water in these areas contains a relatively large quantity of fluoride (about eight parts per million). Further investigation showed that the amount of fluoride in the water in different areas varied from eight parts per million to virtually nothing. In regions with a concentration of one part per million, the inhabitants' teeth showed no mottling and little decay. It was decided, therefore, to add sodium fluoride to the water supply in Britain to bring the concentration up to one part per million. Some people objected to this, saying that the addition of fluoride to drinking water does not improve teeth. How would you, as a scientist, set out to verify this statement? Other people have said that fluorides are poisonous. This is, of course, true of many substances if a sufficient amount is taken. People said this of chlorine when, some hundred years ago, it was first added to the water supply to kill disease-causing bacteria, such as those causing typhoid. Today, we would not dream of drinking untreated water.

On average, we drink about a litre (two to three pints) of water each day. If the water were to contain one part per million of fluoride, as suggested, we would consume one milligramme per day. A fatal dose is 2 500 mg. Do you think, therefore, that death from fluoride poisoning is likely?

The health authorities in Britain investigated the effect on the incidence of dental decay of adding fluoride to water. In three areas they brought the concentration up to one part per million. Paired with these were three other areas where no fluoride was added. These were the control areas. In the experimental areas there was a reduction in dental decay of 60%, as compared with the control areas. What can we conclude?

12.7. Dentition in relation to diet

The arrangement of teeth in a mammal is known as its **dentition**. The dentition of different mammals varies according to the food they eat and their methods of feeding.

Man eats a wide range of foods, both flesh and vegetable, and is called an **omnivore**. His dentition is, therefore, relatively unspecialized.

The arrangement of teeth may be expressed as a dental formula. This shows the number of each type of tooth in one half of the mouth, the left or right side. The following symbols are used:

> i   for incisors
> c   for canines
> pm for premolars
> m   for molars

The dental formula of an adult man is thus:

$$i \frac{2}{2} \quad c \frac{1}{1} \quad pm \frac{2}{2} \quad m \frac{3}{3} = 32 \text{ teeth total}$$

The number above the line indicates the number of this type of tooth in one side of the upper jaw, and the number below the line indicates the number in one side of the lower jaw. Thus:

$$i \frac{2}{2}$$

indicates that man has two incisors on each side of the upper jaw and two on each side of the lower jaw (a total of eight incisors).

Investigation 12d. To compare the dentition of a rabbit, dog, sheep and man

Examine the skulls of the animals or, if these are not available, study Figures 10.5, 12.6, 12.7 and 12.8. Copy the chart (Table 12.1), record the numbers of each type of tooth and work out the dental formula for each animal. The figures for man have already been

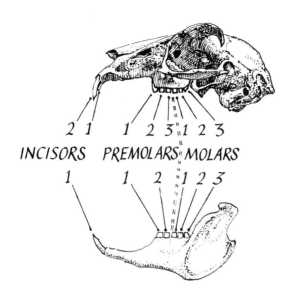

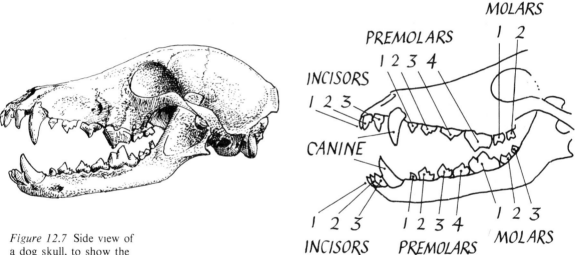

2 1   1 2 3 1 2 3
INCISORS   PREMOLARS MOLARS
1   1   2 1 2 3

Figure 12.6 Side view of a rabbit skull, to show the dentition

MOLARS
1 2
PREMOLARS
1 2 3 4
INCISORS
1 2 3
CANINE
1 2 3   1 2 3 4   1 2 3
INCISORS   PREMOLARS   MOLARS

Figure 12.7 Side view of a dog skull, to show the dentition

entered as an example. Finally, make brief notes about the diet of each animal and suggest how the tooth arrangement is adapted to deal with it.

The dog feeds on the flesh of other animals. A flesh-eating animal is called a carnivore. How is its dentition adapted for such food? How do the incisors of the dog compare with those of man? Why do you think the dog's canine teeth are so strongly developed? Articulate the lower jaw and see how the last upper premolar and first lower molar work together like shears. These are called **carnassial** teeth.

Both the rabbit and the sheep feed on plants and are called herbivores. Can you suggest why the incisors of the rabbit are rather different? Why does the rabbit have no canine teeth? The gap

176

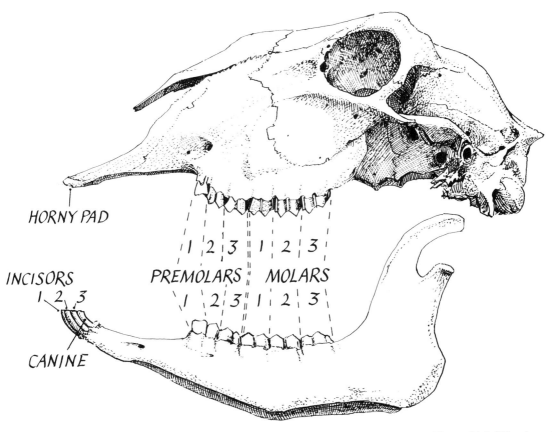

HORNY PAD

INCISORS
1, 2, 3

PREMOLARS   MOLARS
1 | 2 | 3 | 1 | 2 | 3 |
1 | 2 | 3 | 1 | 2 | 3 |

CANINE

Figure 12.8 Side view of a sheep skull, to show the dentition

between the incisor teeth and premolar teeth of the rabbit is called the **diastema**. The premolars and molars are ridged for grinding vegetation. Why does the rabbit have the diastema?

Why has the sheep no upper incisors? What does it feed on? Look at the surfaces of the sheep's premolars and molars. What sort of work do they do? Does the sheep need a diastema?

TABLE 12.1. DENTITION IN RELATION TO DIET

Diet	Animal	Incisors	Canines	Premolars and Molars	Dental Formula
Omnivorous	Man	8, chisel-edged	4, short, conical, incisor-like	20, short-crowned, cusped	$i\frac{2}{2}$ $c\frac{1}{1}$ $pm\frac{2}{2}$ $m\frac{3}{3}$
Carnivorous	Dog				
Herbivorous	Sheep				
Herbivorous	Rabbit				

177

The incisors of the dog are pointed and canine-like for tearing flesh. The canines assist and, being very well developed, serve also to hold the prey. The carnassial teeth are ridged and sharp-edged and have a shearing action which is useful for removing meat from bones and for cracking bones.

The rabbit's incisors are flat but sharp-edged for gnawing grass. These teeth have a persistent pulp which means they continue growing after they have reached adult size. The gnawing action wears the teeth down. If a rabbit loses an incisor, the tooth in the other jaw may grow so long that the rabbit is unable to feed. The diastema separates the mouth into two functional areas so that the gnawed material need not necessarily be ground.

The sheep has a hard pad on its upper jaw against which the lower incisors trap the grass. This is a cropping action.

We see, therefore, that the dentition of an animal is adapted to its diet and its method of feeding.

Test your understanding

Copy and complete the following paragraph:

The four types of teeth in a mammal are the . . . .[1], canines, ...[2] and molars. There are no . . . .[3] in the milk set. The . . . .[4] are the main cutting teeth. Most teeth stop growing once they are fully formed, but this is not true of the . . . .[5] teeth of animals such as the . . . .[6] The hardest part of a tooth is the . . . .[7] The shape and arrangement of an animal's teeth depend upon its . . . .[8] Thus an animal with a set of carnassial teeth is a . . . .[9], whilst one with a wide diastema is probably a . . . .[10] animal, especially if the canines are absent.

1. Draw a tooth in section and explain the functions of the various parts.
2. What are the main causes of dental decay? How may such decay be prevented (a) by the individual and (b) by health authorities?
3. Bears have a similar dental formula to dogs. Why should this be so? Which animals would you expect to have a similar dental formula to sheep?
4. Describe and give the purpose of (a) a diastema and (b) carnassial teeth.
5. The crowns of the molars and premolars of some animals are much taller than those of others. Suggest a reason for this. Which animals would you expect to have molars and premolars with very tall crowns?

TOPIC B: THE CONTINUANCE OF LIFE

Chapter 13

How Life Began

13.1. In the beginning

Man has always been eager to understand his own beginning and the origin of his planet, Earth.

The Universe is made up of at least a thousand million groups of stars called galaxies. The solar system to which our planet, Earth, belongs is a part of the galaxy called the Milky Way. The Milky Way consists of at least 100 000 million stars.

The solar system consists of the sun, a medium-sized star, with a diameter of about 1 390 000 kilometres, and nine planets, together with their satellites, or moons.

The planets revolve in orbits around the sun. The closest planet to the sun is Mercury, circling at about 58 million kilometres; then comes Venus, Earth (circling at about 150 million kilometres), Mars, Jupiter, Saturn, Uranus, Neptune and Pluto (5 900 million kilometres). Figure 13.1 shows the relative diameters of the planets, but it is not possible to show the relative distances of each planet from the sun. To do this, if Mercury were drawn 10 mm from the sun, Earth would be 26 mm and Pluto would be 1 070 mm. It would be impossible to get the diagram on the page. On this scale, the diameter of the sun would be 0·25 mm and the diameter of Earth 0·002 mm.

In our previous investigations, we have not accepted an idea until we have been able to demonstrate it consistently. In our discussions on the origin of the Universe, of Earth and, indeed, of life itself, we shall be considering not proven facts, which can be demonstrated, but speculations, based on the knowledge available at this time. On such evidence one can only suggest theories, so it is not surprising that there are differing theories which attempt to explain the origin of the Universe.

13.2. The origin of the Universe

The Universe consists of energy and matter.

a. The Evolutionary or 'Big Bang' Theory

This theory of the origin of the Universe contends that it

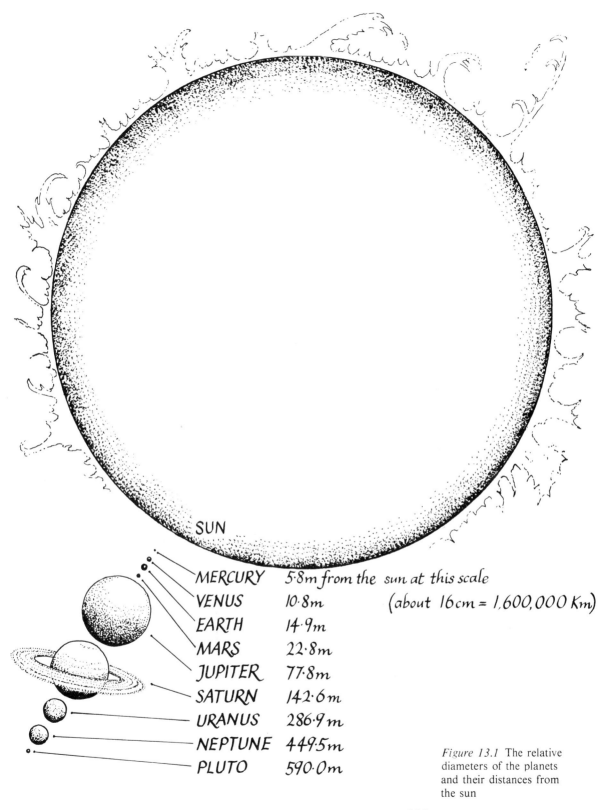

SUN

MERCURY   5·8m from the sun at this scale

VENUS   10·8m   (about 16cm = 1,600,000 Km)

EARTH   14·9m

MARS   22·8m

JUPITER   77·8m

SATURN   142·6m

URANUS   286·9m

NEPTUNE   449·5m

PLUTO   590·0m

Figure 13.1 The relative diameters of the planets and their distances from the sun

181

originated from an explosion of hot, concentrated primordial material, about 10 000 million years ago, and has been expanding outwards into space ever since. As the primordial material thinned out, it cooled and reassembled to form the planets, stars and galaxies. This theory suggests a beginning, with an initial explosion, and a gradual but steady slowing down ever since. It suggests that the primordial matter resembled the nuclear material of atoms, and contained neutrons (sub-atomic particles found in the nucleus of atoms) which break down into protons (the same as a hydrogen nucleus) and electrons. It is possible to see how these protons and electrons formed some of the elements we know today. This theory does not suggest how the primordial matter originated. According to the theory, the primordial matter is the original material from which the Universe arose.

b. The Steady State Theory

This theory, supported by Fred Hoyle, suggests that the Universe has always existed and is infinite, both in space and time, having no beginning or end. Evidence collected by radio telescopes suggests that immense clouds of hydrogen in outer space provide the raw material from which the galaxies and stars are constantly being created.

The Evolutionary Theory suggests that the hydrogen arose as a result of the explosion of the dense primordial matter, each neutron being split into a proton and an electron. The Steady State Theory suggests that the hydrogen gas always has been, and is still being, created by the conversion of energy into matter.

The two theories agree in that hydrogen atoms probably formed the building blocks of the heavier elements we find today.

13.3. The origin of the solar system

As Earth is one of the nine planets of the solar system, its origin must be linked with the origin of the solar system. There are, however, several current theories attempting to explain this origin.

a. Jeans and Jeffreys suggested the **Tidal Hypothesis** that the planets and their satellites were originally all part of the sun around which they now revolve. They suggest that a star passed so close to the sun that its attraction caused a bulge of gas on its surface, which was dragged into a tidal wave of gas that became detached from the sun. The theory suggests that these detached masses of gas went into orbit around the sun, before slowly cooling to form the planets.

b. The English astronomer, R. A. Lyttleton, proposed the **Double Star Hypothesis,** which suggests that the sun had a companion, a larger star which underwent a violent explosion to form a brilliant

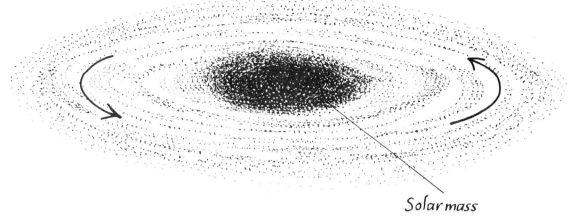

Solar mass

Figure 13.2 A disc of cosmic dust with the solar mass at its centre

star called a **supernova.** This larger body was propelled into space by the force of the explosion, but some of the fragments of the explosion were captured by the sun's gravitational field and remained behind to form the planets.

c. In recent years, the **Condensation Hypothesis** has been proposed by Harold Urey. This hypothesis suggests that an explosion of a star resulted in a cloud of dust and gases, such as hydrogen and helium. The particles of dust were drawn together by gravitational attraction to form a thin plate-like disc with a solar mass at the centre which revolved on its axis (see Figure 13.2). Eventually the disc separated to form the planets, leaving the solar mass as the sun at the centre. The disc became segmented and dust comprising each segment compacted to produce a planet, such as Earth. At first the earth was probably a relatively small mass which grew as more dust and gas were attracted to it by gravity. As it became heavier the forces of gravity increased, squeezing the particles of dust tightly together and causing the temperature to rise. When at last the earth began to cool, the heavy materials sank to the centre and the lighter ones solidified at the surface to form the igneous rocks. We know, by sending shock waves from one side of the earth to the other, that even today the centre of the earth is still a liquid, probably containing a large proportion of iron and nickel.

13.4. The age of the earth

When the earth was formed, crystals containing the element uranium formed in the earth's crust. A particular type of uranium called **uranium isotope 235** is unstable, and gradually 'decays' by giving off alpha (α) and beta (β) particles (radioactivity) until it is eventually converted to the stable element lead. This process of radioactive decay started from the time of crystallization, that is the time that the rocks were formed. Scientists know the rate at which uranium 235 is converted to lead, so by examining the proportion of uranium 235 to lead in the crystals, they have been able to estimate the age of the earth. It is now estimated that the earth was formed about 4 600 million years ago.

13.5. The ancient atmosphere

The gravitational force exerted by the earth enabled it to retain some of the gases around it to form its atmosphere. By examining other stars, we know that the atmospheres of stars and planets undergo gradual changes. It is reasonable to suppose, therefore, that the atmosphere of the earth today is different from that of its early days. The present composition is about 79% nitrogen, 20% oxygen, plus small amounts of other gases such as carbon dioxide and water vapour.

There is evidence which suggests that the ancient atmosphere was made up of water vapour, hydrogen, ammonia and methane.

13.6. Some old ideas of the origin of life

Aristotle, who lived over 2 000 years ago, believed that life could arise spontaneously from non-living material. About 300 years ago, a reputable scientist, van Helmont, supported this view with the following experiment. He placed a few kernels of wheat in contact with a dirty shirt and left them for three weeks. When re-examined, young mice were found in the shirt. From this he concluded that the mice had been generated spontaneously from the shirt and wheat. What was wrong with van Helmont's experiment? How would you have carried it out?

It was not until about 1860 that the French biologist, Louis Pasteur, finally performed experiments which showed that living things could arise only from other living things. You might like to try his experiment yourself.

Investigation 13a. Investigating spontaneous generation (see Figure 13.3)

Biological

Label five test-tubes A, B, C, D and E, and pour nutrient broth into them until they are about one-third full.
1. Plug test-tube A with sterile cotton wool, but do not heat.
2. Leave test-tube B unplugged.
3. Plug test-tube C with sterile cotton wool and tie several layers of tin foil over the open end.
4. Plug test-tube D with sterile cotton wool through which a straight piece of glass tube has been inserted.
5. Plug test-tube E with sterile cotton wool through which one end of an S-shaped tube has been inserted.
6. Then sterilize test-tubes B, C, D and E in a pressure cooker or autoclave for fifteen minutes.

184

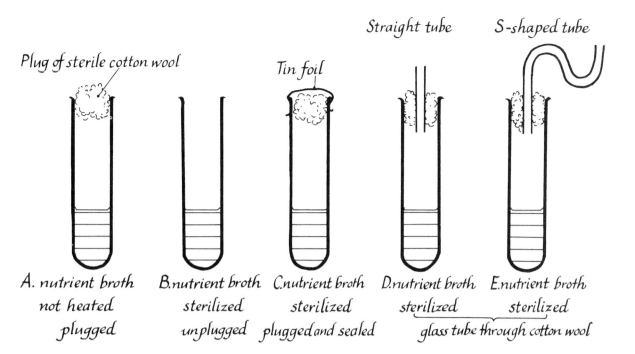

Plug of sterile cotton wool

Tin foil

Straight tube

S-shaped tube

A. nutrient broth
not heated
plugged

B. nutrient broth
sterilized
unplugged

C. nutrient broth
sterilized
plugged and sealed

D. nutrient broth
sterilized

E. nutrient broth
sterilized

glass tube through cotton wool

7. Place the tubes away from heat sources such as radiators and out of direct sunlight. Examine on days 3, 5, 7 and 14.

Figure 13.3 A modern version of Pasteur's experiment

If bacteria are present, the broth in the tubes will become cloudy or turbid. The degree of cloudiness is also some indication of the numbers of bacteria present. Record on the chart below which tubes become turbid and on which day the turbidity appears.

TABLE 13.1. THE RESULTS OF INVESTIGATION 13a

	Day 3	Day 5	Day 7	Day 14
Test-tube A				
Test-tube B				
Test-tube C				
Test-tube D				
Test-tube E				

Carefully examine the bend in the glass tube in test-tube E. What conclusions can you draw from your results? Did the fact that test-tube A was not sterilized have any influence upon the rate at which it went turbid? If the broth in test-tube B was sterilized and yet still went turbid, why was this so? What do the results in tubes C and E show? Are they the same? What accounts for any difference between the tubes D and E? What does tube E show that tube C does not? Why did this experiment disprove the theory of spontaneous generation?

Pasteur used a swan-neck culture flask which was similar in function to tube E. The object of Pasteur's experiment was to discover if bacteria could be formed from dead material in the presence of air. Almost a hundred years earlier, Spallanzani claimed to have disproved the theory of spontaneous generation. He had boiled liquids and sealed them from the air (as you did with tube C). There was no growth of microbes, but people did not believe him and argued that something had happened to the air inside the sealed vessel which prevented the microbes from growing. Perhaps the microbes needed fresh air to grow.

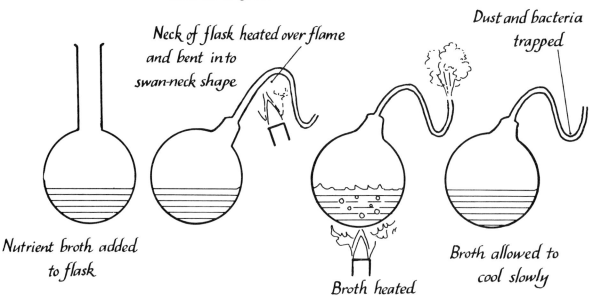

Figure 13.4 Pasteur's swan-neck culture flask

Pasteur poured broth into a flask as in Figure 13.4. He heated the neck of the flask and drew it out into a fine open-ended tube. He then bent this tube into an S-shape, a similar shape to the tube you placed in test-tube E. He then boiled the contents of the flask vigorously to sterilize them. The steam pushed all the air from the flask but, as the flask cooled, air was slowly drawn from the outside, through the swan-neck into the flask. The dust and microbes could pass down but not up, and they were drawn in so slowly that they became trapped in the curve of the neck. Air was able to pass through. There was no growth in this flask, but Pasteur showed that if he cut the neck off the flask, or if the flask was tipped so that broth came into contact with the dust in the tube, then bacteria would soon appear.

13.7. Current theories of the origin of life

Recent evidence suggests that this planet, Earth, was formed about 4 600 million years ago, at which time it had an atmosphere of water vapour, hydrogen, ammonia and methane. The Russian scientist, Oparin, suggested that life has existed on this planet for the past 1 000 million years. Recent workers have discovered micro-fossils of blue-green algae (very simple plants) in rocks 3 400 million years old. We have seen that scientists established that life can only arise from existing living things. How then did life arise initially, perhaps 4 000 million years ago? Oparin suggested that life did not occur in a single instant, but gradually arose by a process of **chemical evolution**. It is extremely difficult to suggest precisely at which point in this process non-life became life. The whole process probably took 1 000 million years, when the conditions on the earth were suitable. It is unlikely that these conditions exist today.

An American scientist, S. L. Miller, made up a mixture of gases similar to the supposed composition of the primitive atmosphere. He then passed a powerful electric spark over this mixture for a week. When he analysed the resulting watery residue, he discovered that it contained a surprisingly high proportion of **amino acids**. Amino acids are the basic building units of proteins, which, in turn, form the basis of the living substance, protoplasm. There is evidence that the climate of the primitive atmosphere was very hot and thundery. The gases could therefore have combined under the electrical discharge of lightning to form amino acids. These probably condensed in the rain drops and fell into the puddles on the hot, rocky surface of the earth. Amino acids can link up with the removal of water to form short chains called peptides. However, a considerable amount of energy is necessary; living organisms use enzymes to assist the process.

Sidney Fox, another American scientist, tried to discover how this might have happened. The water in the puddles on the hot steaming rocks might have contained amino acids. Fox thought that, as these puddles dried on the sun-scorched rocks, water might have been expelled from the amino acids, causing them to link together into peptide chains. He took a mixture of dry amino acids, heated them strongly and then examined the residue. He discovered that some of the amino acids had, in fact, linked together into short chains. He supposed that, somehow, new organic compounds might have been formed on the ancient rocks and then have been washed by the rains into the oceans, forming what J. B. S. Haldane described as 'a hot, dilute primeval soup'.

How could these still relatively simple compounds have formed the more complex proteins and become associated together into a living system? Oparin drew attention to a special group of non-living droplets called **coacervates**. Coacervates are clusters of protein or protein-like molecules which are held together within a droplet of liquid. When proteins are dissolved in water, they become electrically charged and attract to themselves molecules of water, so that a sphere of water molecules becomes organized around a protein molecule. When a cluster of protein molecules become organized within a single sphere of water, a coacervate is formed (see Figure 13.5).

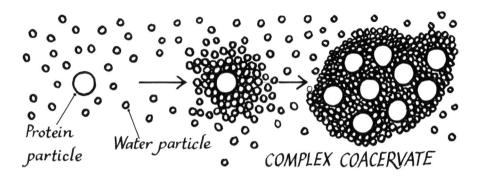

Protein particle

Water particle

COMPLEX COACERVATE

Figure 13.5 Formation of a coacervate droplet

Coacervation is a powerful method of concentrating substances having high molecular weights.

How could the coacervates have become more complex and living, able to utilize energy to maintain their organization? Other molecules could have been absorbed as they collided with the coacervates whilst diffusing. The surfaces of certain organic molecules are sticky, so they tend to stick together when they collide. These molecules may have stuck to the surface of the coacervates.

Some coacervates would be short-lived, but others might have been more stable. Eventually, certain combinations of molecules might have produced an energy-liberating reaction within a coacervate which enabled it to maintain stability. Initially, these reactions probably occurred at a very slow rate, and it probably took a long time for the evolution of the simplest living thing able to maintain and reproduce itself.

Eventually, enzyme systems to speed the chemical reactions were established and a special chemical substance, **adenosine triphosphate** (written as **ATP**), was developed for the storage and transfer of energy. In the successful organisms, a group of large molecules called the **nucleic acids** were able to carry 'instructions', and gained control of the processes of the organism. The best-known nucleic acid is deoxyribonucleic acid, abbreviated to DNA, shown by Watson and Crick in 1953 to have some very interesting properties. So we have a complex aggregate of large organic molecules surrounded by a membrane which controls the substances which enter and leave it. It has a system of enzymes which assist the chemical reactions within it. Some of these reactions produce energy which enables it to maintain and improve its organization. It has a substance called ATP which enables it to store some of this energy until it is needed, and it is able to produce similar 'organisms'.

At this point, we can probably say that a very simple living organism had developed. This stage was probably reached about 3 500 million years ago.

How did this very simple form of life give rise to the multitude of living things that abound on our planet today? This will be considered in the next chapter.

Test your understanding

Copy and complete the following paragraph:

The earth is a ....[1] which is one of a number forming the ....[2] system. At the centre of this system is a star which we call the ....[3] This group of stars is a part of the galaxy called the ....[4] It seems likely that the earth was formed ....[5] million years ago, but that recognizable life did not exist until ....[6] million years ago. At that time, the atmosphere consisted of the gases ....[7], hydrogen, ...[8] and water vapour. It is thought that under the influence of ....[9], these gases may have united to form ....[10] acids which are in fact the building bricks of ....[11]

1. Explain the two most popular theories of the origin of the Universe.
2. How might the solar system have arisen?
3. What was wrong with van Helmont's investigations into the origin of living material?
4. Explain how Pasteur finally disproved the theory of spontaneous generation.
5. What does Pasteur's experiment show that those of Spallanzani did not?
6. How did scientists estimate the age of the earth?
7. Explain how life may have arisen on the earth.

Chapter 14

The Changing World: Evolution

In these books we have considered quite a number of different plants and animals, ranging from simple organisms, such as *Spirogyra* and *Amoeba*, to complex forms, such as flowering plants and mammals. Of course, only a very small proportion of the living world has been considered, for there are well over a million species of animals and over a quarter of a million species of plants. Each species forms a distinct group, interbreeding freely and inhabiting definite geographical areas.

How have these organisms come to be on the earth? Have they always been on the earth in their present form? Will they remain the same in the future? The answers to the questions are not simple, and man has puzzled over them since the dawn of his existence. Indeed, the origin of man himself is as deep a mystery.

We have learnt that, when faced with a mystery, a scientist looks for evidence and then puts forward a hypothesis which fits the facts. Let us now see what evidence there is regarding the origin of species.

14.1. Life in the past: the fossil record

Fortunately, scientists are able to learn quite a lot about life in the past from the study of fossils (palaeontology). A fossil is anything left by a dead plant or animal as evidence of its existence.

Fossils may be divided into four types:

a. Impressions

Here, part of the animal or plant forms a hollow in soft mud which later becomes converted to rock. Dinosaurs, for instance, have left footprints, and ancient flying reptiles (Archaeopteryx) have left impressions of bones and feathers. Even soft-bodied animals, such as worms and jelly-fish, have left markings in the rocks.

b. Whole preservation

This means that the whole animal or plant is preserved in its original form. This method of fossilization is very rare and has occurred only when conditions have prevented the normal processes of decay. Some 25 000 years ago, woolly mammoths became entombed in the polar ice of Siberia. After excavation, the mammoths were found to be so well preserved that, in some cases, the flesh was still edible by sledge dogs, and the stomachs contained undigested grass. Another example of whole preservation are the flies found trapped in amber, the hardened resin from coniferous trees. These insects lived in the Baltic forests some 40 million years ago.

c. Petrification

Here, the organism has been turned into stone. The softer parts of the body have decayed and have been replaced by mineral deposits infiltrating the cavities so produced. Much of our knowledge of early plant life has come from a study of petrifications, such as those from Rhynie chert beds in Scotland. In petrified wood, as found in Lough Neagh in Northern Ireland, the wood grain is still visible throughout.

d. Casts

These are the commonest of all fossils. Their formation is illustrated in Figure 14.1. After its death, the plant or animal becomes

Figure 14.1 Stages in the formation of a fossil cast

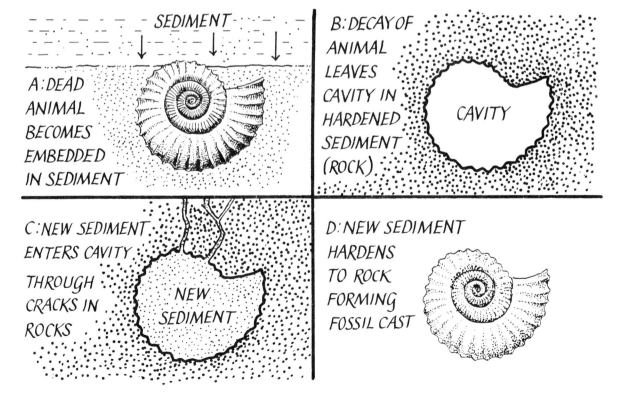

imprisoned in accumulating sediment, which later hardens to rock (for example, sandstone). Decay of the corpse leaves a cavity, the lining of which is a mould of the original body form. Should a different type of sediment subsequently enter this mould and harden, a fossil cast will be formed. Among the animals which are found as fossil casts are trilobites (arthropods), ammonites (molluscs) and sea-urchins (echinoderms).

It should be realized that it is extremely unlikely that a dead organism will leave a fossil. Should it do so, the chance that the fossil will be discovered is remote. As Charles Darwin pointed out, the fossil record is like a book from which many pages have been torn; those pages that remain are largely unreadable.

14.2. How fossils are dated

If you have time and patience, you may well find fossils for yourself. Fossilized plants are sometimes found when lumps of coal are broken open with a hammer and cold chisel. Animal fossils occur in chalk, in sandstone and limestone cliffs, and among the pebbles of the sea-shore. Some areas, for example the coast around Lyme Regis, are particularly abundant in fossils, and should reward the fossil hunter.

Supposing that a fossil is found, how can its age be discovered? This is done by finding out the age of the rock in which the fossil was found. Note the exact location of the fossil, and the nature of the surrounding rock. Reference to a geological map of the area will help to identify the rock. Particular types of rock were laid down during definite periods of the earth's history. Coal, for instance, was formed during the Carboniferous Period, between 275 and 220 million years ago; whilst chalk is younger, being formed in the Cretaceous Period, 140 to 70 million years ago.

Dating is possible because the various rocks occur in layers, or **strata**. The deepest-lying rock is **igneous**, formed when the earth came into being. Above this rock are layers of **sedimentary rock**, formed by the hardening of mud (sediment) deposited by streams, lakes, rivers and seas. By identifying the rocks, and by measuring the thickness of the strata, the geologist is able to estimate how long each took to form. Of course, rocks are not continually added at a particular point, and for millions of years there may be no sedimentation. Thus a younger rock may come to be just above a much older one. The problem is further complicated by the folding, faulting and erosion which has taken place in the earth's crust after the formation of the rock strata (see Figure 14.2).

It is possible to date the more recent fossils by radioactive methods, the best known of which is carbon-14 dating. The method is suitable for fossils aged between 100 and 50 000 years. All living

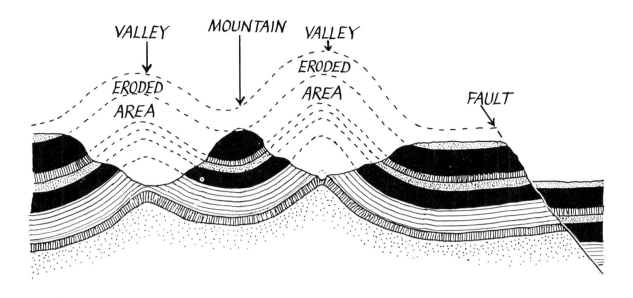

VALLEY   MOUNTAIN VALLEY
ERODED   ERODED
AREA   AREA   FAULT

organisms contain a constant proportion of radioactive ('heavy') carbon, or carbon-14. After the death of the organism, the amount of carbon-14 steadily decreases, decay occurring to normal carbon, or carbon-12. The rate of decay is known (half of the carbon-14 will be converted to carbon-12 in about 5 568 years). By measuring the amount of carbon-14 left in the fossil, its age may be estimated.

Figure 14.2 Stratification of the earth's crust

This method of dating has been checked experimentally by using it to date materials of known age, such as wood from very old trees. Here, carbon dating has given ages which almost agree with those obtained by counting annual rings.

14.3. Great periods of the earth's history

Micro-fossils found in South Africa are estimated to be some 3 200 million years old. Other very old fossils are those of the blue-green algae and iron bacteria preserved in silica of North America, which are about 1 600 million years old. There is then an enormous gap in the fossil record, extending to around 600 million years ago when the Cambrian series of rocks were formed. Thus a thousand million years of Pre-Cambrian history is represented by very few fossils. In the Cambrian rocks, however, are found fossils representing all the major fossil-producing phyla except the Chordata (vertebrates). The first chordates, the armoured fishes, occur in Ordovician rocks, approximately 420 million years old.

Study of the fossils in other rock series shows the following:

a. Many plants and animals, such as dinosaurs and giant horse-tails, have existed in the past, but do not exist today. They are said to have become **extinct**.

b. Each period of the earth's history has been dominated by

193

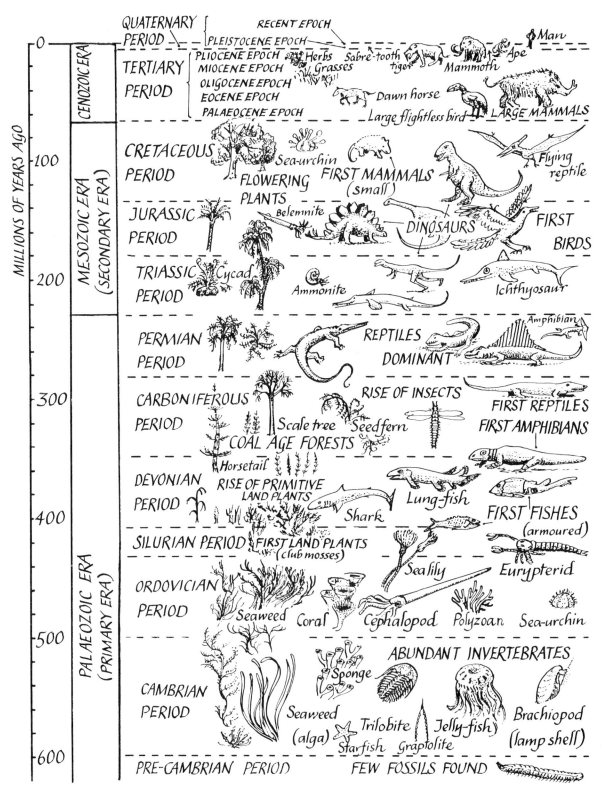

Figure 14.3 Fossils of the various geological periods

194

certain groups of plants and animals. Thus the Carboniferous Period, when coal was formed, was dominated by a variety of large amphibians which inhabited the swampy forests of giant ferns and horsetails.

c. The groups of plants and animals which dominated the more recent periods are the more complex forms. Thus, flowering plants (angiosperms) appeared first in rocks about 150 million years old, and soon became the dominant plants. About the same time, the most advanced animals, the birds and mammals, appeared, the latter becoming the dominant group.

The major periods of the earth's history, with the dominant life-forms, are shown in Figure 14.3.

What conclusions may be drawn from the fossil record regarding the origin of species? It seems reasonable to assume that there has been a **succession of life** in geological time, with new species arising and some existing forms becoming extinct. Each group has enjoyed periods during which the numbers and range of form have increased, whilst during other periods these have declined. Each dominant group has been replaced by one comprising more advanced organisms. Thus the Age of Fishes was followed by the Age of Amphibians, which, in turn, was followed by the Age of Reptiles. We have a picture of life constantly changing, with the simple giving way to the complex.

14.4. Fossil horses

In a few cases, sufficient fossils have been discovered to suggest how one particular modern animal may have arisen. The best-known example is that of the horse (see Figure 14.4).

The modern horse, *Equus caballus*, is an animal which is adapted and suited to fast running and to a grazing habit. Its legs are long, and each possesses only a single toe, on the nail (hoof) of which the animal runs. Grinding rough grass tends to wear the teeth down; to compensate for this, the teeth are taller than those of other, non-grazing mammals. The molar surfaces are so constructed that they remain sharply ridged, even as the tooth is worn down.

Horses of the genus *Equus* first appear as fossils in rocks one to two million years old. In older rocks, around ten million years old, are found fossils of horse-like animals which are smaller than *Equus*, and have bones of three toes in each foot. Only one of these toes seems to have touched the ground. Earlier fossils show this same toe pattern. The teeth were shorter and less ridged than those of *Equus*. The series of fossils may be traced back to one called Hyracotherium (the 'Dawn Horse'). This was about the size of a fox, had short teeth and possessed four functional toes on the front foot and three on the back foot.

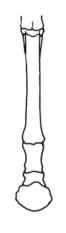

FORE-FOOT WITH
ONE TOE

MODERN HORSE
(EQUUS)

VERY TALL MOLARS
WITH COMPLEX CROWNS

FORE-FOOT WITH
THREE TOES (ONE
TOUCHED GROUND)

FOSSIL HORSE FROM MIOCENE PERIOD
(15-35 MILLION YEARS AGO)

FAIRLY TALL MOLARS
WITH COMPLEX CROWNS

FORE-FOOT WITH
FOUR TOES

SHORT MOLARS WITH CUSPS

HYRACOTHERIUM (THE 'DAWN HORSE') A FOSSIL FROM
THE EOCENE PERIOD (50-70 MILLION YEARS AGO)

Figure 14.4 Fossil horses

Hyracotherium lived some sixty million years ago, when the warm, damp climate allowed a luxuriant growth of vegetation. Probably, a number of such forms of animal arose and spread from North America to other continents. Some twenty-five million years ago, the climate is believed to have become cooler and drier, reducing the forests and increasing the area of grassland. The Dawn Horse gave way to animals more able to graze and to run rapidly when attacked. When we run, we run on our toes, and it follows that an animal constantly needing to run would be more adapted if it were permanently up on its toes. Since the centre toe was longer than the other four, there would be a tendency for this to survive when the other toes were lost or became mere splint-bones.

The onset of the Ice Age probably caused the decline of many of these horse ancestors, so that only the genus *Equus* survives today. All the modern types of horse belong to this one genus.

14.5. The geographical distribution of plants and animals

Species of plants and animals are not distributed evenly over the earth's surface, but have restricted areas. Thus, for instance, birch trees occur in Europe and South America, but not in other continents; whilst giraffes occur only in Africa. Is this uneven distribution due to the fact that conditions of life are unsuitable elsewhere? This cannot be entirely true, for there are many examples of animals and plants failing to occur in a continent or area where conditions are quite suitable for them. Thus rabbits and the cactus called prickly-pear did not exist in Australia until man took them there, yet, once established, they flourished and their spread soon went out of control. By 1925 prickly-pear, introduced to Australia as a garden plant, had spread to cover an area of some 24 million hectares (60 million acres), an area larger than that of England and Wales combined! One could hardly say that conditions did not suit this plant.

The geographical distribution of plants and animals was a subject of great interest to Charles Darwin, who made a careful study of the flora and fauna of many parts of the world during the voyage of H.M.S. *Beagle* from 1831 to 1836. As the ship surveyed the eastern coastline of South America, Darwin was able to go ashore at many points. He noted the plants and animals that occurred and compared them with those of a previously studied area a few miles away. He was struck by the fact that no two places had exactly the same species. He also collected fossils of a number of extinct large mammals, and became impressed with the way life has changed with time. Darwin was fortunate because on the same cruise he was able to visit a number of oceanic islands, such as the Galapagos, and was amazed at the unique forms of life that occurred there. For instance,

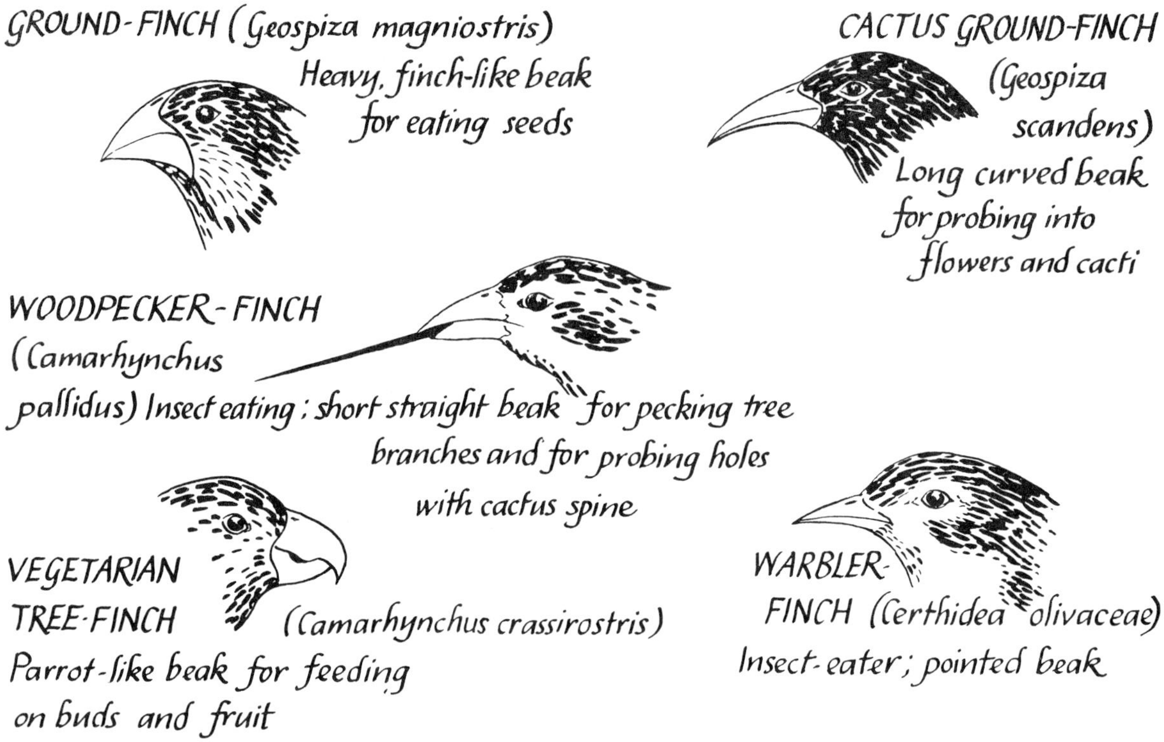

GROUND-FINCH (Geospiza magniostris)
Heavy, finch-like beak
for eating seeds

CACTUS GROUND-FINCH
(Geospiza
scandens)
Long curved beak
for probing into
flowers and cacti

WOODPECKER-FINCH
(Camarhynchus
pallidus) Insect eating; short straight beak for pecking tree
branches and for probing holes
with cactus spine

VEGETARIAN
TREE-FINCH   (Camarhynchus crassirostris)
Parrot-like beak for feeding
on buds and fruit

WARBLER-
FINCH (Certhidea olivaceae)
Insect-eater; pointed beak

Figure 14.5 Some of the Galapagos finches, discovered by Charles Darwin

out of 193 species of flowering plants growing on the Galapagos Islands, only 93 were found in other parts of the world.

Darwin also saw that the plants and animals inhabiting a particular area were adapted to their various ways of life. He was particularly interested in the Galapagos finches, each of which possessed a beak suitable for dealing with its particular type of food (see Figure 14.5).

On his return to England, Darwin spent many years pondering over his strange discoveries, and wondered at the explanation behind them.

14.6. Homologues and vestiges

The various groups of vertebrates use the fore-limbs for different purposes. The bird and the bat use them as wing supports, as did the pterodactyl. The whale, on the other hand, uses them as flippers; the mole as soil-scrapers; the horse as legs; and man as arms. One might imagine, therefore, that the structure of these various limbs would be very different, but this is not so. The limbs have a similar bone-pattern and each may be considered to be a variation of a basic pattern, termed the **pentadactyl limb** (see Figure 14.6).

198

Structures such as these, which have different functions but have a fundamental similarity of structure, are said to be **homologous**. They may be explained if we assume that the animals have arisen from a **common ancestor**, each having adapted the basic limb pattern to suit its own way of life. Many examples of homologues occur in the animal and plant kingdoms.

Vestiges are structures which are possessed by an animal or plant, but which have no apparent function. Thus pythons, like all snakes, are limbless, yet their bodies contain some bones of the hind limb and of the pelvic girdle. Flightless birds, such as the kiwi and ostrich, have fore-limbs with a full wing pattern, though much reduced in size. Some 180 vestiges are known in man, including the appendix and the third eyelid.

The existence of vestiges is, again, an indication that animals and plants have ancestors, from which they inherit their body pattern. Some structures are inherited and continue to develop even though their function has been lost.

Figure 14.6 Modifications of the pentadactyl limb

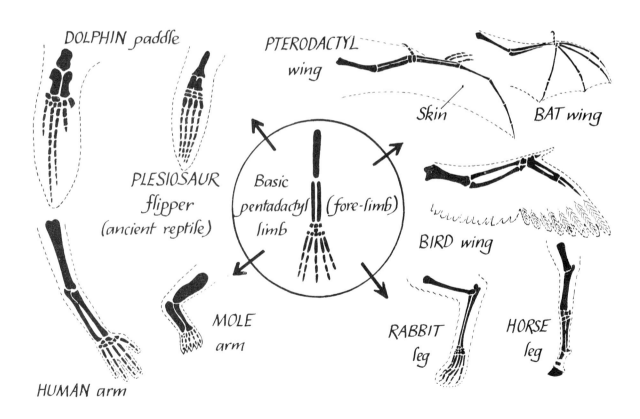

14.7. The meaning of evolution

In this chapter we have only been able to outline a few pieces of evidence regarding the origin of species. A mass of such evidence supports the theory that modern plants and animals have arisen from earlier forms, or ancestors, by a process of gradual change. This process is known as **organic evolution.**

The first forms of life were almost certainly unicellular, and from these forms the algae (unicellular plants) and the protozoans (unicellular animals) arose. This is thought to have occurred some 4 000 million years ago, since which time life has constantly changed, producing more complex forms. From our point of view the most important stage in the evolutionary process has been the evolution of man, which has occurred within the last 15 million years.

14.8. The mechanism of evolution: Darwin and natural selection

If we accept that evolution has occurred, with the implication that all modern species of plants and animals have their origin in ancestral forms, it is right that we should consider how such changes could have come about. The modern theory of evolution is based on that put forward jointly by Charles Darwin and Alfred Wallace in 1858. The main points of this theory are as follows:

a. For all species the *number of potential offspring* far exceeds the number which actually develop into adults. For instance, each acorn is capable of developing into an oak tree, and each year one tree will produce thousands of acorns. However, the number of oak trees in existence remains much the same from year to year, and it follows that many acorns never develop into oak trees.

b. Since only a small proportion of offspring can survive, there would seem to be *competition for survival*, and a *struggle for existence* must occur. Thus, if several acorns fall within the same area of soil and germinate, the resulting seedlings will compete for water, light and air.

c. If all offspring were identical, it would be sheer chance which ones survived and which perished. However, all offspring are not identical, for *variation* exists. Just as no two human beings are identical, so, too, no two individuals of any other species are identical. Our oak seedlings will differ from each other in certain respects.

d. It is quite possible that one offspring will possess a feature which gives it an advantage in the battle for survival. Thus, in oak seedlings, it might be that rate of growth is a variable feature. Any seedling which has inherited the ability to grow rapidly will tend to flourish, and will establish itself to the exclusion of seedlings which have not inherited this tendency. Which offspring survive, therefore, will depend on the number of *advantageous variations* possessed by each. This is known as the **survival of the fittest.**

e. Since, through heredity, the characters of the parent are transmitted to the offspring, *the advantageous feature may be passed on and may benefit future generations.* Disadvantageous variations, on the other hand, will tend not to be passed on, since their possessors will tend to fail in the struggle for existence and will not survive to reproduce. Thus our rapidly growing oak seedling will grow into an oak tree which may produce many more seedlings possessing this advantageous feature.

f. The environment determines which features are advantageous, which are disadvantageous and which are of neutral survival value. For instance, on salt marshes, land plants which are able to tolerate immersion in salt water are at an advantage over those that cannot. This feature is of no advantage in, say, a meadow. Thus, in a sense, nature decides which individuals survive. Darwin referred to this as **natural selection.**

14.9. An example of natural selection at work

It will be easier for us to understand how natural selection can bring about change in a species if we consider an actual example.

The **peppered moth** (*Biston betularia*) occurs in woods, and feeds by night and rests by day on the bark of trees with its wings outspread (see Figure 14.7). The moth is greyish-white and mottled with black marks, so that it blends well with the lichen-covered bark of trees. It can only be distinguished if it moves. The moths vary in a number of features, and there is one variant which is almost black in colour (the melanic form). The first melanic form in the Manchester area was recorded in 1848, and at that time such forms were rare. Fifty years later, records show that some 98% of the moths in the Manchester area were dark. What caused this change in the moth population?

The selective factor here is the hedge-sparrow, nuthatch and spotted flycatcher, all of which feed on the moths. In normal country areas these birds find it difficult to distinguish the fawn moth, but easily see the black variant. The black coloration is, therefore, a disadvantageous variation. In 1848 the area around Manchester was rural, but since then the advance of industrialization has brought soot and grime, darkening the bark of the trees. The tables have been turned, for now it is the black moth which is well camouflaged and the fawn moth easily distinguished.

To verify this theory, H. B. D. Kettlewell collected and marked peppered moths and released them in two contrasted areas, Dorset (rural) and Birmingham (industrial). He then spent many nights capturing the moths, using traps containing mercury vapour lamps.

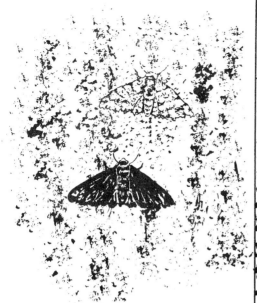
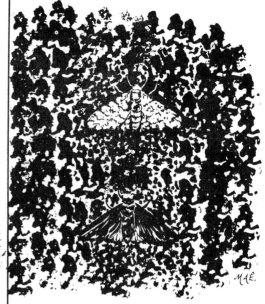

A

IN COUNTRY AREAS
THE MELANIC FORM IS MORE
EASILY DISTINGUISHED AGAINST
THE LIGHT-COLOURED BARK

B

IN INDUSTRIAL AREAS
THE NORMAL FORM IS MORE EASILY
DISTINGUISHED AGAINST THE SOOT-
- COVERED BARK

Figure 14.7 An example of
natural selection: the
peppered moth

In this way he was able to estimate hcw many of the released moths
had survived. A record of Kettlewell's results is given in Table 14.1.

TABLE 14.1. RESULTS OF INVESTIGATION ON
PEPPERED MOTHS

	DORSET		BIRMINGHAM	
	Fawn	Black	Fawn	Black
Released	496	473	137	447
Recovered	62	30	18	123
Percentage recovered	12·5	6·3	13	27·5

Do these results support the theory of natural selection as applied
to peppered moths?

14.10. Artificial selection

Through the ages, man has imitated the process of natural selection. By selective breeding he has produced plant and animal forms
differing considerably from the original stock. Thus the various
types of horse, from the Shetland pony to the great Shire horse, have
their origin in the Arabian Wild Horse. For some 2 000 years man

has selected, for breeding purposes, those horses which show some desirable attribute. The English thoroughbred racehorse, as we know it today, has been developed in the last 300 years by the careful compilation of pedigree and selection of breeding stock. Successful horses, such as those that win the Derby, immediately become highly valued for breeding purposes. Such horses have also been exported on a large scale, and the racehorses of many countries owe their origin to the English thoroughbred.

Charles Darwin was very interested in the results of artificial selection, and even took up pigeon breeding to further his knowledge. In his opinion, the various breeds of pigeon differ so much that if they were wild birds they would be placed in separate species. However, they are all varieties of one species, and have all been developed from the wild rock-pigeon by selective breeding. The rock-pigeon still exists and is a very variable animal, so it is easy to see how different forms could be bred over the long period of domestication (some 3 000 years).

14.11. The importance of isolation

We have seen how natural selection ensures that only the fittest survive to reproduce themselves. Constant change, over many generations, will ensure that the species becomes highly **adapted** to its environment. Thus, a woodpecker is adapted to its way of life by its short and powerful beak, which is strong enough to withstand the rapid pecking of hard wood. The tongue is extremely long, enabling it to reach into the tunnels of ant colonies. The feet are unusual in that two of the four toes are directed backwards, enabling the bird to support itself as it climbs the vertical tree trunk. It is hard to see how such a highly adapted animal can be improved by further evolution, or that it could be ousted by a new species. Within an interbreeding population, natural selection serves to perfect the adaptation of the species.

However, let us suppose that part of the population becomes cut off, or isolated, from the main breeding group. If the isolated group were to find itself in a slightly different environment, the selective factors would be different, and different adaptations would result. Darwin found that, of the twenty-six species of land birds on the Galapagos Islands, twenty-one were peculiar to those islands. Moreover, each of the twelve islands had its own species of finch, adapted to a particular method of feeding (see Figure 14.5). None of these finches occurs on the South American mainland, but must have evolved from ancestors that migrated, or were blown by storms, from there. Once settled on the various islands, the ancestral finches became isolated from each other and evolved independently.

In this example, the isolation was geographical, but this is not always the case. Anything which prevents two members of the population from reproducing will be an isolating factor. Thus two species may inhabit the same area, but be isolated from each other by their behaviour. This is true of the crow and the rook. The carrion-crow is a solitary bird, which nests in trees and on cliff-faces. It mates in April. The rook, on the other hand, nests in communities (rookeries) at the tops of tall trees. Mating occurs in March. It is easy to see how these two closely related species are isolated from each other.

14.12. The causes of extinction

In some cases, animals and plants may have become extinct because of disease or because of a sudden change in climate (for example, the coming of the Ice Age). However, it is probable that the main cause of extinction is **loss of adaptation**. If changes occur in the environment and the animal or plant fails to become adapted to the new conditions, then it will perish. Thus, an animal which is highly adapted to one method of feeding may become extinct if its normal food becomes no longer available.

Another important cause of extinction is **competition**. Since true (placental) mammals were introduced by man into Australia, the pouched mammals (marsupials) have declined seriously, and some have become extinct. This is because the placental mammals are more highly evolved and the marsupials cannot compete successfully with them.

The changes that man has brought about in the environment by farming, hunting, etc., have caused the extinction of many forms of life. Much of this extinction could have been avoided. Only now is concern being expressed over this problem, and action taken.

14.13. The evolution of man

Man has not evolved from apes, as is sometimes stated, but many people believe that man and the modern apes have common ancestors. These ancestral forms are believed to have inhabited the warm forests of Asia and Africa some fifteen million years ago.

The change in environment that brought about the evolution of man seems to have been a descent from the trees, for what reason is not clear. Having left the safety of the trees, it was an advantage to think fast and to run rapidly. Three important changes from the ape-form took place. Firstly, the foot changed from the prehensile (gripping) foot of the ape to the more rigid, walking foot of man. Secondly, the skeleton changed, so that the posture became upright and the eyes became directed forward. The legs became longer than the arms, and the hands became free to hold objects. Thirdly, the brain case (cranium) increased in size, enabling a more complex brain to evolve. Thus, early man compensated for his lack of claws, fangs or other natural weapons by grasping stones, bones, etc., in his hands. Speed of foot, coupled with a cunning brain, enabled him to capture his prey and to escape from his enemies. Probably, from the beginning, man was a social animal, hunting in groups. The development of the power of language meant that the members of the group could communicate with each other. Parents could pass on the benefit of their experience to their offspring, and the ways of the species improved. The ability to make tools and the ability to communicate through language separate the human species from all others.

What of the future? Will man continue to evolve? All that we have said in this chapter implies that evolution will continue. In the case of man, the main evolution will be towards the perfection and improvement of those extra 'limbs', his tools. Before this century, the tools served merely to aid man's limbs, but now, with the development of the computer, man has found a tool to assist his brain also, and the future possibilities of the combination of these two types of tool are unlimited.

Test your understanding

1. Name the various types of fossil and say how each is formed.
2. Explain the two methods by which fossils are dated.
3. In what respect is the Pre-Cambrian Period of the earth's history a mystery to palaeontologists?
4. What is meant by the statement that the Carboniferous Period was the Age of Amphibians?
5. What main conclusions may be drawn from a study of fossils?
6. What particular features of the horse had to develop during its possible evolution from Hyracotherium?
7. What were Charles Darwin's main impressions during the voyage of the *Beagle*?
8. Explain the meaning of the terms homologous structures and vestigial structures. Give examples of each.
9. What is meant by organic evolution?
10. Explain, briefly, the theory of natural selection.
11. How did the population of peppered moths in the Manchester area change between 1848 and 1898? How would you expect the population to change over the next fifty years?
12. Explain how some organisms are adapted to their ways of life (choose examples other than those mentioned in this chapter).
13. Name some animals and plants that have become extinct. Indicate, for each, the probable date and cause of extinction.
14. Find out as much as you can about the fossils of man (for example, Neanderthal Man). Find out how these men may have differed from modern man, in anatomy and way of life.

Chapter 15

How Life Is Handed On

15.1. Sexual reproduction

In previous chapters we have seen that living organisms can only arise from other living organisms. In all but the simplest animals and plants, new organisms arise as a result of sexual reproduction. Sexual reproduction involves two organisms of the same species, the male which contributes the male gametes (sperms in the case of animals and the male nuclei of the pollen grain in the case of plants) and the female which contributes the female gametes (the ova in the case of animals and the egg cells within the ovule in the case of plants).

What is the relationship between parents and their offspring? You have all heard the expression 'like father, like son'; you have probably been rather annoyed when a fond aunt has declared, 'Isn't she like her mother?' A teacher in school may have asked you if you have an older brother in the school. Comments such as these imply that children may share certain characteristics with their parents, and that the children of a family may share certain characteristics with one another. These characteristics may be physical features like hair colour or nose shape, or perhaps the sound of a voice or a behavioural feature.

The process whereby characteristics are transmitted from one generation to another is known as **inheritance**, and the science of the behaviour of inherited characteristics is known as **genetics**.

By what means could the 'instructions' causing a particular characteristic to develop pass from the parents to their offspring? In Chapter 9 we observed the process of fertilization, using the marine worm, *Pomatoceros*. The sperm united with the ovum to produce a single-celled zygote from which the new organism developed. We may suggest that any 'instructions' from parent to offspring are transmitted by the male and female gametes. What part of the gametes contain these instructions? Can you remember the structure and relative sizes of sperms and ova that you observed in the *Pomatoceros* (Investigation 9a)?

If the organism is to gain instructions equally from the male gamete and female gamete, these instructions are most likely to be carried by some common structure. Study Figure 15.1 carefully, noticing that the two gametes are very different in both size and structure. Can you see a similar structure in each?

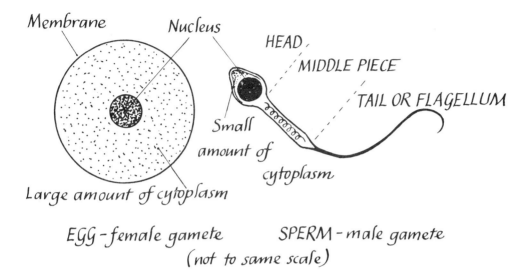

Membrane

Nucleus

HEAD

MIDDLE PIECE

TAIL OR FLAGELLUM

Small amount of cytoplasm

Large amount of cytoplasm

EGG — female gamete   SPERM — male gamete
(not to same scale)

15.2. The structure of the nucleus

Figure 15.1 Diagram to show the parts of the sperm and ovum (egg)

If the nuclei of the male and female gametes carry the instructions which control the development and structure of the offspring, let us examine some nuclei to see how these instructions might be carried.

Investigation 15a. Observing the structure of the nucleus

Onion root tips provide a convenient and suitable material to use to observe the structure of the nucleus. This is most easily observed when the cells are dividing to produce new cells by the process called **mitosis** (see Book I, Chapter 2).

1. Grow some onion root tips by placing a small onion on a test-tube almost full of water, as in Figure 15.2. A good crop of roots should be obtained in five to seven days.
2. Cut the roots about 5 mm behind the tip. Store any root tips not needed for immediate use in ethanoic ethanol (30% ethanoic acid, 70% ethanol).
3. Place a root tip into a watchglass (not a 'solid' one), and add nine drops of 1% ethanoic-orcein stain and one drop of dilute hydrochloric acid.
4. Remove the funnel from a bunsen burner, and light the bunsen to produce a small flame.

Corrosive

Toxic

Flammable

Harmful

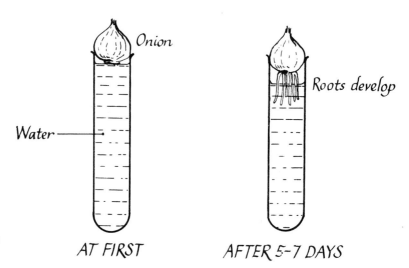

Water ————

Onion

Roots develop

Figure 15.2 Growing onion
root tips

AT FIRST   AFTER 5-7 DAYS

5. Hold the watchglass in forceps and heat over the flame (keep the watchglass moving) until its contents steam. Do not allow them to boil.
6. Add another two drops of dilute hydrochloric acid and repeat the heating.
7. Repeat this procedure two or three times, adding a little dilute hydrochloric acid on each occasion.
8. Cover the watchglass with a second inverted watchglass, and leave for ten minutes.
9. **Place the root tip in a drop of ethanoic-orcein on a microscope slide.**
10. Carefully place a cover-slip over the root tip, and cover with a piece of filter paper.
11. Whilst taking care not to move the cover-slip, press it firmly with the blunt end of a pencil to squash the root tip.
12. The nuclei of the cells are more easily seen if they are spread out. Carefully tap the cover-slip with the tip of a needle or pencil. Great care must still be taken not to move the cover-slip or the cells will become rolled up and their nuclei will not be visible.
13. Study the slide, first with the low-power objective of a microscope. When you have found the small area of dividing cells, carefully revolve the nose-piece of the microscope so that you can use the high-power objective. It should automatically be almost in focus. Remember you should only use the fine adjustment with high power. (This is a temporary preparation which will fade after a few hours. It can be made to last a little longer by ringing the cover-slip with a rubber solution and by placing in a refrigerator.)

14. Search your slide carefully. Compare what you see with Figure 15.3.

Look carefully at the nuclei of the dividing cells. The nuclear membrane has broken down. Can you see the thread-like structures arranged in various ways? These are the **chromosomes.** The nuclei of all organisms contain these thread-like bodies, but they can only be stained, and therefore observed, at the time when the cell is about to divide into two daughter cells. The number of chromosomes in the nucleus is constant for a particular species; for example, the nucleus of an onion cell always contains sixteen chromosomes and the nucleus of a human cell always contains forty-six chromosomes. The number varies from species to species, but is constant for a particular species.

When examined carefully, it can be seen that each chromosome has a partner, a second chromosome in the nucleus which is similar in size and shape to itself. This is called its **homologue.** The chromosomes, then, are arranged in pairs. The onion has eight pairs making the total of sixteen, and man has twenty-three pairs making the total of forty-six.

TABLE 15.1. TABLE SHOWING THE NUMBER OF CHROMOSOMES FOUND IN THE BODY OF CELLS OF COMMON ORGANISMS

Species	Number of Chromosomes	Number of Pairs
Drosophila	8	4
Garden pea	14	7
Onion	16	8
Man	46	23
Horse	66	33

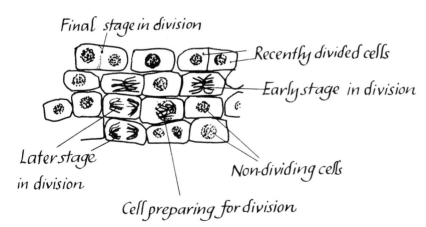

Final stage in division

Recently divided cells

Early stage in division

Later stage in division

Non-dividing cells

Cell preparing for division

Figure 15.3 Dividing cells in the root tip of an onion

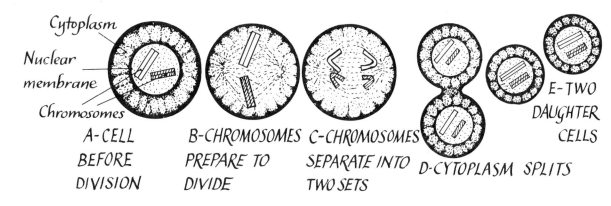

Cytoplasm

Nuclear membrane

Chromosomes

A-CELL BEFORE DIVISION

B-CHROMOSOMES PREPARE TO DIVIDE

C-CHROMOSOMES SEPARATE INTO TWO SETS

D-CYTOPLASM SPLITS

E-TWO DAUGHTER CELLS

Figure 15.4 Diagrams showing the behaviour of the chromosomes during mitosis (normal cell division), as in the onion root tip

Figure 15.5 Diagrams showing the behaviour of the chromosomes during meiosis, or reduction division, as in the formation of sperms

15.3. The function of the chromosomes

What role do the chromosomes play in inheritance? Let us see how they behave during the formation of the sex cells or gametes. Compare Figure 15.4 with Figure 15.5. The chromosomes are visible in both processes, but they behave in different ways.

In the onion root tip normal growth was taking place, and the process of cell division which you observed was normal mitosis. In mitosis, a cell divides to produce two identical daughter cells. During the process, the number of chromosomes is duplicated so that the two daughter cells contain sixteen chromosomes—two sets of eight. This occurs in the formation of normal body or somatic cells, which

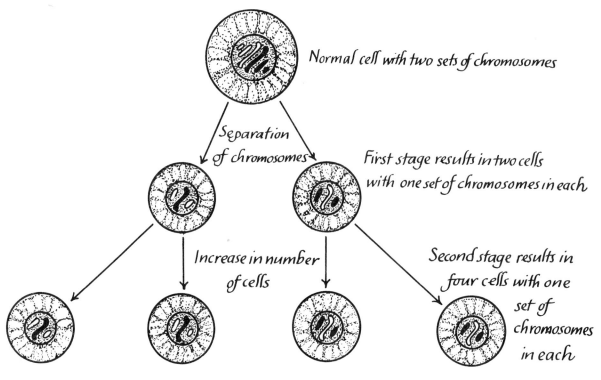

Normal cell with two sets of chromosomes

Separation of chromosomes

First stage results in two cells with one set of chromosomes in each

Increase in number of cells

Second stage results in four cells with one set of chromosomes in each are referred to as **diploid** cells and are given the symbol 2n because their nuclei have two sets of chromosomes.

In the production of sexual gametes, such as the formation of sperms and ova, the process of cell division is called **meiosis,** or reduction division. By this process, the number of chromosomes in the resulting gametes become half that of the parent cell. In other words, each gamete only receives one from each pair of chromosomes and has therefore only one set of chromosomes, not two like the parent cell. These cells with just one set of chromosomes are described as **haploid** and are given the symbol n.

15.4. The chromosomes at fertilization

We have already seen that, at fertilization, a male gamete fuses with a female gamete to produce a zygote. In due course, the zygote develops into a new organism. We have seen that the diploid cells of the sex organs produce haploid gametes. So each gamete is contributing just one set of chromosomes to the zygote (see Figure 15.6).

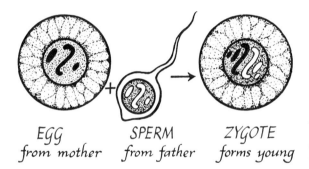

EGG
from mother

SPERM
from father

ZYGOTE
forms young

Figure 15.6 The recombination of chromosomes at fertilization

At the beginning of this chapter, it was observed that children appear to exhibit characteristics of each of their parents. An organism receives a single cell, the gamete, from each of its parents. It has now been shown that each of these gametes contains only one set of chromosomes so that the zygote, and in due course the new organism, has the normal complement of two sets. The new organism therefore receives one set of chromosomes from each of its parents. Of a pair of homologous chromosomes, one has been received from the male parent and its partner from the female parent. It would seem possible that the chromosomes may have something to do with the transmission of inherited characteristics.

15.5. Some breeding investigations

In order to gather clues concerning inheritance, it is necessary to study the results of crosses producing large numbers of offspring over several generations. Human beings are not very good subjects because the average time between generations is about twenty-five years, and normally only one child is born at a time. An entire family usually consists of the parents and just two or three children. Even cats and dogs take a long time to provide enough useful data. We need a small animal which is easy to handle and keep in the laboratory. It must breed rapidly, produce large numbers of young and have clearly marked characteristics.

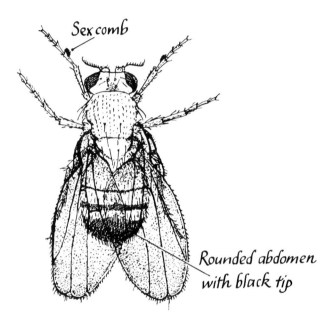

Figure 15.7 A male *Drosophila*

The fruit fly, *Drosophila,* has a life-cycle which takes about two weeks, at 25 °C, and a single female can lay more than a hundred eggs at a time. The sexes can be distinguished quite easily. The male, shown in Figure 15.7, has a rounded abdomen which appears black at its posterior end. The male also has a sex comb, a line of bristles, on the tarsi of the front pair of legs. The female, shown in Figure 15.8, has a more pointed abdomen which appears to be striped with black bands. She has no sex comb.

15.6. *Drosophila* culture

Biological

Toxic

Drosophila can be kept in the laboratory in culture jars (which may be small, wide-necked milk or cream bottles) or in similarly proportioned bottles. Into the bottom of the bottles is poured 30 mm of warm culture medium. The culture medium contains the food for the larvae, set in a jelly made from agar. It is important that a fungicide such as 'Nipagin' should be added to the culture medium to inhibit the growth of moulds and mildews.

212

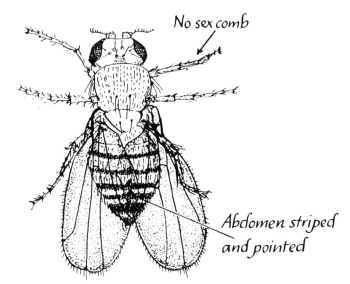

Figure 15.8 A female *Drosophila*

A suitable culture medium can be made by dissolving 5 g of agar powder in 250 cm³ of boiling water in a porringer or similar vessel. Add to this a mixture containing 200 cm³ of maize meal, 100 cm³ of black treacle and a trace of Nipagin or similar mould inhibitor. Heat for five to ten minutes, stirring well.

This will make enough for ten bottles. It should be poured whilst warm (about 50 °C), and allowed to set before the flies are introduced. A piece of crepe paper should be placed down the side of the jar so that the larvae can climb up it when they are ready to pupate. A bung of cotton wool wrapped in muslin allows air to enter for respiration, but keeps out bacteria (see Figure 15.9).

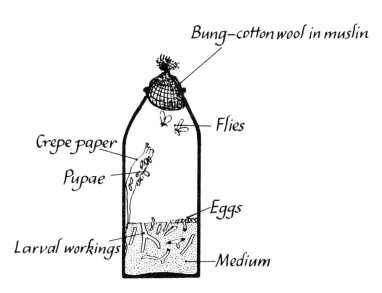

Figure 15.9 A *Drosophila* culture jar

213

The eggs are laid on the surface of the medium. After about twenty-four hours, these hatch into larvae which feed on the medium and burrow into it. The presence of burrows in the medium is evidence that larvae are present and active. About ninety-six hours (four days) after hatching, a larva will crawl up the crepe paper, or the side of the container, and pupate. In another four days, the pupa becomes brown and wrinkled, and the adult hatches. A few drops of yeast suspension should be added to a culture jar for the adults to feed on.

Once a female fly has mated, the sperms she receives are stored in her sperm sacs and may fertilize several generations of eggs. It is important, therefore, that any female flies used for experimental crosses must be virgins. The female flies become fertile and will mate about eight hours after hatching, so it is important that the male and female flies be separated by that time. The virgin females are usually very pale in colour and their wings may be folded. Simple crosses can be carried out in a 75×25 mm specimen tube with about 30 mm of medium in the bottom.

The flies used for laboratory experiments are descendants of the wild species which are found around decaying fruit. The normal fly, which resembles his non-captive cousins, has long wings, red eyes and a grey body. From time to time, flies with different characteristics appear in the normal population. These flies which have changed from the normal 'wild' type are called **mutants**, and it is these that are normally used in experimental crosses to study the behaviour of inherited characteristics. Common mutants are vestigial-winged, ebony-bodied and white-eyed (see Figure 15.10).

15.7. Handling *Drosophila*

Figure 15.10 The wild type and various mutants of *Drosophila*

Drosophila is a very active insect and will not sit still to be sexed, counted, or studied in any other way. It is therefore necessary to

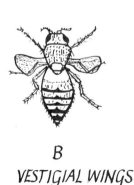

A

WILD TYPE –
RED EYES, LONG WINGS,
GREY BODY

B

VESTIGIAL WINGS

C

WHITE EYE

D

EBONY BODY

214

anaesthetize the flies before examination. An etherizer can quite easily be made from a short-stemmed filter funnel, a specimen tube, a cork and a piece of cotton wool, as in Figure 15.11. The cotton wool is simply tied to the stem of the funnel with cotton.

Figure 15.11 (left) An etherizer

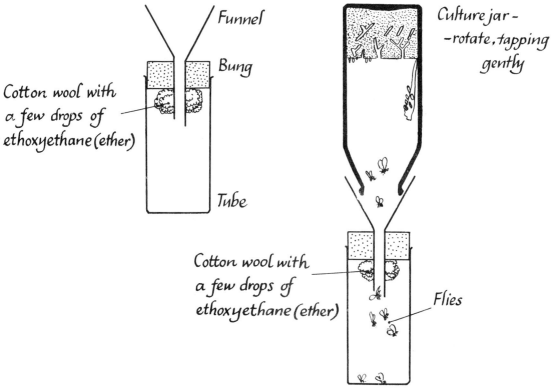

Funnel

Bung

Cotton wool with a few drops of ethoxyethane (ether)

Tube

Culture jar - -rotate, tapping gently

Cotton wool with a few drops of ethoxyethane (ether)

Flies

Figure 15.12 (above) Transferring flies to the etherizer

Investigation 15b. Etherization technique

1. With a pipette, add a *few* drops of ethoxyethane (ether) to the cotton wool.   Take care to return unused ether to the bottle and cork it securely and immediately.
2. Shake the culture bottle to remove any flies from the neck and the bung. Do not be too vigorous or you may dislodge the medium and crush the flies.
3. Remove the bung from the culture bottle, and quickly invert it over the funnel of the etherizer (see Figure 15.12). The flies are quickly anaesthetized and will be killed if left too long. Gently tap the culture bottle to dislodge any hesitant flies. As the flies tend to move upwards, the culture bottle and etherizer together may be gently inverted, so that any remaining flies can make their way up into the etherizer.
4. As soon as all the flies are in the specimen tube and are still, remove the etherizer and replace with a stopper.

★ WARNING.
Ethoxyethane (ether) is highly inflammable and all naked flames should be extinguished before the bottle is opened.

5. Carefully tip the flies to be examined on to a white tile and lay them out in a line across the middle. Examine with a mounted lens or binocular microscope.

6. Go along the line and push flies of one type, such as long-winged, to one side and vestigial-winged to the opposite side. If the flies start to crawl away, they can be re-anaesthetized with an emergency etherizer,ᵃ a piece of cotton wool soaked in ethoxyethane under a dish, as in Figure 15.13.

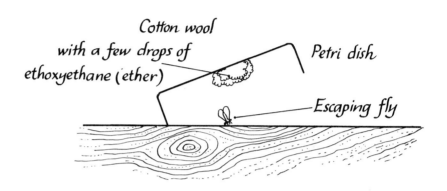

Figure 15.13 An emergency etherizer

When starting your experimental crosses, it is necessary to use flies bred pure for the characteristic to be studied. In other words, if the parental flies with long wings are crossed over several generations with similar long-winged flies and the offspring all have long wings, then such a culture of flies would be a pure-line, long-winged culture.

Investigation 15c. Crossing pure-breeding, long-winged flies with pure-breeding, vestigial-winged flies

1. Place five or six male flies into a tube with the same number of virgin female flies.

2. As soon as larval activity is observed in the medium, remove the parents. Destroy the females by dropping them into either oil or ethanol.

3. On the morning and evening of the ninth and tenth days, segregate the male and female flies into separate tubes, to ensure the conservation of virgin females.

4. On the eleventh day, examine all the flies, count them and record their characteristics on a table, as in Table 15.2. This is called the first filial or F.1 generation. Record the combined results of the class. Do all the flies have long wings or vestigial wings in this generation? If not, what is the proportion of long-winged flies to vestigial-winged flies? Have all the characteristics of the parental

Flammable

Biological

216

generation been inherited by at least some of the first filial generation?

5. Now cross flies from the F.1 generation and breed a second generation. This is called the second filial or F.2 generation. Add your results to the table you have drawn. Did the rest of the class get similar results to your own? Again record the combined results of the entire class. Can you explain the results in both the first filial and second filial generations?

TABLE 15.2. RESULTS FROM INVESTIGATION 15c

	Number of Flies with Long Wings		Number of Flies with Vestigial Wings	
	Own Results	Class Results	Own Results	Class Results
Parental Cross F.1 Generation F.2 Generation				

15.8. Breeding experiments with mice

Similar experiments can be carried out using pure-breeding mice. The mice are best kept in plastic cages with wire tops—the Cambridge pattern.

Investigation 15d. Coat colour inheritance in mice

1. (a) Take a pure-breeding male mouse with a black coat and put it into a cage with a pure-breeding female mouse with a chocolate coat. OR
   (b) Take a pure-breeding female mouse with a black coat and put it into a cage with a pure-breeding male mouse with a chocolate coat. Hold the mouse firmly at the base of the tail with your thumb and first finger. A male mouse may be distinguished from a female mouse by its prominent genital papilla and the distance between the anus and the genital orifice, which may be more than 10 mm. In the female, this distance is usually rather less than 5 mm. Mature females may also be recognized by the presence of nipples.

Biological

2. Keep the mice fed, watered and clean for the next twenty days.
3. The young will be born after about twenty-one days. If the parent mice have been handled from birth, they will not mind you handling their babies.
4. Ten days after the birth of the young, you should be able to

record the coat colour. Record both your own results and the combined results of the class in table form, as in Table 15.3.

TABLE 15.3. RESULTS FROM INVESTIGATION 15d

	Number of Mice with Black Coats		Number of Mice with Brown Coats	
	Own Results	Class Results	Own Results	Class Results
Parents F.1 Generation F.2 Generation				

5. The mice become sexually mature at about six weeks and can be expected to have produced their first litter by about ten weeks. When the young are about seven weeks old, set up crosses between members of the first filial generation. Add these results to your table.

One could just as easily use other characteristics, such as long ears and short ears or dark eyes and pink eyes. Explain the results obtained in both the first filial and second filial generations. Suggest how the characteristics in these two investigations might have been inherited.

15.9. The work of Gregor Mendel

The pioneer investigations on inheritance were carried out a little more than a hundred years ago by Gregor Mendel, a monk who lived and worked in a monastery at Brünn, which is now in Czechoslovakia. He experimented with the ordinary garden pea (*Pisum sativum*), which exhibits a number of clearly defined characteristics.

First of all, Mendel grew a number of different strains of pea plant, taking care to keep them separate from one another and allowing them only to self-pollinate for several generations. To prevent cross-pollination, he covered the flowers with little muslin bags. When his pea plants had bred true for a particular characteristic for several generations, he knew he had a pure line and was ready to begin experimenting.

You could repeat his first experiment. He crossed pure-bred **tall** pea plants, which grew up to about 2 metres, with pure-bred **dwarf** pea plants, which grew up to between 0·2 metre and 0·5 metre high. These were the parental generation. He avoided the possibility of self-pollination by removing the stamens of the flowers and then dusting pollen from the other parent on to the stigma with a brush. When the pods were ripe, he collected the pea seeds, sowed them and carefully examined the plants of the first filial generation which grew from them. All these plants grew to about 2 metres high, so they were all tall plants. What can we deduce from this? What has happened to the characteristic for dwarfness? Did you get results like this in the first filial generation of your own breeding experiments?

The 'instruction' which determines the development of tallness would appear to be stronger than the 'instruction' which determines the development of dwarfness. We call the characteristic which appears in the first filial generation the **dominant** characteristic and the characteristic which is over-ridden, the **recessive** characteristic. Which characteristics were dominant and which ones recessive in your own investigations?

Mendel then allowed these tall plants of the first filial generation to self-pollinate. Again, he harvested the ripe pods and sowed the seeds they contained. These gave rise to a total of 1 064 plants in the second filial generation, of which 787 were tall plants and 277 were dwarf plants. This is approximately in a ratio of three tall plants to every one dwarf plant in the second filial generation.

The crosses can be summarized as below:

PARENTS   TALL   X   DWARF
                                     ↓

F.1 GENERATION   ALL TALL

                          TALL   X   TALL
                                     ↓

F.2 GENERATION   3 TALL TO 1 DWARF

You have, no doubt, noticed that the characteristic of dwarfness has reappeared in the second filial generation after missing a generation. Did this happen in your own investigations? The 'instruction' for the characteristic of dwarfness must have still been present in plants of the first filial generation although it was over-ridden by the dominant instruction for tallness. Why were there three tall plants to every one dwarf plant?

Mendel repeated this experiment using different characteristics:

Yellow Seeds × Green Seeds
Round Seeds × Wrinkled Seeds
Green Pods × Yellow Pods

In every case, he obtained similar results to those obtained with the tall and dwarf plants.

15.10. How are the 'instructions' inherited?

You will remember that in Section 15.4 we discovered that the common contribution of both parents to a zygote was the nucleus of its gametes. We saw that a feature shared by all nuclei was that they contained thread-like bodies which we called chromosomes. The nucleus of each somatic or body cell contained two sets of chromosomes (see Figure 15.14). In other words, each chromosome had a partner which was similar to it in size and shape. Furthermore, we learnt that in the formation of the gametes the number of chromosomes was halved so that they come to contain only one set. Each gamete, therefore, contributes one set of chromosomes to the zygote, which then has a full complement of two sets. Could the chromosomes represent the 'instructions' which cause an organism to develop a particular characteristic?

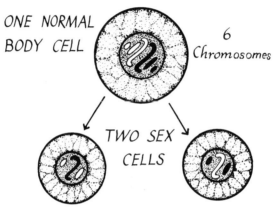

ONE NORMAL BODY CELL — 6 Chromosomes

TWO SEX CELLS

3 Chromosomes

Figure 15.14 The formation of sex cells

The fruit fly has four pairs of chromosomes, but a much greater number of characteristics. The pea plant has seven pairs of chromosomes, but Mendel experimented with more than seven pea characteristics. So the chromosomes do not simply represent the 'instructions'. Mendel called the 'instruction' which determined the development of a particular characteristic a germinal factor. Today it is called a **gene**. What then is the relationship between the chromosomes and the genes? There is a relatively small definite number of chromosomes, but a very large almost indefinite number of genes.

Morgan carried out a large number of breeding experiments with *Drosophila* in the early 1900s, and discovered that some characteristics usually appeared together, such as a certain wing length and a certain body colour. These characteristics were said to be **linked** together. As a result of further work, he observed that the characteristics were linked into four groups. Morgan knew that *Drosophila*

220

had four pairs of chromosomes, so he suggested that a group of linked genes were carried on the same chromosome.

We know now that the development of a particular character is controlled by a particular part of a chromosome, the gene. Each chromosome carries many genes which are believed to be arranged in a row—one after another along the chromosome like oarsmen in a rowing eight. In the same way that an oarsman always occupies the same seat in a boat, each gene would seem to have its own particular place, or **locus**, on the chromosome.

15.11. Why is each chromosome duplicated?

Let us think for a moment about your own investigation and Mendel's first experiment with his tall and dwarf plants. In the first filial generation the characteristic of dwarfness was not shown (it was over-ridden by the dominant character for tallness), but its gene must have been present in those tall plants of the first filial generation because it reappeared in approximately 25% of the offspring in the second filial generation.

Each of a pair of chromosomes bears the genes for the same characteristics in the same position along its length. So a zygote receiving a pair of chromosomes (see Figure 15.15), one from the

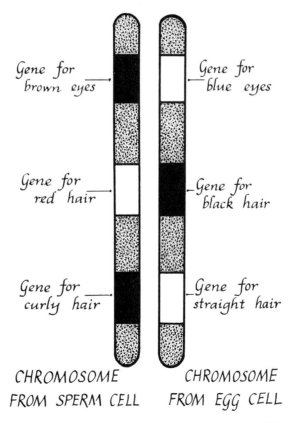

Gene for
brown eyes

Gene for
blue eyes

Gene for
red hair

Gene for
black hair

Gene for
curly hair

Gene for
straight hair

CHROMOSOME
FROM SPERM CELL

CHROMOSOME
FROM EGG CELL

Figure 15.15 A pair of chromosomes

221

male gamete and the other from the female gamete, will receive two genes for the development of a particular characteristic. The characteristic determined by the dominant of the two genes will develop. An individual will only exhibit a characteristic controlled by a recessive gene when similar recessive genes are received from both parents.

When an organism receives similar genes for a characteristic from both of its parents, it is said to be a **homozygote**. If crossed with another organism homozygous for that character, it will breed true and produce a pure line in which all the offspring resemble the original parents. If an organism, as in your F.1 *Drosophila*, receives different genes for a particular characteristic from its parents, then it is called a **heterozygote**, and will resemble the parent contributing the dominant gene.

All the gametes produced by a homozygote will contain similar genes for that particular characteristic, but half the gametes produced by a heterozygote will contain dominant genes and the other half will contain recessive genes. The heterozygous tall plant of the first filial generation is physically indistinguishable from its homozygous parent.

The external appearance of an organism is called its **phenotype**, whilst the genetical make-up is called its **genotype**.

15.12. An explanation of Mendel's results and your own

The parent plants Mendel started with were pure-breeding for height, so they would be homozygotes.

Let us represent the gene for tallness by the symbol T.

Let us represent the gene for dwarfness by the symbol t.

From Table 15.4, we see how each somatic cell produces two gametes. Each gamete has only one set of chromosomes and therefore the gene for only one of a pair of characteristics. The gene which would determine the development of the other characteristic has gone into the other gamete. At fertilization, the original number of chromosomes is restored, but when two different genes for the same character come together in a zygote, as they do in the first filial generation above (Tt), only one can develop, the dominant characteristic. In Mendel's experiment, drawn out in Table 15.4, the dominant gene for tallness over-rides the recessive gene for dwarfness. All the first filial generation are heterozygotes; half of the gametes (pollen grain nuclei and egg cells) that they produce contain the dominant gene T and the other half contain the recessive gene t.

When these meet at fertilization, there is an equal chance for any of the following four combinations to occur in the second filial generation:

a. If a pollen grain T meets an egg cell T, then the zygote will contain TT and will give rise to a homozygous tall plant.

TABLE 15.4. THE RESULTS OF MENDEL'S EXPERIMENTS

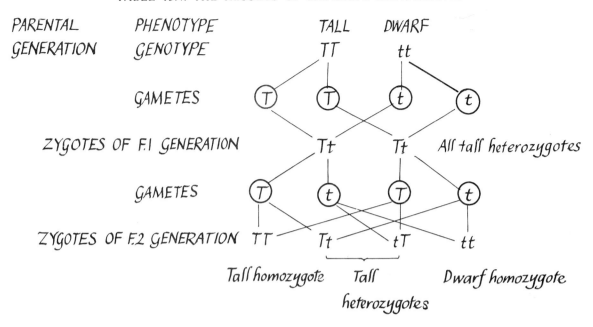

b. If a pollen grain T meets an egg cell t, then the zygote will contain Tt and will give rise to a heterozygous tall plant.

c. If a pollen grain t meets an egg cell T, then the zygote will contain tT and again will give rise to a heterozygous tall plant.

d. If a pollen grain t meets an egg cell t, then the zygote will contain tt and will give rise to a homozygous dwarf plant.

It can be seen that in three cases out of four, tall plants will be produced. The greater the number of offspring in the second filial generation, the more nearly will the results approach the theoretical ratio of three to one. Which of your investigations gave a result nearest 3:1—*Drosophila* or the mice? Why?

If you are not convinced that the laws of probability will produce such a neat result, carry out the following investigation.

Investigation 15e. Chance combinations of beads

Take a bag containing an equal number (at least twenty) of, say, black beads and white beads (or marbles). The more beads in the bag the better. Let the black beads represent the dominant characteristics and the white the recessive characteristics. Put your hand in the bag and, without looking, take out two beads. Make a note of the combination and then put the beads back and shake. Repeat as often as time allows. Record, as shown in Table 15.5, first your results and then the results of the whole class added together.

If no beads or marbles are available, you can carry out this investigation with the toss of a coin. If you and a partner both toss

223

TABLE 15.5. THE RESULTS OF INVESTIGATION 15e

	Own Results	Class Results
Black and Black		
Black and White		
White and Black		
White and White		
Totals		

Ratio— . . . containing black . . . containing no black

pennies simultaneously and record on Table 15.5 the number of times both of the coins came down heads, the number of times one coin is heads and the other is tails and the number of times both come down tails, the ratios can then be worked out in exactly the same way.

This section explains Mendel's results, but we must not forget that Mendel did not know, as you do, that the nucleus contained genes and chromosomes. He showed that characteristics remain distinct from generation to generation, but that they may be masked by a more dominant characteristic and so appear to miss a generation. From this he deduced his First Law of Inheritance which states that *of a pair of contrasted characters, only one can be represented in a single gamete*. In other words, of T and t in the parent plant, a single gamete can only carry T or t.

15.13. The back cross or test cross

If we have a tall pea plant, a long-winged *Drosophila* or a mouse with a black coat, how do we know whether it is a homozygote (TT, + + or BB) or a heterozygote (Tt, +vg or Bb)? We have to carry out a back cross or test cross. Cross the phenotype under test, such as the tall pea plant, with a double recessive. (*Note.* + represents the gene for long wings and vg the gene for vestigial wings in *Drosophila*; B represents the gene for black coat and b the gene for chocolate coat in mice.)

Investigation 15f. A back cross

Biological

1. Make up a breeding tube of *Drosophila*, containing long-winged flies of unknown genotype and vestigial-winged flies (vg vg).
2. Count the offspring after eleven or twelve days and record their characteristics.

The unknown genotype is either (+ +) or (+vg). What is the unknown genotype if all of the offspring have long wings? What is the unknown genotype if 50% of the offspring have long wings and 50% have vestigial wings?

This experiment can be repeated using either pea plants or mice. In the case of the mice, it will take about a month to obtain a result, and it will take rather longer with the pea plants.

With peas, if we have a tall pea of unknown genotype, we know that one of the height-determining genes is the one of tallness T. It is the other that we are attempting to discover, so, employing the symbols used previously, we can represent the unknown zygote as Tx. When it is crossed with the recessive tt, the result will be at least 50% tall (see Table 15.6). If the other 50% are also tall, what is x? What is x if the second 50% are dwarf?

TABLE 15.6

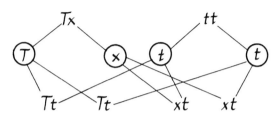

15.14. The dihybrid cross: two-character inheritance

The crosses so far considered have only involved the inheritance of a single pair of characters. These are called **monohybrid** crosses. Mendel went on to investigate the inheritance of two pairs of characteristics. For example, he crossed peas with round yellow seeds with peas with green and wrinkled seeds.

The first filial generation had 100% round yellow seeds. What does this tell us about the characteristics of roundness and yellowness? When the flowers of the first filial generation were allowed to self-pollinate, four types of seed coat were produced: out of a total of 556 plants, 315 had round yellow seeds, 108 had round green seeds, 101 had wrinkled yellow seeds, and 32 had wrinkled green seeds. This is approximately a ratio of 9:3:3:1.

From these results, Mendel proposed his Second Law of Inheritance, the Law of Independent Assortment of Characters, which stated that '*each of a pair of contrasted characters can be combined with each of another pair*'.

This idea is most important because it is one of the causes of variation. The characters can be rearranged to produce new types. Mendel started off with two types of pea: round yellow and wrinkled green. In the second filial generation he had four types: round yellow, round green, wrinkled green and wrinkled yellow. Roundness had recombined with greenness and yellowness with wrinkledness. These new combinations help to explain how a child may have his mother's eye colour and his father's hair colour.

15.15. The inheritance of sex

In humans and most other animals, there is a special pair of chromosomes called the **sex chromosomes**. The pair of sex chromosomes is the major factor determining the sex of an organism, although hormones and sometimes environment play a part. Associated with these sex chromosomes are the genes concerned with the inheritance of the secondary sexual characteristics. There are two types of sex chromosome: the X chromosome which bears a number of genes and a Y chromosome which is small and hardly carries any genes. In humans, in *Drosophila* and in most organisms, if a zygote receives an X chromosome from each of its parents it will develop into a female, but if the zygote receives an X chromosome from one parent and a Y chromosome from the other, then it becomes a male. Half of the male's gametes contain an X chromosome and half contain a Y chromosome, but all the gametes produced by the female contain an X chromosome. The X chromosome of a male will always have been received from its mother.

TABLE 15.7

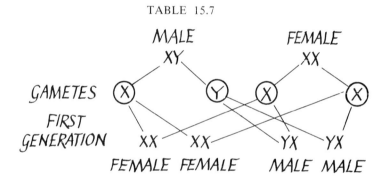

This mechanism ensures a fifty–fifty ratio between males and females, which is quite a satisfactory arrangement.

15.16. Incomplete dominance

Sometimes the idea established by Mendel that a characteristic is inherited completely, or not at all, seems to be disobeyed. This occurs both in the inheritance of petal colour in antirrhinums and coat colour in certain cattle.

As can be seen from Figure 15.16, when a red-flowered antirrhinum is pollinated by a white-flowered antirrhinum, the first filial generation consists entirely of pink antirrhinums. If these pink antirrhinums are allowed to self-pollinate, they give rise to 25% reds, 50% pinks and 25% whites in the second filial generation. This is explained by the fact that the red antirrhinums contain two similar genes RR, both of which cause the production of red pigment in the petals. The

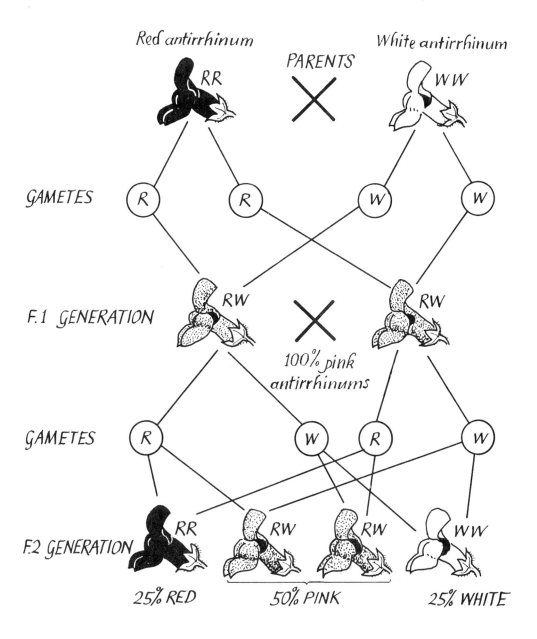

Red antirrhinum   PARENTS   White antirrhinum

RR ✕ WW

GAMETES   R   R   W   W

F.1 GENERATION   RW   ✕   RW

100% pink
antirrhinums

GAMETES   R   W   R   W

F.2 GENERATION   RR   RW   RW   WW

25% RED   50% PINK   25% WHITE

two genes contained in the white flower, WW, are for the absence of pigment formation. The pink flowers in the first filial generation are heterozygotes and contain one gene R for the formation of pigment and one gene W for the formation of no pigment. The result is that, in the heterozygote, the one dose of pigment produced by R has to go as far as two doses produced by RR in the red flower. The result is that the heterozygote flower is pink.

The roan cattle arise in a similar way. The roan is the heterozygote Rr with only one dose of pigment in the fur; this gives it the characteristic roan appearance.

Figure 15.16 An example of incomplete dominance

15.17. Mutations

Occasionally, new characteristics arise spontaneously in a population. Sometimes people are born with 'webbed' fingers or toes, or more than five fingers or toes. In most cases, such an unusual characteristic can be traced through a person's family history, even though it may have missed several generations. Eventually, however, a point is reached when it arose for the first time. These spontaneous changes in the genetical make-up of an organism are called **mutations**.

In Investigation 15c we made use of a mutant form of *Drosophila*, namely the vestigial wing. Over 600 different mutants of *Drosophila* have been recorded.

Originally, many of our garden flowers and domesticated animals and plants arose as a result of mutation. Most mutations, however, are harmful to the organism with the result that the organism containing a mutation often does not develop. Although mutation occurs in all types of organism, it is a relatively rare occurrence. It is estimated that a particular mutation may occur as little as once in a million births.

15.18. Chromosome mutations

There are two types of mutation. The first type are changes which take place in the structure, number or arrangement of the chromosomes and are called chromosome mutations. The second type are gene mutations (see below).

Chromosomes may be broken or extra chromosomes may occur. Sometimes the number of chromosomes may become doubled and produce a larger, more vigorous organism. This occurred in the development of many of our garden flowers and food plants, such as cultivated wheat and strawberries.

Occasionally, humans are born with cells containing an extra chromosome, having forty-seven chromosomes instead of forty-six. Such unfortunate people have very limited mental capabilities and can only perform simple tasks. They are called mongols and rarely reach a great age. They cannot normally reproduce. Can you suggest why?

15.19. Gene mutations

Most mutations do not upset the number, size or arrangement of the chromosomes, but affect individual genes on the chromosomes and are called gene mutations.

Mutations occur at random within a population, so it is impossible to predict when mutation will occur. Every gene has its own rate of mutation. This rate can be artificially accelerated, as we shall learn in the next section.

Exactly how mutants are produced is not yet fully understood, but it is almost certainly due to changes in the chemical nature of the gene molecules. It is not surprising that most observable mutations are harmful if not lethal, because any change is more likely to upset the delicate physiological balance of an organism rather than improve it. Dominant mutations, therefore, tend to be eliminated. There is an unseen pool of recessive mutations which may be manifest in later generations if two similar recessive mutant genes happen to recombine and thus produce an undesirable characteristic.

15.20. The effect of radiation on mutations

As mentioned previously, the actual cause of mutation is not fully understood, but it is known that radiation, such as X-rays and gamma rays, greatly increase the mutation rate. For this reason great care is taken not to expose people to excessive doses of radiation. Radiographers wear lead-lined aprons to protect themselves; persons handling radioactive materials in research and atomic power stations wear badges containing film which records the amount of radiation they are exposed to.

Test your understanding

1. Explain the difference between a homozygote and a heterozygote.
2. Explain, with an example, when you would use a back cross.
3. What are the advantages of sexual reproduction?
4. What is the difference between (a) diploid cells and haploid cells, (b) dominant and recessive characters and (c) phenotypes and genotypes?
5. What is a gene?
6. What is a mutation?
7. In human eye colour, brown is dominant to blue. If a man with brown eyes married a woman with blue eyes, what colour eyes would the children have if (a) the man was homozygous for brown eyes and (b) he was heterozygous for brown eyes?
8. What would the eye-colour pattern of the grandchildren be if children of the homozygous father married a partner with similar eye-colour genes?
9. Could two brown-eyed parents produce a child with blue eyes? Explain.
10. In a laboratory were two cages of black rabbits. The rabbits in one cage were homozygotes and those in the other cage were heterozygotes resulting from a cross between a pure-bred black rabbit and a pure-bred white rabbit. Unfortunately, the technician left the cages open and the rabbits got mixed up. Describe what experiments you would perform to sort them out again. (You may use other rabbits.)

TOPIC C: HEALTH AND HYGIENE

Chapter 16

Micro-organisms and Disease

The term micro-organism, or microbe, is used to cover all living things which are not visible to the naked eye. Apart from their small size, these organisms have little in common, for they include both plants and animals of many different types. The study of micro-organisms is called **microbiology**, a study which began with the observations of the early microscopists, **Robert Hooke** (1635–1703) and **Anton von Leeuwenhoek** (1632–1723). Serious study of the structure and mode of life of microbes did not begin until the middle of the last century, with the work of **Louis Pasteur** (1822–95) and **Robert Koch** (1843–1910).

Many micro-organisms have proved to be useful to man. Examples are the yeasts used in wine-making and baking, and bacteria used to turn milk into cheese. In this chapter, however, we shall be mainly concerned with microbes which are man's enemies—ones which contaminate his food and cause disease.

16.1. Bacteria

Bacteria are unicellular organisms of very small size, ranging from 0·2 micrometre (μm) to 2 μm in width and 2 μm to 10 μm in length. Therefore, if bacterial cells were placed end to end, a row of from 100 to 500 would measure only 1 mm. Bacteria are the smallest living organisms that can exist in the free state (viruses are smaller, but they can only exist within the cells of other organisms). Even with the high-power lens of our school microscopes, it is not possible to see bacteria, except as vague dots and dashes. How, then, can we detect their presence? The answer lies in the rapid reproductive power of bacteria. Bacterial cells may divide as often as every twenty minutes, so that, beginning with one cell, we have 8 after one hour, 64 after two hours, over 32 000 after five hours and over 2 000 000 after seven hours. The resulting bacteria form a **colony**, which is visible to the naked eye. Since the reproduction of the bacterial cell is asexual, all the organisms forming the colony will be identical in the characters they inherit.

The first person to observe the multiplication of bacteria, and to grow them in cultures, was the German, **Robert Koch**, the first true bacteriologist. The methods he devised are still used today, and, in our first investigation, we shall use one of them.

Most bacteria, unlike green plants, are unable to synthesize organic substances from simple inorganic materials. Instead, they must obtain organic and inorganic substances from the medium on which they grow. In other words, they are **saprophytic**. For their growth, bacteria also require moisture and a suitable temperature (around body temperature—37 °C). Some require oxygen (aerobic bacteria), whilst others can exist in its absence (anaerobic bacteria).

In the laboratory, bacteria are fed on a **nutrient broth**, which may be made using one of various recipes, or may be purchased ready-made, in powder or tablet form. The broth is made into a jelly by mixing it with **agar**, an extract of seaweed. The nutrient agar is sterilized by heating and is then poured into sterilized tubes, bottles or petri dishes. After the agar has been incubated at 37 °C, the growth of bacteria is indicated by the appearance of round patches on the surface of the jelly.

Investigation 16a. Culturing bacteria on nutrient agar

For this investigation you will be provided with a petri dish containing nutrient agar (preferably made from a blood-agar base). The jelly and dish have already been sterilized. Proceed as follows:

1. Without removing the lid, turn the petri dish over and, with a wax pencil, mark lines dividing the base into quarters. Letter the quarters A, B, C and D.
2. Turn the dish back again and carefully remove the lid. Now press the fingertips of one hand gently on to the surface of the jelly in quarter A. Replace the lid quickly.
3. Remove a strip of Sellotape (approximately 100 mm) and turn back about 20 mm at the end so that you have something to hold. Place the sticky surface of the tape in contact with any surface in the room (desk, table, floor, wall, window-sill, etc.). Open the lid of the petri dish and place the sticky part of the tape in contact with the jelly in quarter B (see Figure 16.1). Remove the tape and replace the lid.
4. Repeat this procedure, using another strip of tape applied to another surface and then to quarter C.
5. Leave quarter D untouched.
6. Invert the petri dish and incubate at 37 °C for two days, and then look to see where the colonies of bacteria have grown.

Biological

When you have finished examining the culture, place the whole dish in a container of disinfectant, and then wash your hands well. Why do you think that this is advisable?

Have any bacterial colonies grown in quarter D? How do you

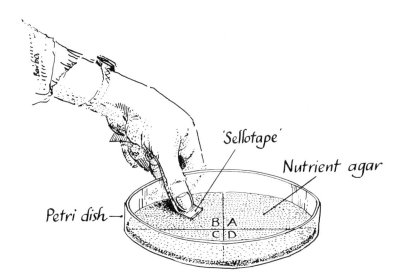

Figure 16.1 Preparing a bacterial culture

account for this? What does the distribution of colonies in the other three quarters show? What does this investigation suggest about the occurrence of bacteria? Is there any indication that bacteria of more than one species have grown in your dish?

16.2. Types of bacteria

Investigation 16a has suggested that bacteria are very common organisms, for they seem to occur on many surfaces around us, and even on our bodies. Bacteria have, indeed, been found to occur in almost all parts of the earth, from the polar regions to the tropics.

All bacteria are single cells, or aggregations of single cells. For convenience, they may be divided into three groups according to their shape:

a. Spherical bacteria, or **cocci** (singular, coccus).

b. Cylindrical, rod-like bacteria, or **bacilli** (singular, bacillus).

c. Spiral bacteria, or **spirilla** (singular, spirillum).

There are many variations within these basic forms (see Figure 16.2).

The wall surrounding the bacterial cell differs from that surrounding plant cells in that it does not consist of cellulose. Many bacteria secrete a slimy layer on to the outside of this wall, which has the effect of making the organism more resistant. Certain bacteria are able to form resistant **spores** which can withstand boiling water and prolonged periods of drought. Such spores may survive for many years under adverse conditions, ready to 'germinate' when conditions improve.

16.3. How bacteria may be killed

a. Pasteurization

The great French biologist, **Louis Pasteur**, was the first to tackle the problem of how bacteria may be killed. About the middle of the last century, the French wine industry was suffering great financial loss because wine was turning sour in the vats, especially during warm weather. The wine turned to vinegar and had to be thrown away. The worried wine growers appealed to Pasteur for help. Pasteur placed some of the sour wine under his microscope and was able to detect the presence of bacteria which were absent from sound wine. After some fruitless attempts, he found that if he heated the wine to a temperature of 50–60 °C for a few moments the bacteria were destroyed. When the wine was cooled again, it was found to keep almost indefinitely. This simple discovery saved the fortunes of the wine growers, and the name **pasteurization** was given to the heating and cooling process.

Investigation 16b. The effect of pasteurization on milk

1. Sterilize two boiling tubes and, into each, pour 30 cm³ of raw, skim milk. Plug the tubes with cotton wool and mark them P (for pasteurized) and C (for control), respectively.
2. Place tube P in a water-bath and heat the milk to 62–63 °C for thirty minutes. Do not heat tube C.
3. Place both tubes in a rack in a warm part of the laboratory.

Biological

Figure 16.2 Some forms of bacteria

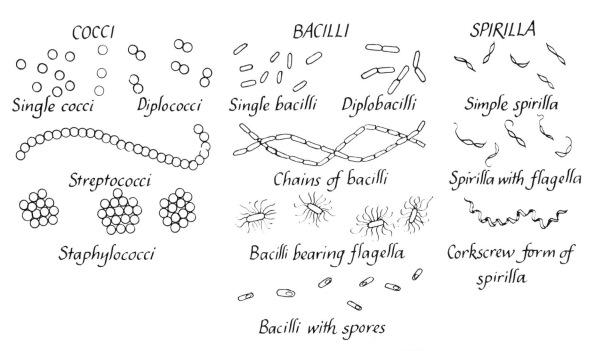

COCCI

Single cocci   Diplococci

Streptococci

Staphylococci

BACILLI

Single bacilli   Diplobacilli

Chains of bacilli

Bacilli bearing flagella

Bacilli with spores

SPIRILLA

Simple spirilla

Spirilla with flagella

Corkscrew form of spirilla

4. After two days, boil the milk in each tube. If the milk has soured, it will clot on boiling.

Is there any difference in the freshness of the milk in the two tubes? How do you account for this difference?

Commercially, milk is pasteurized by one of two methods:
a. By heating to 62 °C for thirty minutes, or
b. By heating to 71 °C for fifteen seconds.

If milk or wine is heated to higher temperatures than those mentioned, the flavour and other qualities are affected. Bacteria which do not form spores are seldom able to survive long at temperatures above 55 °C, for their enzyme systems are destroyed. Spore-forming bacteria are much more resistant and require subjection to steam pressure at 120 °C for forty minutes before they are destroyed.

It might be thought that cooling would also kill bacteria, but this is not so, although it does slow down their growth and reproductive rates. Thus, foods remain fresh for several days if kept in a refrigerator at 0–10 °C. That bacteria are able to resist cooling is illustrated by the fact that the typhoid bacillus was found to survive immersion for six months in liquid air (-180 °C).

b. Disinfectants and antiseptics

The pioneer work in the control of bacteria by chemicals was done by the Edinburgh surgeon, **Joseph Lister** (1827–1912). At the time when Lister was practising medicine, surgery was a 'hit and miss' affair, for operations frequently caused the patient's death because the wound became septic. One practice in an attempt to combat the sepsis was to cover the wound with tar. Lister wondered if it was the phenol (carbolic acid) in the tar that was killing the bacteria. He tried soaking the wound dressings in a solution of phenol, and also sprayed the air around the wound with this chemical. Although this must have been most unpleasant for the doctors and nurses, it did have the effect of considerably reducing the number of deaths through septic wounds.

Substances such as phenol, which kill or inhibit the growth of germs, are called **antiseptics**. A more general word, **disinfectant**, is used for those chemicals used to kill bacteria other than those which cause sepsis. Phenol is still widely used as a germ-killer. Many other disinfectants, such as Lysol, Jeyes' Fluid, etc., contain some 50% of phenol. The cheapest and best disinfectant for home use is soap and hot water.

It is very important to use the disinfectant at the correct concentration, for at some dilutions bacteria are not killed, and may even feed on the disinfectant!

236

Investigation 16c. The effect of dilution on disinfectant action

1. Set up seven test-tubes in a rack, and number them from 1 to 7 with a wax pencil.
2. Into tube 1, pour 20 cm³ of 0·4% phenol.
3. Into each of tubes 2 to 7 pour 10 cm³ of distilled water.
4. Pour 10 cm³ of the phenol from tube 1 into tube 2, and mix the acid and distilled water thoroughly.
5. Now pour 10 cm³ of this mixture into tube 3 and again mix well.
6. Repeat this procedure as far as tube 6, so that a series of dilutions of disinfectant are made, each tube being half the strength of the tube before it. It will be necessary to tip away half of the fluid in tube 6. Each tube now contains 10 cm³ of liquid. Smell each tube to see if you can detect the phenol.

Biological

7. Add a little rich garden soil to some water in a beaker. Allow to settle for a few minutes, and then add 10 cm³ of the soil water to each of the seven tubes. The soil water is used here as a source of bacteria.
8. Plug each tube with cotton wool, and leave for about a week. Tubes in which the bacteria have been killed will remain clear and continue to smell of phenol. Tubes in which the bacteria have not been killed, but have broken down the phenol, will become cloudy and lose their smell.

The tubes are illustrated in Figure 16.3.

At what dilution does phenol seem to lose its disinfectant power? Can you suggest any reasons for variation in the results gained by the class?

Figure 16.3 The contents of the tubes used in Investigation 16c

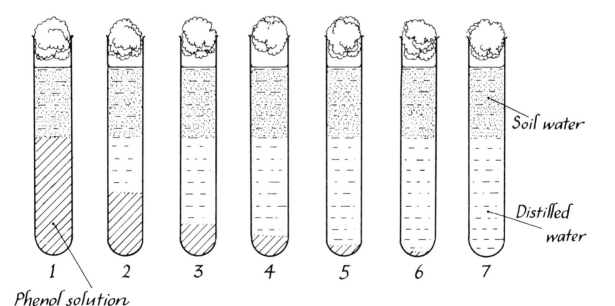

Soil water

Distilled water

1   2   3   4   5   6   7

Phenol solution

16.4. Bacteria and disease

Pasteur's discovery that wine became 'sick' because of the presence of bacteria led him to suggest that other diseases might be due to bacterial invasion. Support for this theory came from Pasteur's own discovery that bacteria were the cause of a disease of silkworms. In 1845 this disease threatened to ruin the French silkworm industry. Pasteur solved the problem by devising methods whereby infected moths were detected, and only healthy forms were used for breeding the valuable caterpillars.

A great advance in the understanding of disease came some thirty years later through the work of Robert Koch on anthrax. This is a disease mainly of cattle, though it can cause the death of humans. The carcases of dead animals have greatly enlarged spleens, filled with a black fluid. The disease caused much loss of cattle in France, Russia and other parts of Europe around 1870. In the bodies of victims, Koch discovered chains of rod-shaped bacteria (bacilli). Were these the cause of the disease? Koch realized that this assumption could only be made if he was able to do three things:

a. To find the same bacillus in every victim of the disease examined (this was found to be so);

b. To cultivate the bacillus outside the body of an animal (Koch found it was possible to grow the bacteria in the clear fluid from inside the eye of an ox); and

c. To give the disease to a healthy animal by introducing the cultured bacillus into its body (Koch inoculated a variety of animals, including rabbits, guinea pigs and mice, and found that they all died of anthrax within two days).

Thus Robert Koch proved that an important disease is caused by a micro-organism, the anthrax bacillus. His principles and methods have enabled the bacteria which cause many diseases to be isolated. Some of these diseases are listed in Table 16.1.

TABLE 16.1. SOME DISEASES CAUSED BY BACTERIA

Bacilli	Streptococci	Spirilla
Anthrax	Bacterial pneumonia	Cholera
Bubonic plague (Black Death)	Scarlet fever	Meningitis
Diphtheria	Tonsillitis	
Leprosy		
Salmonella food poisoning		
Tetanus		
Tuberculosis		
Typhoid		
Whooping cough		

It should not be thought that bacterial diseases are confined to animals. In the last hundred years, well over one hundred plant diseases have been found to be caused by bacteria.

16.5. Viruses

Not all diseases were found to be caused by bacteria. This was clearly shown by work on a disease which causes the wrinkling of leaves of the tobacco plant. In 1872 it was shown that, if the juice of an infected plant was extracted and strained through a fine porcelain filter, the filtrate could still be used to infect a healthy plant. No bacterium was known to be small enough to pass through such a filter. The name **virus** was given to the non-filterable particle, but not until 1935 was the tobacco virus actually isolated, when it was found to have a silvery, crystalline appearance. Today, the electron microscope enables us to magnify the virus particles tens of thousands of times, and their secrets are gradually being revealed.

TABLE 16.2. SOME DISEASES CAUSED BY VIRUSES

(The figures in brackets are the sizes of the particles in nanometres, where 1 nm = 1/1 000 000 mm.)

Foot and mouth (15)	Rabies (125–175)
Poliomyelitis (28)	Mumps (140)
Yellow fever (40)	Smallpox (240)
Influenza (85)	Chicken pox (240)
Parrot fever (250–450)	

Viruses are only able to grow and reproduce within the cells of another organism; in other words, they are **intracellular parasites.** Some viruses (bacteriophages) parasitize the cells of bacteria, and their reproduction has been closely studied (see Figure 16.4). It

Figure 16.4 Reproduction of a virus (a bacteriophage)

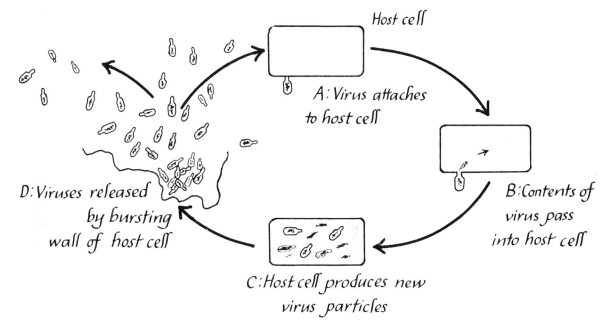

Host cell

A: Virus attaches to host cell

B: Contents of virus pass into host cell

C: Host cell produces new virus particles

D: Viruses released by bursting wall of host cell

appears that once the virus has entered the 'host' cell it is able to 'take over' the cell's metabolism and harness it to the manufacture of more virus particles. Thus the host cell loses its own identity and, in a sense, becomes part of the virus.

16.6. How bacteria and viruses enter the body

Micro-organisms enter the body by three main routes: through the skin, through the alimentary canal and through the respiratory tract.

a. Infection through the skin

Provided that the individual is healthy and well nourished, the skin forms an almost impenetrable barrier to the entry of bacteria and viruses. Germs can enter, however, through the sweat pores, through hair follicles and through cuts and abrasions. Skin resistance is reduced by the accumulation of dirt, the excessive use of cosmetics and the artificial removal of hair. The commonest skin infection, the boil, is caused by the entry of staphylococci into hair follicles.

b. Infection through the alimentary canal

The alimentary canal houses many millions of harmless bacteria, especially in regions such as the large intestine (colon). In a sense, these bacteria are not *in* the body, for they are separated from the body tissues by the wall of the gut itself. Harmful bacteria may be ingested in contaminated food (for example, salmonella food poisoning) or water (for example, typhoid). If such bacteria penetrate the wall of the gut, infection will result.

c. Infection through the respiratory tract

Many diseases, such as the common cold, influenza, diphtheria, scarlet fever and pneumonia, result from infection through the throat, trachea or lungs. The germs are carried in dust or in droplets in the air ('coughs and sneezes spread diseases'). Tiny droplets may remain suspended in the air and travel a considerable distance.

An **infectious disease** is one which is able to be transferred from one person to another. Such diseases may spread by direct human contact (**contagious diseases**) or indirectly (by airborne infection or by contaminated food and water). Bacteria and viruses causing **noncontagious diseases** do not occur in man alone, but may be spread to him by contact with lower animals. Parrots harbour the virus of psittacosis (parrot fever); rats harbour the typhus and plague bacilli; cows harbour tuberculosis bacilli; and dogs harbour the virus of rabies.

16.7. The body's reaction

When we consider the large number of harmful organisms that are around us, we might well wonder why we are not permanently in our sick beds! That we are not is due to the body's natural defence system against infection. To understand how these defences work, we must first consider the nature of disease itself.

The symptoms of a disease (fever, sore throat, headache, spots, etc.) are due to:

a. the rapid multiplication of bacteria or viruses, and the subsequent invasion of body tissues, and

b. the release of poisons, or **toxins**.

Let us consider an example. If a spore of the anthrax bacillus gains entry to the human skin through a cut, it multiplies rapidly beneath the skin, causing the death of the surrounding tissue. Toxins are liberated into the blood and are carried to all parts of the body, lowering the resistance of the patient. Soon, the multiplying bacteria themselves enter the blood stream and set up colonies in other tissues and organs. Unless this process is arrested, death will result.

The body's natural defence against such attack is two-fold:

a. **White blood cells**, or leucocytes, are able to ingest bacteria, rather as an amoeba ingests its prey.

b. **Antibodies** are produced by the body. The cells of the body and, particularly, some of the white cells (lymphocytes) are able to release chemicals or **antitoxins** which neutralize bacterial poisons and may cause the death of the bacteria themselves.

In many cases this defensive mechanism is so efficient in dealing with infection that we are not conscious that an invasion of bacteria or viruses has occurred (we show no symptoms of disease). At other times the 'germs' are more numerous or stronger, and the battle between them and the body's defence cells results in inflammation, or reddening of the infected area. There are losses on both sides and yellow **pus** may accumulate. This contains the dead bacteria, white cells and tissue cells. Whether the body will win the battle against the infective organism will depend on:

a. the virulence, or strength, of the micro-organism,

b. the extent of the dose of infection,

c. the general health of the patient and

d. the treatment given.

In the next section we will see how the body's defences may be reinforced.

16.8. Prevention of disease: immunity

If the body is capable of resisting the attack of a particular germ, it is said to possess **immunity** to this germ. The defence mechanism that has been described gives the body a certain **natural immunity** to various diseases. Thus man has a natural immunity to distemper which attacks his dogs, and foot and mouth disease which attacks his cattle. We also know that immunity may be **acquired** as a result of recovery from an attack of the disease. Thus, second attacks of mumps, measles, chicken pox, scarlet fever and diphtheria are rare. Diseases such as the common cold and influenza, however, are caught over and over again.

16.9. Vaccination

A Gloucestershire doctor, **Edward Jenner** (1749–1823), wondered if it would be possible to give the body immunity to a disease to which it was not naturally immune. The particular concern at that time was the dreaded disease **smallpox**, which killed many people and disfigured many others.

It was generally believed, in the West Country, that a person who had suffered from cowpox could not catch smallpox. Cowpox is a mild disease caught through contact with cows, which causes skin sores resembling those of smallpox. In 1796, Jenner performed an experiment to try to save a boy, James Phipps, whose family were dying of smallpox. He transferred some of the pus from cowpox sores on the hands of a dairymaid, Sarah Nelmes, into scratches that he had made on the arm of James Phipps. As expected, the boy soon suffered a mild attack of cowpox. Jenner waited to see if the boy contracted smallpox from contact with the family. When he did not, Doctor Jenner wondered if it was the mild attack of cowpox which had given him immunity from the more dangerous disease. The only way to check this was to actually put smallpox germs into James Phipps' body. After a great deal of heart-searching, Jenner did this, and to his great relief found that the boy remained healthy.

The name **vaccination** (from *vacca*, cow) was given to the method whereby contact with one germ is used to give immunity to another. For many years, people looked on vaccination with great suspicion, but eventually Edward Jenner was able to convince them of its great value.

Of course, few diseases have related, milder diseases which may be used for vaccination. Louis Pasteur was the first to show that vaccination could be performed using a weakened dose of the germs of the same disease. Using this method, he was able to give cattle immunity against anthrax, and fowl immunity against chicken cholera.

Today, vaccines are used to protect us against many diseases, such as typhoid, poliomyelitis, diphtheria, tetanus and whooping cough. The immunity that these confer is said to be **active**, for it is the body itself that has been stimulated to produce antibodies in response to the weak germs of the vaccine. These antibodies remain in the blood, ready to deal with any subsequent attack of the disease before it can gain a foothold. Sometimes, vaccines containing only bacterial toxins, and not the actual germs, are used. These toxins are obtained from laboratory cultures of the bacteria, the extracted toxin being weakened by mixing it with a chemical such as formaldehyde. The enormous reduction in the number of deaths from diphtheria has been largely due to vaccination using a weakened toxin.

Let us suppose that a patient is found to be suffering from disease. Will vaccination be of any use? It will not, for it is then too late to 'put back the clock' and get the body to produce its own antibodies. The solution here is to give the patient an inoculation of antitoxin. It has been found that, when diphtheria toxin is injected into a horse, the horse's blood develops abundant antitoxin, and the animal does not suffer from the disease. The antitoxin can be extracted from the blood and the resulting **serum** used for injecting a patient that has diphtheria. Immunity acquired in this way is said to be **passive**.

In many cases, acquired immunity weakens with time, and vaccination has to be repeated. Another problem is that new strains of bacteria and viruses are constantly evolving, so that the body may not be immune to the new type. Thus, since the isolation of the influenza virus in 1932, several new strains have appeared and caused epidemics (widespread infection). The 'Asian' 'flu epidemic of 1957 is an example.

16.10. Antibiotics: the discovery of penicillin

In Section 16.6 it was mentioned that boils are caused by bacteria of the staphylococcus type. In 1928, Professor **Alexander Fleming** (1881–1955) was carrying out research on this germ in London. He had prepared cultures of the bacterium, using petri dishes of nutrient agar similar to those used in Investigation 16a. There were many such cultures in the laboratory, and whilst Fleming was away on a few days' holiday one of the dishes became contaminated when its lid slipped off. A less observant worker might have thrown the culture away, but Fleming noticed a curious fact. Colonies of a blue-green mould were growing among the bacterial colonies on the jelly. Around each mould patch there was a clear area, devoid of bacteria. Fleming reasoned that the mould, which he identified as a species of *Penicillium*, must give out some substance which diffuses into the jelly and inhibits the growth of bacteria. He named this substance **penicillin**.

Fleming grew more of the mould in glass dishes containing broth, the mould appearing as a thick, velvety 'carpet' on the surface of the broth. He found that the broth contained penicillin and was effective in killing bacteria, even if diluted to one part in a thousand. However, he was unable to extract penicillin from the broth.

Later, other workers extracted penicillin, and showed not only that it can kill many types of bacteria but also that it is safe to give it to humans. In America, penicillin began to be produced on a large scale. This was no mean task, for earlier work at Oxford had shown that the broth from 600 flasks was needed to produce enough penicillin powder to treat one patient for one day! The Americans discovered a new type of mould which could grow in, and not just on, the surface of the broth, so tanks and vats could be used instead of bottles and dishes. Towards the end of the Second World War, enough penicillin was shipped to Britain to save many lives.

A substance, such as penicillin, which is produced by a living organism and is able to retard the growth of bacteria, is called an **antibiotic**. Another important antibiotic is **streptomycin**. This is produced by the soil fungus, *Streptomyces*, and is used mainly in the treatment of tuberculosis.

16.11. Other causes of disease

The diseases mentioned in this chapter have all been caused by bacteria or viruses. Some diseases have other causes. We learnt, in Section 1.7, that lack of essential vitamins can result in such diseases as scurvy and rickets. These are called **deficiency diseases.** Other diseases, such as ringworm and athlete's foot, are caused by the growth of **fungi** in the skin. Finally, a number of important diseases are caused by one-celled animals or **protozoans** (see Book I, Section 4.1). These include malaria, dysentery and sleeping sickness.

16.12. Malaria

Malaria is a disease of major importance in tropical countries. It has been estimated that each year some 300 000 000 cases occur and 3 000 000 people die of the disease. The effects of this one disease on the advance of civilization have been enormous.

A patient with malaria at first feels chilled and is then feverish for five or six hours, but then becomes 'well' again. Two or three days later the sickness returns, with another attack of chill and fever. This cycle of events may be repeated fifteen to twenty times. If the patient lives through these attacks, the disease may appear to have left him. However, it is a feature of malaria that for a period of one, three, or even twenty years, the patient may be subjected to further attacks of fever.

The drug **quinine**, extracted from the bark of the cinchona tree, was used extensively during the seventeenth, eighteenth and nineteenth centuries to treat the disease. In the latter part of the nineteenth century, it was discovered that the blood of patients suffering from malaria contained microscopic parasites (protozoans of the genus

Plasmodium). A British army doctor, **Ronald Ross**, was able to prove that these parasites can be transmitted from an infected person to a healthy person by the bite of a female mosquito of the genus *Anopheles* (see Book I, Sections 6.13 to 6.15).

From early times, malaria had been associated with swamps and foul places (Latin: *malus*, bad; *aer*, air). Ross had now shown why this is so, for swamps are breeding grounds of the mosquito. Today, the World Health Organization is tackling the enormous task of the eradication of malaria. The main method of control is to eradicate the insect-carrier by spraying the adult mosquitoes with insecticides and by preventing them from breeding by draining swamps, etc., or by spraying them with oil. This oil prevents the larvae from clinging to the water surface in order to breathe air.

Test your understanding

1. What are the requirements for the growth of bacteria, and how are these requirements satisfied in the laboratory?
2. Name the three basic types of bacterium and give two examples of each.
3. What is the difference between a streptococcus and a staphylococcus?
4. Explain two ways in which bacteria may protect themselves.
5. What is meant by pasteurization?
6. What treatment must be given to an article to make it completely sterile?
7. What major contributions to the study of disease were made by (a) Robert Koch, (b) Joseph Lister, (c) Edward Jenner, (d) Alexander Fleming and (e) Ronald Ross?
8. Distinguish between antiseptics and disinfectants.
9. What three requirements must be satisfied before it can be assumed that a disease is caused by a particular micro-organism?
10. In what respects do bacteria differ from viruses?
11. Name the three main routes by which germs enter the body. For each route, suggest how the risk of such entry may be reduced.
12. Distinguish between contagious and non-contagious diseases, and give an example of each.
13. Explain the exact meaning of these terms: toxin, antitoxin, pus, natural immunity, acquired immunity, active immunity, passive immunity, vaccination, antibiotic.
14. What methods are being used to control the spread of malaria?

Chapter 17

Maintaining a Healthy Environment

In the previous chapter, we learnt that many diseases are caused by micro-organisms, by bacteria, viruses, and certain microscopic animals. In addition, some diseases are caused by poisonous substances which may contaminate the air we breathe, or the food we eat. All too often these poisonous substances originate from waste which man thoughtlessly, carelessly or ignorantly throws away in a haphazard manner. Other diseases are caused by radiation and by working in unhygienic conditions.

The disease-causing agents are carried by droplets of moisture in the air, by water, by food and drink, by dust particles and by animals such as dogs, cats, flies, fleas and lice which live with man. Sewage contains human excreta which is rich in bacteria. It is important, therefore, that it is treated promptly and thoroughly to make it harmless. If untreated sewage contaminates the water supply, then there is a great danger of infection.

In the late nineteenth and early twentieth centuries, a great deal was learnt about the causes of infectious diseases, and their cures. In recent years, attention has been paid to preventing the spread of these diseases by ensuring clean air; a clean water supply; adequate inspection, storage and preservation of food; thorough treatment of sewage; the control of disease-carrying organisms; and the efficient disposal of refuse. In addition, we are becoming increasingly aware of the dangers of dumping industrial waste into the environment without due consideration of the long-term effects on health or of the destruction of amenities.

17.1. Clean air

Many germs, including those causing the common cold, influenza, measles, mumps and tuberculosis, are carried in dust or in droplets in the air. These specks of dust and tiny droplets may be carried for great distances by air currents. In addition to germs and dust, the air may contain smoke from fires and furnaces, carbon monoxide and lead from car exhausts, pollen from flowers, and a variety of chemicals from various factories.

Smoke contains grit, dust, carbon, tar and sulphur dioxide gas. It damages the lungs and may cause chronic bronchitis. Especially, it is a hazard to the respiratory systems of the very young and very old. When smoke is mixed with fog, **smog** is formed, in which the harmful impurities of smoke are concentrated, and not allowed to disperse. Smog is very dangerous, and it is estimated to have caused 3 000 deaths in three weeks in London in December 1952. In 1956, the Clean Air Act was introduced. This made it an offence in certain areas, called 'smokeless zones', to burn fuels which produce smoke. Instead, householders are obliged to burn specially processed 'smokeless fuels' which have had the harmful substances, such as sulphur and tar, removed during manufacture. Since the Act, there has been much less smog and less respiratory disease in these areas.

17.2. Ventilation

In Chapter 2 we learnt that the body removes oxygen from the air and that it returns carbon dioxide and water vapour to it. Fires and heating boilers also need oxygen and produce carbon dioxide and water vapour. Ventilation is concerned with maintaining comfortable and healthy atmospheric conditions around the body. It is important that the air in a room should circulate like the air does outside. In this way, it is frequently changed and the expired carbon dioxide and water vapour are dissipated and are replaced with fresh, cool, oxygen-rich air. A crowded room with poor ventilation rapidly becomes hot and stuffy as the air becomes stale and saturated with water vapour. In such an atmosphere, the body becomes hot and sweaty, and we feel tired and yawn a great deal. We may even faint. The discomfort is not caused, as was once thought, by the increase in the carbon dioxide in the air, but by the air immediately around the body becoming saturated with water vapour and interfering with the temperature control mechanism of the body (see Section 5.5).

The temperature, humidity and movement of the air in a room affect the comfort of its occupants. The air in a room should be changed at least once an hour, the relative humidity should not exceed 75% and the temperature should be at least 16 °C.

It is also important that fires and central heating boilers should have a good supply of air if they are to function safely and efficiently. The Gas Boards have regulations concerning ventilation in rooms which contain a gas appliance. Air bricks in the wall are frequently used at a low level to ensure an adequate supply of fresh cool air to the boiler.

Natural ventilation depends on **convection currents**, the tendency for hot air to expand and rise, being replaced by heavier cooler air, and on **diffusion**, the tendency for gases to pass from a region of

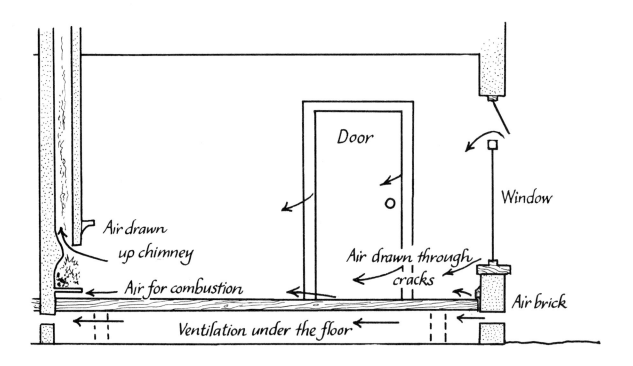

Figure 17.1 Ventilation in a room

high concentration to a region of lower concentration and hence to become dispersed. Normal dwelling-houses are ventilated by chimneys, windows and doors (see Figure 17.1). The movement of the wind over ventilating flues and chimney pots has a suction effect, and draws stale air and smoke out of the top of the house. In addition, kitchens are frequently fitted with an extractor fan to remove the smells and fumes of food preparation and cooking (see Figure 17.2).

Communal buildings, such as office blocks and theatres, which are designed for the use of large numbers of people, are fitted with mechanical ventilation systems which either suck stale air out of

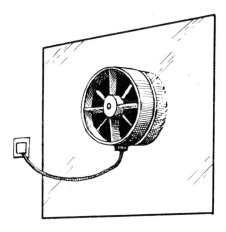

Figure 17.2 An extractor fan as used in a kitchen

248

the building or pump fresh air into it. Many buildings have air-conditioning which maintains a constant circulation of fresh air by means of electric pumps. The equipment filters out dust and dirt, cools or warms the air to the required temperature, absorbs waste gases and adds water vapour to it.

Discomfort such as a sore throat and drowsiness may be caused in homes when the atmosphere is too dry. This frequently occurs when central heating radiators or gas fires are used. In addition, dry air may cause woodwork to shrink and crack, and may easily damage musical instruments. This dryness or low humidity can easily be cured by using a humidifier to moisten the air (see Figure 17.3).

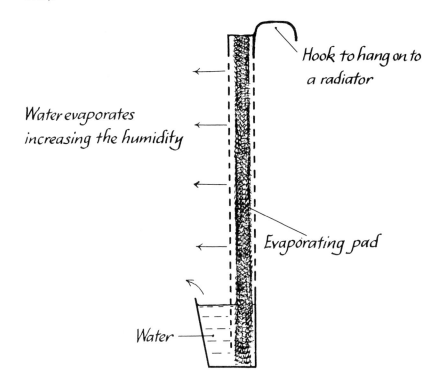

Hook to hang on to a radiator

Water evaporates increasing the humidity

Evaporating pad

Water

Figure 17.3 A domestic humidifier seen in vertical section

17.3. Heating and lighting

Healthy living conditions demand adequate heating and lighting, both at work and at home. It is particularly important that the very young and the old should have adequate heating. The temperature-regulating mechanism of a very young baby is not fully developed and the baby must be kept warm. Old people, who do not move around a great deal, often suffer from 'poor circulation' and feel the cold far more than younger and more active people. An accepted temperature for people in sedentary occupations is 20 °C. Fires should always be carefully guarded, particularly where children and old people are concerned. Mirrors should not be mounted above an open fire grate, in case the clothes of the person using the mirror catch fire. Similarly, parents should not put children's toys on the mantle shelf above the fire.

The open fire is dirty and inefficient, and it can be dangerous. It is difficult to light, it needs constant attention and only heats one room. Slow combustion stoves are much more efficient and need less attention; they may also heat the domestic water and may provide the heat for radiators in other rooms. Fires and stoves need a chimney which must be swept periodically, but the chimney does provide some ventilation. Gas convector fires are fairly efficient, are easy to light, are clean to operate and warm a room up very quickly. They, too, need an efficient chimney. Electric fires do not need a flue, and can easily be moved from room to room. They are clean and easy to operate.

Central heating systems are most efficient. They get their heat energy from a central boiler which may be fired by solid fuel, oil or gas. The heat produced is distributed round the building either by hot water through a system of pipes and radiators, or by hot air which is pushed round the house through a system of ducts and grills.

Adequate lighting is very important for both health and safety. Natural lighting from the sun is the most efficient and pleasant to work by. It is therefore important that windows should be large and well positioned. Natural lighting in a room can be improved by the careful choice of pale-coloured paints and wall-papers which reflect the light. Artificial light is supplied by electricity, using tungsten bulbs or fluorescent tubes. Lighting should be arranged to give sufficient light for close work without eye strain. It should be even, without glare, and it should not cast shadows.

Stairways, difficult passages and porches should be well lit to minimize the possibility of a fall, particularly if elderly people are using them.

17.4. Clean water

Our demand for water is constantly increasing for both industrial and domestic uses. It is estimated that an average of between 200 and 300 litres of water are used per person, per day. About half of this is used for domestic purposes.

In nature water circulates. It falls from the heavens as rain, hail and snow. It may then evaporate again and return to the atmosphere as water vapour, or it may run off the ground into lakes, streams, rivers or the sea. Water may soak into the soil until it reaches an impervious layer of rock which it cannot pass through. It then collects in the spaces in the porous rock, such as chalk or sandstone. If this rock is exposed at the surface, a spring may form and the water will run into the streams and rivers. Some water may be trapped between layers of rock; deep wells may be dug to bring the water to the surface. This circulation of water through the environment is known as the **water cycle** (see Figure 17.4).

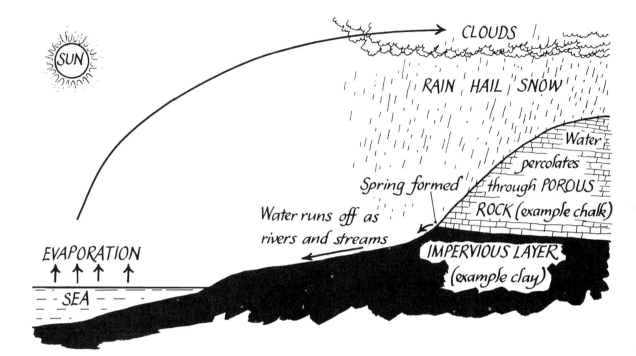

Figure 17.4 Some of the main stages in the water cycle

The community needs water for domestic purposes (cooking, drinking and washing) and for municipal and industrial purposes (sewers, public lavatories and swimming baths, fire services and cooling processes). As one of the principal routes of infection is through the mouth, and as poisonous substances may enter the body in food and drink, it is essential that the water supply should be free from micro-organisms and poisonous substances. In addition, drinking water should be clear and sparkling and without taste, smell or colour.

If each one of us needs more than 200 litres of water per day, water must be collected when it is available and stored until it is needed. On a small scale, rain water can be collected from roofs into barrels or tanks. This water is very soft and suitable for washing or watering the garden, but may be contaminated and is unsuitable for drinking.

On a larger scale, surface water is collected in hilly areas and runs into the streams and rivers. River valleys may be blocked by huge dams which stop the flow of the streams and rivers and form reservoirs, in which the water is stored. From the reservoir, the water flows through pipes to small reservoirs or tanks near the town to be supplied. The water in the mountain stream may be almost pure, but there is a danger that, as the water percolates down to inhabited, cultivated or industrial areas, it may become contaminated with organic impurities, fertilizer residues, industrial waste and even sewage.

Many diseases are spread by water; this is usually due to the contamination of water by untreated human faeces. Typhoid fever, dysentery, cholera and poliomyelitis are just a few of the diseases which are spread in this way. Waste which has been carried in lead pipes may result in lead poisoning if it should contaminate the water supply. Waste must therefore be tested and purified before it is introduced into water from which the domestic water supply is taken.

Drinking water is tested for purity by estimating the numbers of coliform bacteria, such as *Escherichia coli*, present. Coliform bacteria are found in the alimentary canals of man and animals, and hence occur in their faeces. They are not necessarily harmful, but their presence indicates contamination by sewage or animal faeces. This means that the water may also contain some of the disease-causing bacteria mentioned above. The presence of one or two bacilli per 100 cm^3 of water is not regarded as dangerous, but if the number exceeds five per 100 cm^3, then the water is considered to be unfit for drinking.

Investigation 17a. Testing the purity of water samples

Collect several samples of water, such as pond water, rain water, tap water and distilled water. Use boiled water as a control.

Biological

This is a bacteriological test and the principles and precautions learnt in the previous chapter must be observed. MacConkey Nutrient Agar is the medium used. This is available from Oxoid Ltd, either as the ready-made sterile medium in McCartney bottles or as tablets. If tablets are used, soak two tablets in 9 cm^3 of distilled water in a McCartney bottle and autoclave for fifteen minutes to sterilize it. When the medium has cooled to about 45 °C, add 1 cm^3 of the water sample to be tested, and then pour the medium into a sterile petri dish. If the ready-made medium is used, heat the McCartney bottles containing it in a beaker or saucepan of water until it melts. Allow the medium to cool to 45 °C and then add 1 cm^3 of the water sample to be tested and pour into a petri dish (see Figure 17.5). When pouring into the sterilized petri dish, great care should be taken to open the dish as little as possible, and for as short a time as possible, to prevent any contamination. Invert the petri dish, and incubate at 37 °C for two days.

MacConkey Agar contains lactose sugar which is fermented by

252

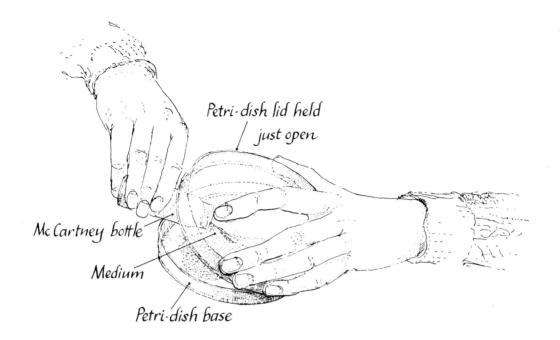

Petri-dish lid held just open

McCartney bottle

Medium

Petri-dish base

any coliform bacteria present in the water sample. Pink or red colonies of bacteria growing on the surface of the medium indicate the presence of coliform bacteria in the water sample. Each colony arises from a single bacterium. Counting the number of colonies on the petri dish will give you some idea of the number of bacteria in the 1 cm^3 sample.

Figure 17.5 Pouring the medium into a petri dish

17.5. Purification of water

Water is obtained from a number of different sources and may, therefore, need different treatment. Water drawn from deep wells or from deep springs is unlikely to be contaminated and needs little treatment, but water taken from a river, such as the Thames, is very likely to be contaminated and it therefore needs very thorough treatment.

The general principles used in the treatment of water are illustrated in Figure 17.6. As the water enters the water-works it passes through a number of screens to remove any large pieces of debris such as twigs. It may then be stored for some time, during which any particles suspended in the water settle out as a sediment. Bacteria settle out with the sediment and, during storage, disease-causing micro-organisms which multiply under natural conditions tend to die out. Aluminium salts are sometimes added to the water to speed up this rather slow sedimentation process.

The next process is filtration, which is a purely mechanical process in which the water soaks through a bed of sand under the influence

253

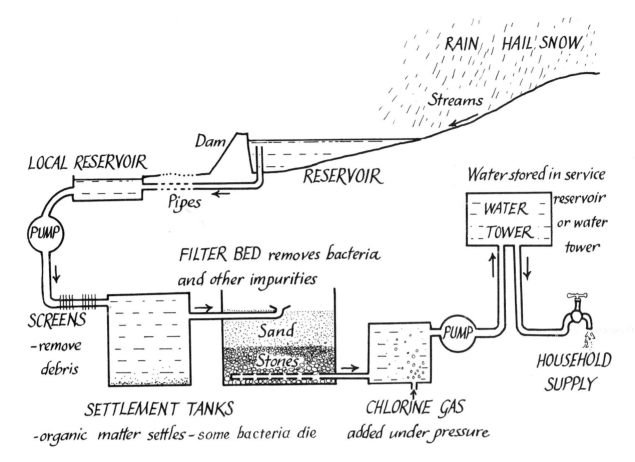

RAIN HAIL SNOW

Streams

Dam

LOCAL RESERVOIR

RESERVOIR

Pipes

Water stored in service

WATER TOWER

reservoir or water tower

PUMP

FILTER BED removes bacteria and other impurities

SCREENS

-remove debris

Sand

Stones

PUMP

HOUSEHOLD SUPPLY

SETTLEMENT TANKS

-organic matter settles - some bacteria die

CHLORINE GAS

added under pressure

Figure 17.6 Water collection and purification

of gravity. Various micro-mesh filters have been developed to replace or supplement the sand filter-beds, and the water may be pumped through these to speed up the process.

As a final precaution, chemical purification is used. Chlorine gas is forced through the water under pressure. Normally, 0·1 part of chlorine per million of water is added, but for water taken from heavily contaminated rivers, such as the Thames, 0·25–1 part per million is used. The chlorine oxidizes and destroys any remaining organic matter, including micro-organisms. In some areas sulphur dioxide is added to remove excess chlorine.

Investigation 17b. To discover the effect of bleaching powder and boiling on coliform bacteria in water.

Biological   Harmful

Collect a sample of river water and divide it into three portions labelled A, B and C. Put sample C on one side as a **control**. Dissolve 1 g of bleaching powder in 500 cm³ of water. Add 2 cm³ of this solution to 100 cm³ of sample A and leave for one hour. Boil sample B for fifteen minutes. Test all three samples for the presence of coliform bacteria with the technique used in Investigation 17a.

254

Examine the results after twenty-four hours. Is there any difference between the plates from samples A, B and C? What is the effect of boiling water or treating it with bleaching powder?

On a small scale, water can be made safe by boiling for fifteen minutes or by the addition of bleaching powder. Bleaching powder contains chlorine. Water may also be sterilized by ultra-violet light.

17.6. Sewage disposal

In Chapter 4 we learnt about the ways in which the body gets rid of its waste. In many poorly developed countries, untreated human faeces are used as a fertilizer for the food crops. It is not surprising that there is a high incidence of parasitic infection and diseases of the alimentary tract in these regions. In fact, it is these infections which reduce the vigour of the population and contribute to the slow development of the region.

In our own country, one of the main dangers of the water supply is that it may become contaminated with untreated sewage and may become an agent for the spread of diseases caused by the micro-organisms in the sewage.

Sewage consists of human faeces, rain water and waste water from houses and factories. In a camp, faeces are simply deposited in a hole or trench and covered with soil. Provided that the hole is deep, and the waste well covered, this is a perfectly satisfactory method. In isolated country cottages or caravans a pail is used, which is emptied regularly. The pail may be situated in a privy some way from the house, but, nowadays, the 'chemical closet' type are found to be more wholesome, and contain chemicals to destroy any micro-organisms and to neutralize any unpleasant smells.

Septic tanks are often used in country houses which have piped water but no main drainage. The faeces and waste water flow into a septic tank some way from the house. A film of bacteria covers the surface of the sewage and encourages the breakdown of organic substances. The sludge settles to the bottom of the tank, and is emptied at regular intervals.

Urban areas have a **water carriage** system in which the faeces, rain water and waste water are carried from the house by pipes into a sewer which is usually beneath the road. This system relies on a plentiful supply of water to flush the waste into the sewer. Sanitary appliances are made of glazed non-absorbent porcelain or stoneware. Sinks and water closets both have S-shaped bends in which water lodges and acts as a water seal. This prevents foul smells in the pipes and sewers from entering the house (see Figure 17.7).

Sewage is heavily contaminated with coliform bacteria to the extent of 100 000 bacilli per 1 cm^3. The aim of sewage treatment is to remove the solids and to reduce the bacterial content to a safe level

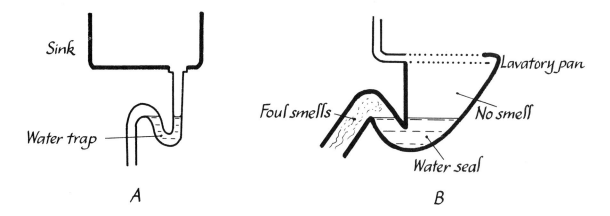

Sink

Water trap

A

Foul smells

Lavatory pan

No smell

Water seal

B

Figure 17.7 A water seal beneath a sink and a water closet

and so produce an effluent which can be released into the rivers or allowed to percolate through the soil. Even then, as we learnt in Section 17.5, it is not fit for drinking without further treatment.

In coastal districts the sewage was frequently discharged directly into the sea without treatment. The sewage entered the sea below low-tide level, but even then there was the danger of the currents washing the sewage back on to the beach. The position of the sewage-outfall pipe could often be located by the ever-present sea-gulls waiting for some tasty tit-bit to emerge. With an increase in coastal populations, this is no longer an acceptable method, as many of the beaches of our resorts were regularly polluted with sewage, toilet paper, etc., and the sea was no longer pleasant to swim in.

In inland areas sewage must be treated (see Figure 17.8). The first stage is to pass it through a **grid** with bars about 1·5 cm apart. This breaks up the solids and removes solid objects such as toilet paper and lost articles. The grid is then removed as the sewage passes slowly through the **grit chamber**. The suspended matter settles out in the next stage in which the sewage flows slowly through the **continuous sedimentation tanks**, forming a sludge which is removed from the tank every few days. This sludge may be dumped in the sea or on land, but in modern treatment plants it is dried and sold as manure, or 'digested' to extract methane and fat.

The liquor from the sedimentation tanks still contains organic substances in solution and in suspension. This liquor needs to be oxidized by exposure to the air in the presence of bacteria. When land was more plentiful, this was done on a **sewage-farm,** by spreading the liquor on to the land and allowing it to percolate into the soil. Bacteria and enzymes break down the nitrogenous materials to ammonia which is then converted into nitrates by the soil bacteria. The crops grown on the sewage farm benefited from these nutrients. This process is called **land filtration**, but now it is more usual to filter the liquor through beds of clinker in large, round tanks. The liquor is normally sprinkled on to the clinker beds from revolving

256

arms. The clinker offers a very large surface area on which a film of bacteria forms. In the presence of atmospheric oxygen, the bacteria convert the organic matter into carbon dioxide, nitrogen and other simple chemical substances. The effluent leaving the clinker beds is now safe and can be released into rivers or streams.

17.7. Refuse disposal

In our modern society, a thousand people produce between them a thousand kilograms (about a ton) of dry refuse each day. This refuse consists of wrapping and packing materials, tins and bottles, ashes, broken crockery, old newspapers and kitchen waste. It is the responsibility of the Local Authority to dispose of it.

At home, the refuse is stored in a dustbin, which should have a well-fitting lid to prevent houseflies from entering and laying their eggs on the waste food. Before putting scraps of food in the dustbin, they should be wrapped in newspaper. It is also a good idea to sprinkle some disinfectant powder into the bottom of the dustbin. In many areas, householders are supplied with strong paper sacks which can be easily removed and replaced each week. This makes the work of the refuse collector lighter and more hygienic. It also greatly reduces the chance of refuse being spilt whilst being transfered to the dustcart, and eliminates the chance of sticky foods

Figure 17.8 The sequence of events in the treatment of sewage

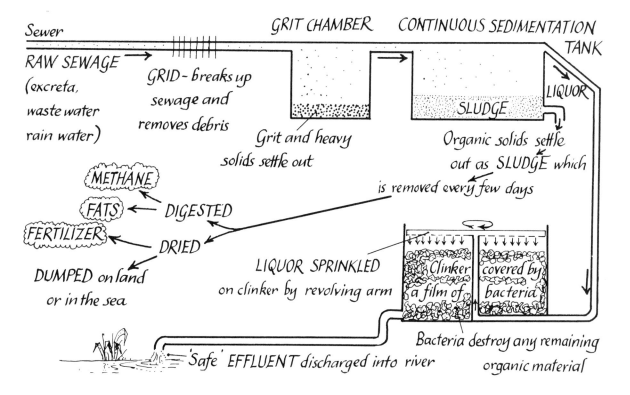

257

accumulating in the bottom of the dustbin and becoming putrid and noxious.

The Local Authority may dispose of the refuse in a number of ways. Some coastal authorities send the refuse out to sea in barges and dump it. This is a very short-sighted policy and is no longer really acceptable as it inevitably adds to the increasing pollution of the coastal waters.

Usually the refuse is sorted, sometimes from a conveyor belt. Bottles are collected, tins and other metal objects are picked out (often by magnets) and papers are sorted out for re-pulping. All these can be sold. Burnable rubbish is then burnt in an incinerator. Finally, the remaining rubbish is disposed of by **controlled tipping**. It is spread on waste ground in layers about 1·5 m deep, sprayed with a disinfectant and then covered by a layer of soil about 0·3 m deep. This is then allowed to settle before adding a further layer of rubbish. Tipping is often used to raise the level of useless low-lying ground. After the rubbish has had time to settle completely, this land may be built on.

17.8. Clean food

One of the principal routes of infection is through the mouth, in food and drink. Precautions must, therefore, be taken to ensure that our food and drink are free from disease-causing micro-organisms and poisonous substances. Food offers nourishment for bacteria as well as ourselves, so it is not surprising that they flourish on untreated foods. Fungi also readily attack fresh foodstuffs, and although they do not often cause disease they decay the food and make it inedible.

Fresh fruit and meat are safe if they are eaten immediately, but it is impracticable to pick fruit or slaughter animals every time we need fruit or meat. Food must be preserved in a safe and edible form until it is needed. Much of our food is imported from countries many thousands of miles away. This food must be preserved during its long journey to Britain.

In order to grow and multiply, and thus infect and decay food, bacteria have certain essential requirements. These are moisture, a suitable temperature and, for most bacteria, oxygen. Food can be preserved by storing in conditions which lack these essential requirements for bacterial growth.

Drying deprives the bacteria of moisture. Fish is dried in certain parts of the world, and at one time meat was preserved by this method. Fruits, such as grapes, are dried to form raisins, sultanas and currants, etc. Apricots and figs are often dried. Milk and eggs may have their moisture removed so they can be stored and transported as a powder.

Salting may be used to preserve ham and fish. The salt kills any invading bacteria by removing the water from them by osmosis. **Jam-making** has a similar effect, but in this case sugar rather than salt is added.

Canning is one of the safest methods of preserving meat and fruit for a long period. It also conserves the vitamin content. The food is put into the can, which is then closed except for a small hole. It is then heated to force out all the air. The can is then completely sealed, sterilized by heating it to a high temperature and cooled in chlorinated water. Imperfectly sealed cans will bulge or 'blow' due to gases produced by decomposing food inside. The condition of all canned food should be checked on opening.

Investigation 17c. To study the effects of temperature on the growth of bacteria

Prepare two petri dishes of nutrient medium and label them A and B. Inoculate both from a bacterial culture. A disc impregnated with *Bacillus subtilis* (obtainable from Oxoid Ltd) is also suitable. Incubate petri dish A at 35 °C and place petri dish B in a refrigerator. Examine the dishes after about four days and comment on the development of the bacterial colonies in them. What has been the effect of keeping petri dish B in the cold?

Biological

Freezing is perhaps the most important method of preserving food today. The domestic refrigerator keeps food at a temperature (around 4 °C) at which bacteria do not multiply, and will keep food and milk in a fresh, edible condition for several days. Modern refrigerators have a freezing compartment in which frozen foods may be kept for a week, a month or even several months, depending on its efficiency.

Chilled meat will keep for about six weeks, but deep-frozen meat will keep very much longer. Meat from Australia and New Zealand is frozen and carried in refrigerated ships. Turkeys are now bred all the year round and put into deep-freeze to be sold at Christmas. If they are not sold one Christmas, then, provided they have not been de-frosted, they can be put back and sold later.

Domestic deep-freezes are becoming increasingly popular. They allow housewives, particularly those living some distance from shops, to buy perishable food in bulk and at advantageous prices. Garden produce can be harvested when the crop is ripe, frozen at -21 °C in the deep-freeze and then eaten as needed throughout the year.

Chemical additives are used to preserve some foods, by inhibiting bacterial growth. Sulphur dioxide is often added to sausages to preserve them.

Investigation 17d. To study food shop hygiene

Study Figure 17.9 carefully, and make a list of the practices which are not in the interest of food hygiene! Explain why these practices are unhygienic and say what should be done to remedy them.

Figure 17.9 An unhygienic food store

17.9. Clean milk

Milk, in nature, is intended as the food for young mammals and, as such, contains all the nutrients necessary for a healthy life. With such great nutritional value it is not surprising that man uses cows' milk as a food throughout his life. Milk is, therefore, a wonderful medium for the growth of bacteria, as can be observed by leaving a bottle of milk for just two or three days. It goes sour and becomes thick with bacteria. It is important, then, that milk is treated carefully and used quickly or stored in a refrigerator.

In Section 16.3 we learnt how milk is protected by pasteurization. Sour milk can be recognized by the fact that it clots when boiled.

Investigation 17e. To test milk for freshness

Take 10 cm³ each of three samples of milk: A—raw milk, B—fresh laboratory-pasteurized milk as in Investigation 16b, and

260

C—fresh commercially pasteurized milk. Place them in sterile tubes. Make up a solution of **resazurin**, by dissolving one resazurin tablet in 50 cm³ of distilled water. Add 1 cm³ of this blue resazurin solution to each of the samples of milk. Seal each tube with a sterile bung. Invert each tube several times to mix up the contents. Set up a fourth tube, D, with boiled milk to act as the control. Place all four tubes in a water-bath maintained at 37 °C (see Figure 17.10). Examine the tubes after twenty minutes and note any colour change. Replace the tubes and examine them again after an hour. Compare the colour of each tube with that of the control tube D. Has there been any change from blue to pink or white? Milk-souring bacteria reduce the resazurin from a blue colour to pink and finally to white. This degree of colour change can be used for estimating the bacterial content of milk. Pink and white samples have failed the freshness test.

Biological

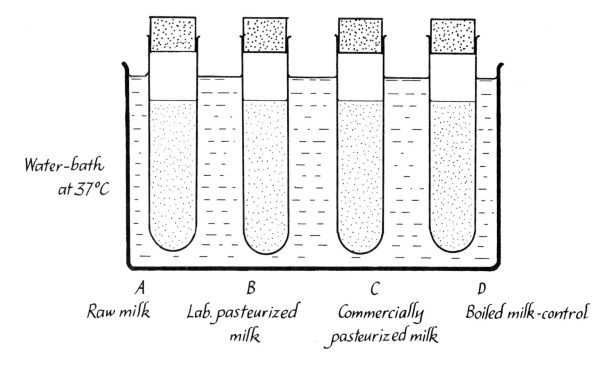

Water-bath at 37°C

A
Raw milk

B
Lab. pasteurized milk

C
Commercially pasteurized milk

D
Boiled milk -control

Figure 17.10 Testing the freshness of milk

17.10. Clean living

Venereal diseases are infectious diseases of the genital organs which are spread by sexual intercourse. **Gonorrhoea** and **syphilis** are the two commonest venereal diseases and both are extremely unpleasant, particularly if they are not treated promptly.

Gonorrhoea has an incubation period of three to ten days. It appears as soreness of and inflammation of the genital organs, accompanied by pain when passing water. In the female, the inflammation may reach the Fallopian tubes, causing sterility and peritonitis.

Syphilis has an incubation period of two to three weeks, and appears first as a hard **chancre** on the penis, vulva or cervix, accompanied by inflammation. Later symptoms are sore throat, rashes and enlargement of glands. Years later, ulcers may develop, and there may be a loss of muscular power which eventually leads to paralysis. Children born to parents suffering from this venereal disease may be infected, and may suffer from blindness and deformity.

These diseases can be avoided by abstaining from casual and promiscuous sexual intercourse. It is vital that sufferers from the diseases do not have intercourse and that they seek *prompt* medical treatment at the special V.D. clinics. This treatment is confidential and, if taken as soon as the symptoms appear, is not painful. Antibiotics are used to control these diseases. Frank co-operation with the social worker attached to the clinic is important, so that the contact who infected the patient, and probably many others, can be traced, informed of their condition and treated.

17.11. Safety in the home

Far more accidents occur within the 'safety' of the home than outside it. Most of these accidents can be avoided by care and forethought to prevent falls, poisoning, cuts, electrocution and burns.

Investigation 17f. To study safety in the kitchen

Figure 17.11 is a picture of a kitchen in a high block of flats. Study it carefully, and list the potential hazards to the toddlers shown in the picture.

17.12. Industrial safety and hygiene

Many working days are lost each year as a result of industrial accidents. Most of these could have been avoided if good working conditions were provided and reasonable precautions taken. Many jobs, such as coal mining, have special dangers. Inadequate lighting and ventilation, faulty heating and excessive noise, together with exposure to poisonous substances, are all health hazards. Boredom and fatigue also contribute to accidents.

Safety regulations exist for dangerous jobs, and it is important that these should be observed. Machinery with moving parts should not be operated without the guards being in position, or cleaned whilst in motion. Protective clothing, including boots with steel toe caps, should be worn when appropriate. Long hair should be covered and loose ties and belts avoided when operating rotating machinery. Protective goggles and gloves should always be worn when using welding or grinding equipment. Inexperienced operators should not be allowed to operate dangerous machinery without training and supervision. Industrial dermatitis, a skin complaint common amongst workers handling chemicals, can be avoided by the use of protective gloves, barrier creams and by the provision and use of good washing facilities. Boredom and fatigue can be prevented by occasional changes in posture, the provision of background music and occasional ten-minute breaks for refreshment and relaxation.

Figure 17.11 Spot the dangers in this kitchen

17.13. Doomwatch

The latter part of the twentieth century is a time when the world population is increasing at a faster rate than ever before. This results in pressures on food supply, living space, natural resources and amenities. About 30% of the world's population are eating 70% of the world's food supply. Over 50% of the world's population are suffering from malnutrition, whilst many of the remainder are suffering from the effects of over-eating. We must devote some of our technological power to achieving a more just distribution of the world's food. Responsibility must be exercised in the size of our families. Family planning should be encouraged and contraception made available, particularly in under-developed countries.

Our way of life and our industry are producing more waste than we know what to do with; because of this the environment is becoming polluted to a dangerous degree. Insecticides are accumulating in our food and bodies, although we must not forget that their use has greatly increased the productivity of the land. Industrial waste, such as detergent, is being allowed to pollute rivers and lakes and is destroying all the life therein. Excess fertilizer is washed from the fields into the rivers and lakes, where it encourages excessive algal growth. This decays and blots out all other life. Oil is being transported in ever-increasing quantities in larger and larger ships. Accidents to this traffic are causing pollution of our beaches, and destruction of bird and marine life. Poisonous metals, such as mercury, are being carelessly disposed of and are accumulating in fish which we eat. Fumes from motor vehicles contain carbon monoxide and lead.

Particularly gloomy pundits have predicted that the loss of trees and vegetation from the earth's surface, together with the increase in industry, is causing an increase in the carbon dioxide content of the air. This, they claim, could have a 'green-house effect', resulting in a rise in the temperature of the atmosphere and the melting of the polar ice caps. This would produce a considerable rise in sea-level, causing vast areas of low-lying ground in the world to be swamped. Happily this is not very likely, but it is the duty of all of us to protest against and prevent practices which endanger the future of our environment and, ultimately, of mankind itself.

Test your understanding

1. Why was the 1956 Clean Air Act necessary?
2. Why do people sometimes faint in hot crowded rooms?
3. What are the main stages in the purification of the water supply?
4. Why is sewage treatment necessary?
5. Draw a flow diagram to show the sequence of events in the disposal of sewage.
6. Describe four methods of preserving food.
7. Why is it important for venereal diseases to be treated promptly?
8. What precautions should be taken in the home to protect the very young and the very old?
9. What precautions should be taken when working with moving machinery?
10. Write an essay on the dangers of pollution.

Analytical Contents List

15 How Life Is Handed On

15.1 Sexual reproduction 15.2 The structure of the nucleus
15.3 The function of the chromosomes
15.4 The chromosomes at fertilization
15.5 Some breeding investigations
15.6 *Drosophila* culture
15.7 Handling *Drosophila*
15.8 Breeding experiments with mice
15.9 The work of Gregor Mendel
15.10 How are the 'instructions' inherited?
15.11 Why is each chromosome duplicated?
15.12 An explanation of Mendel's results and your own
15.13 The back cross or test cross
15.14 The dihybrid cross: two-character inheritance
15.15 The inheritance of sex 15.16 Incomplete dominance
15.17 Mutations 15.18 Chromosome mutations
15.19 Gene mutations
15.20 The effect of radiation on mutations

16 Micro-organisms and Disease

16.1 Bacteria 16.2 Types of bacteria
16.3 How bacteria may be killed
16.4 Bacteria and disease 16.5 Viruses
16.6 How bacteria and viruses enter the body
16.7 The body's reaction 16.8 Prevention of disease: immunity
16.9 Vaccination 16.10 Antibiotics: the discovery of penicillin
16.11 Other causes of disease 16.12 Malaria

17 Maintaining a Healthy Environment

17.1 Clean air 17.2 Ventilation
17.3 Heating and lighting 17.4 Clean water
17.5 Purification of water 17.6 Sewage disposal
17.7 Refuse disposal 17.8 Clean food 17.9 Clean milk
17.10 Clean living 17.11 Safety in the home
17.12 Industrial safety and hygiene 17.13 Doomwatch

Analytical Contents List for Book I

For the convenience of the users of this book, we are setting out below the contents of the companion volume, *General Plant and Animal Biology*, Biology Book I.

responses   Plant hormones   Types of response   Differences between plant
and animal responses

15 The Economy of Nature

Materials of life   The carbon cycle   The nitrogen cycle   The water cycle
The source of energy   Food-chains: interdependence of living organisms
Food-webs   Balance of nature

16 Soil

The meaning of soil   The composition of soil   Soil analysis   Types and
properties of soil   Soil and plant life   Soil organisms   Soil improvement

17 Communal Life

The habitat   Communities   Habitat factors   Colonization of bare ground
Field studies   A woodland study   A hedgerow study   A grassland study
A pond or stream study   A study of the habitat of the earthworm

Index

Where the subject is illustrated the page number is shown in bold type